Successful Wire Antennas

Edited by

Ian Poole, G3YWX

and

Steve Telenius-Lowe, 9M6DXX, KH0UN

Radio Society of Great Britain

Published by the Radio Society of Great Britain, 3 Abbey Court, Fraser Road, Priory Business Park, Bedford MK44 3WH. Tel: 01234 832700. Web: www.rsgb.org

Published 2012.

Reprinted 2012 & 2014

ISBN: 9781 9050 8677 1

Cover design: Kim Meyern

Design and layout: Steve Telenius-Lowe, 9M6DXX, KH0UN

Production: Mark Allgar, M1MPA

Printed in Great Britain by Berforts Information Press of Stevenage

Contents

Foreword

THE RSGB PUBLISHED *Practical Wire Antennas* in 1989. It had fewer than 100 pages and had diagrams but no photographs. Sixteen years later *Practical Wire Antennas 2* appeared, which was a much more comprehensive and up-to-date publication running to 172 pages. Now, in 2012, the Society has published its newest antenna book which has 240 pages of information that is free from any difficult mathematics but is full of the latest designs and wire antenna developments.

This new lavishly illustrated guide to wire antenna design and construction has nine chapters where full details of the latest wire antenna designs will be found. Doublet antennas and their derivatives took up just 10 pages in the first *Practical Wire Antennas* book, but the 'Doublets' chapter in this latest book occupies no fewer than 29 pages. There are also more than three and a half pages of the most comprehensive Index seen in a book of this length.

Successful Wire Antennas will occupy an important space on my book shelf and I am sure that it will be of inestimable value to radio amateurs world-wide, whatever their level of experience may be.

This book will surely become a 'must' for wire antenna enthusiasts at all levels of expertise and technical skill. It is stuffed with very clear diagrams and has numerous photographs that amplify the easy-to-read text, much of which is new material describing antennas that did not even exist 23 years ago.

John D Heys, G3BDQ
January 2012

Preface

A BOOK SUCH AS THIS is the sum of very many people's work. *Successful Wire Antennas* is based on the 2005 RSGB book *Practical Wire Antennas 2*, edited by Ian Poole, G3YWX, which - in turn - was based on the original *Practical Wire Antennas* written by John Heys, G3BDQ. In 2005, G3YWX added much new material of his own to John Heys's original work, while also bringing to our attention wire antenna designs by other authors that had appeared in the RSGB's monthly magazine, *RadCom*, in the period since G3BDQ's book was published.

The fundamentals of antenna design have not changed since the time of Hertz and Marconi and so readers will certainly find some material from both of the previous two books within these pages. What *has* changed in the last quarter of a century is the widespread use of antenna modelling programs such as *EZNEC*, which make it possible to predict with reasonable accuracy such parameters as the gain, azimuth and elevation patterns, feed impedance, SWR, etc of an antenna design, as well as the effects of different types of earth on the antenna. In this new book, therefore, can be found many examples of the results of modelling of the antenna designs featured.

But that's not all that's new. While the fundamentals remain the same, the ingenuity of radio amateurs knows no bounds and numerous new designs for wire antennas have been published since 2005. We have taken the opportunity to trawl through the pages of both *RadCom* and the ARRL's *QST* for the last six years (some 18,000 pages!) to bring you the best of them, while retaining many of the timeless older designs. Here we must thank the authors who have spent a huge amount of time and effort in developing their antennas and then taking the trouble to write them up for publication so that we may all benefit from their work. Each of these authors is acknowledged in the text and is also listed in the index at the back of this book. We would also like to thank several of the regular columnists from these magazines who have shared their knowledge of antennas (and many other subjects) with us over the years and from whom we have quoted in this book: in particular Peter Dodd, G3LDO; Ian White, GM3SEK; Eamon Skelton, EI9GQ; Pat Hawker, G3VA; Richard Newstead, G3CWI; Ward Silver, N0AX, and *QST* Technical Editor Joel R Hallas, W1ZR. This book would also not have been possible without the cooperation of *QST* editor Steve Ford, WB8IMY, who gave permission for articles to be republished, and who provided the photographs and diagrams from *QST*.

In addition to the new antenna designs, subjects that get covered either for the first time or in much greater detail in this book include inverted-L antennas, phased verticals, verticals by the sea, automatic ATUs, receive-only antennas, impedance matching and baluns. As a result, this book is 36% bigger than its predecessor, with the chapter on vertical antennas in particular including a huge amount of new material. That is not to say that old favourites have been forgotten and, indeed, we go back to the original words used by Louis Varney, G5RV, to describe his eponymous antenna - as well as providing a 21st century analysis of it.

We feel sure that in this book there will be something for every radio amateur who enjoys experimenting with wire antennas - and surely that includes most of us?

Ian Poole, G3YWX;
Steve Telenius-Lowe, 9M6DXX, KH0UN

Editor's note

A FEW WORDS about the very term "antenna". There are those who say that insects have antennae and that wireless equipment has *aerials*: "antenna", they say, is a recent American import and so its use in British English should be avoided. Nothing could be further from the truth. No less an authority than the *Wireless Telegraphy Manual for HM Fleet*, dated 1917, has a chapter headed 'The Aerial Wire or Antenna', proving that both terms have been in use in the UK, side by side, for close on 100 years. It is true that "aerial" used to be more commonly used in Britain, but that has not now been the case for decades: antenna guru Louis Varney, G5RV, used the term "aerial" in articles published in 1958 and 1966, but by 1983 he too was calling them "antennas".

Although some British radio amateurs still prefer "aerial", to many the term now sounds somewhat old-fashioned and quaint, rather like the term "wireless" in its original meaning of "radio", before it received a renaissance in connection with computers and Internet connectivity. It is also the case that the word "antenna" is used in just about every other language and so, for all these reasons, that is the term employed throughout this book.

As an aside, according to *The Concise Oxford Dictionary*, the plural of "antenna" is "antennas" when it refers to radios' antennas: only insects have "antennae".

Similarly the term "ATU" may need some clarification. In the UK there has been some controversy for many years over the name ATU, standing for Antenna Tuning Unit (or Aerial Tuning Unit), and it is indeed peculiar that arguably the most common piece of ancillary equipment in an amateur radio station should have so many different names.

There are those who say that since an ATU does not actually tune the antenna to resonance it should not be called an antenna tuning unit at all. Louis Varney, G5RV, probably started this line of argument. In an article called 'ATU . . . or ASTU?', published in the August 1983 *Radio Communication*, he argued that the device should, strictly, be called an antenna system tuning unit (ASTU). More recently, others have argued the case for other more technically accurate terms such as AMU (Antenna - or Aerial - Matching Unit). More accurate or not, none of these names has caught on. In the USA they sometimes get around this issue by calling the unit simply a 'tuner', while in continental Europe the same device is often called a 'matchbox'.

Whatever the name, they all do the same job and, so as to avoid confusion, in this book we will use the term 'ATU' throughout, as that is by far the most commonly-used term in the UK as well as throughout much of the world.

Finally, a note about *EZNEC*. This antenna modelling software is mentioned frequently throughout the book and many of the polar diagrams showing antenna azimuth and elevation patterns have been derived from this program. Several versions of *EZNEC* are available from the website of its developer, Roy Lewallen, W7EL, at www.eznec.com

Steve Telenius-Lowe, 9M6DXX, KH0UN
February 2012

1 Antenna Basics

ANTENNAS ARE ELECTRIC circuits and follow the rules of normal electric circuits, but they have one major difference and that is that they are designed to radiate as much energy as possible as electromagnetic waves in order to travel over great distances. It is this property that makes them different to other circuits.

In view of this difference, antennas are often treated in slightly different ways to more normal electrical circuits. It also makes them very interesting to study and use. In the HF portion of the spectrum, antennas can be relatively large, with their dimensions extending to many metres, making them ideal for experimentation.

To be able to gain successful results it is first necessary to have a basic understanding of the fundamental aspects of antennas. Fortunately a deep mathematical understanding is not required and mathematics will be kept to a minimum in the following chapters. Instead, an overview of the concepts is given here as a useful basis.

RADIATION

The aim of any antenna is to convert the electrical energy supplied to it into an electromagnetic wave that is launched into the ether, and in the opposite direction to take electromagnetic waves that impinge on the antenna and convert them into electrical energy that can be transferred to the receiver.

The actual physics of the radiation of energy from the wire is involved, using Maxwell's equations and differential calculus, and accordingly it is best left to theoretical textbooks. It is sufficient to say here that the current flowing up and down the wire gives rise to a magnetic field around the wire, while the charges in motion (which constitute the current) carry with them an electric field. Due to the reversing nature of the current, the two fields are mutually supporting and expand outwards from the wire, carrying with them energy from the exciting current. There exists in the immediate vicinity of the wire an oscillating field known as the *induction field* (similar to that surrounding an induction coil or a magnet), but this decays in strength rapidly as the distance from the wire increases. At a distance of $\lambda/2\pi$, or approximately one-sixth of a wavelength, it is equal in strength to the radiation field but beyond one or two wavelengths it has fallen to a negligible level.

Radiation takes place from any elevated wire carrying a radio frequency current unless prevented by screening or cancelled by an opposing field of equal magnitude. At any given frequency, and for a given direction relative to the wire, the field strength produced at a distant point is proportional to the current multiplied by the length of wire, as it appears to the observer, through which it flows.

RESONANCE

An antenna is a circuit that has capacitance, inductance and resistance. This means that its impedance is frequency dependent and the antenna is a tuned circuit that resonates. Most antennas are operated at or near resonance although this is not always the case.

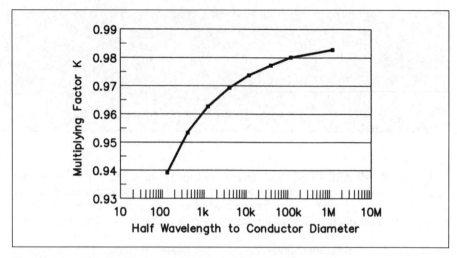

Fig 1.1 : The K factor (from *The ARRL Antenna Book*).

The resonant frequency of a length of wire is dependent upon its length. The shortest length that resonates at a given frequency is one that is just long enough for an electric charge to travel from one end to the other and back again in the time of one cycle of the energy exciting the antenna. As the charge travels the wire twice, i.e. to one end and back again, the length of wire needed to permit this is a *half wavelength*.

Taking the velocity of an electromagnetic wave to be 299,800,000 metres per second, it is possible to calculate that the wavelength of a signal in free space is:

$$\text{Length (metres)} = \frac{149.9}{\text{Frequency (MHz)}}$$

The actual length of a half-wave antenna is not exactly the same as a half-wavelength of a signal travelling in free space. There are several effects that change this somewhat, making the actual length of a half-wavelength antenna shorter than the free space half-wavelength. The first is that insulators with a different dielectric constant to air are often required at the end of an antenna for support. Other nearby objects may also have a similar effect. However, the main effect depends on the ratio of the wire length to its diameter. The thicker the wire in relation to the wavelength, the shorter the antenna. A factor known as the *K factor* is the figure by which the free space half-wavelength must be multiplied to give the length for a half-wave antenna. A curve of the K factor is shown in **Fig 1.1**. At HF where wires are used, the K factor may be around 0.98, and this means that an antenna for a frequency that has a free space half-wavelength of 10.0m would need to be only 9.8m long.

In practice it is always good practice to cut an antenna slightly longer than required, and then once it has been installed to trim its length to give the optimum performance. It is far easier to remove wire by cutting it than to have to replace wire when it has been cut too short. It is also a fact that despite all the calculations, spurious effects sometimes mean that lengths are not quite what they are anticipated to be, especially when antennas are mounted in real situations where they may pass close to other objects that may detune them or where they may have to be bent to fit into the available space.

CURRENT AND VOLTAGE DISTRIBUTION

It has already been mentioned that a charge travels along an antenna wire when it is excited by a signal. If the wire antenna were infinitely long, the charge (voltage) and

the current (the electric charge in motion) would both steadily decrease in
amplitude with the distance from the
source. This would result from the fact
that energy is dissipated in the form of
radiated energy as well as there being
some heat dissipated as a result of the
resistance in the antenna wire.

When the antenna has a finite
length, charge is reflected when it
reaches the far end of the antenna. As
the energy is being continually supplied
in the form of a sine wave of the signal
in question, this can be considered as
a series of charges of different amplitude being supplied.

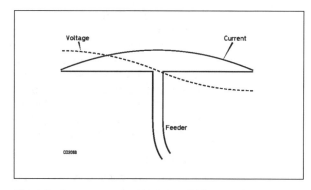

Fig 1.2: Current and voltage waveforms along a half-wavelength dipole.

When a half-wavelength antenna is excited with a signal, there is not just a
single charge, but a continuous supply of energy, varying in voltage according to a
sine wave cycle. It is possible to consider this as a series of charges, all with slightly
different amplitudes. When a charge reaches the end of the antenna and is reflected,
the direction of current flow is reversed. As there is a continuous supply of charges,
the forward and reflected currents add together. At the point of reflection, the charge
moving towards the end and the one that has just been reflected are virtually the
same. As they are flowing in opposite directions they cancel each other out and no
current flows at the end of the antenna.

Away from the end of the antenna, the magnitudes of the outgoing and returning
currents differ from each other. This is because the charges have been supplied at
different parts of the RF cycle, and the returning charge takes a different time to reach
the end of the antenna and be reflected back than the charge that is travelling towards the end. As both charges at a given point have a different magnitude, they do
not completely cancel out and a measurable current exists. The greatest difference,
i.e. the largest resultant current, exists at a distance of a quarter-wavelength from the
end of the wire. Back still farther from this point the current decreases until, a half-
wavelength away from the end of the antenna, it reaches zero again. Thus, in a half-
wavelength antenna, the current is zero at the ends and maximum at the centre, as
shown in **Fig 1.2**.

The voltage along the wire behaves in a different manner to the current. It reaches
its greatest amplitude at the end because, at this point, two practically equal charges
add together. Back along the wire, however, the outgoing and returning charges are
not equal and their sum is smaller. At a point a quarter-wavelength from the end, the
returning charge is equal in magnitude but opposite in phase with the outgoing
charge. This is because at this time the polarity of the voltage wave from the source
has reversed. The two voltages therefore cancel each other and the resultant voltage
is zero. Beyond the quarter-wavelength point, the voltage again increases, but this
time with the opposite polarity.

From this it can be seen that the voltage is at its maximum at every point when the
current is at its minimum, and vice versa.

DIRECTIVITY

The radiation field which surrounds the wire is not uniformly strong in all directions.
It is strongest in directions at right angles to the current flow in the wire and falls in
intensity to zero along the axis of the wire. In other words, the wire exhibits directivity
in its radiation pattern, the energy being concentrated in some directions at the
expense of others.

One of the methods of increasing the directivity is to use further wires in the antenna, along with phasing techniques so that signals in some directions are reinforced, whereas in others the signals from the various wires cancel. These antenna arrays are often called beams because they concentrate radiation in the desired direction like a beam of light from a torch. Because a number of wires or elements are needed to create this directivity, beam antennas usually require more space than simple ones, and this limits the extent to which they can usefully be employed at the longer wavelengths. As a result of the added complexity and space required, few beam antennas are described in this book.

DIPOLES

One of the most commonly used words in antenna work is *dipole*. A dipole is simply some device (in the present context an antenna) which has two 'poles', or terminals, into which radiation-producing currents flow. The two poles may be of any length, and a certain amount of confusion sometimes arises from the failure to state the length involved. In practice it is usually safe to assume that when the word 'dipole' is used by itself, it is intended to describe a *half-wavelength antenna*, i.e. a radiator of electrical half-wavelength fed by a balanced connection at the centre. Any reference to gain over a dipole is assumed to refer to this half-wavelength dipole. When reference to another form of dipole is intended, it is usual to state the overall length, e.g. a full-wavelength dipole, short dipole etc. A short dipole is less than half a wavelength long, but needs to be tuned to resonance by the addition of inductance, usually in the centre, or some form of capacitive end-loading as discussed later. Shortening has little effect on the radiation pattern but, if carried too far, leads to poor efficiency and excessively narrow bandwidth.

Loops containing between two-thirds and one-and-a-half wavelengths of wire have radiation patterns very similar to those of half-wave dipoles.

A further reference sometimes encountered is to the monopole or unipole. This is an unbalanced radiator, fed against an earth plane, and a common example is the ground-plane vertical.

GAIN

If one antenna system can be made to concentrate more radiation in a certain direction than another antenna, for the same total power supplied, then it is said to exhibit gain over the second antenna in that direction. In other words, more power would have to be supplied to the reference antenna to give the same radiated signal in the direction under consideration, and hence the better antenna has effectively gained in power over the other.

Gain can be expressed either as a ratio of the powers required to be supplied to each antenna to give equal signals at a distant point, or as the ratio of the signals received at that point from the two antennas when they are driven with the same power input. Gain is usually expressed in *decibels*. Gain is, of course, closely related to directivity, but an antenna can be directive and yet have a power *loss* as a result of energy dissipated in antenna wires and surrounding objects. This is actually the reason why it is not possible to obtain high gain figures from electrically small antennas.

It is important to note that in specifying gain for an antenna, some reference to direction must be included, because no antenna can exhibit gain simultaneously in all directions relative to another antenna. The distribution of radiated energy from an antenna may be likened to the shape of a balloon filled with incompressible gas, with the antenna at the centre. The amount of gas represents the power fed to the antenna, and the volume of the balloon can only be increased by putting in more gas. The shape of the balloon may be distorted into many different shapes, and elongated greatly in some directions so that the amount of gas squeezed in those directions is increased, but this can only be achieved by reducing the amount of gas in some other part of the balloon: the total volume must remain unaltered. Likewise the antenna can only direct extra energy in some required direction by radiating less in others.

The gain of an antenna is expressed in terms of its performance relative to some agreed standard. This enables any two antennas to be directly compared. For example, if two antennas have a gain 6dB and 4dB respectively, relative to a given standard, the first has a gain of 6 - 4 = 2dB relative to the second.

It is unfortunate that two standards exist side by side and will be encountered in other references to antennas. One standard often used is the theoretical *isotropic radiator*, which radiates equal power in all directions, i.e. its solid polar diagram is a sphere (*isotropic* means having the same physical properties in all directions). This is a strictly non-practical device which cannot be constructed or used, but has the advantage that the comparison is not complicated by the directional properties of the reference antenna.

The other standard is the *half-wave dipole* which has its own directional pattern. This is a practical antenna which can be built and is therefore a more realistic basis for comparison, but it should be noted that gain expressed relative to a half-wave dipole (*dBd*) means by inference relative to the *maximum radiation* from the dipole.

Gain relative to an isotropic radiator is designated as *dBi* but beware of a common tendency to quote the gain of an antenna gain without reference to the standard employed. This can lead to a disparity of 2.15dB in claimed results, this being the difference of the two standards employed (the gain of a half-wave dipole relative to the isotropic source). In some cases it is safer to assume the more conservative figure when comparing different antenna performance unless one is sure that the same reference has been used in each case.

Because direction is inevitably associated with a statement of gain, it is usually assumed in the absence of any qualifying statement that the gain quoted for any antenna is its gain in the direction of its own maximum radiation. Where the antenna system can be rotated, as is often the case on 14MHz and higher frequencies, this is not so important, but when the antenna is fixed in position the superiority it exhibits in one direction over another antenna will not hold in other directions, because of the different shapes of the two directivity patterns. Antenna A may have a quoted gain of 6dB over antenna B, but only in the directions which favour the shape of its radiation pattern relative to that of antenna B.

There is an important distinction between transmitting gain and effective receiving gain. In the first case it is required to maximise the power transmitted and in the second case we have to maximise the signal-to-noise ratio, and the two gains will be the same only if there are no power losses and noise is isotropic, i.e. arriving equally from all directions. In the HF bands, the useful receiver sensitivity is limited by external noise which is usually well above the receiver noise level and, as long as this remains true, signal-to-noise ratio is unaffected by losses in the antenna system. Typically, with a low-noise receiver, antenna losses could reduce the power transmitted by up to 10dB or more before starting to affect the performance adversely when the same antenna is used for reception.

RADIATION RESISTANCE AND ANTENNA IMPEDANCE

When power is delivered from the transmitter into the antenna, some small part will be lost as heat, since the material of which the antenna is made will have a finite resistance, albeit small, and a current flowing in it will dissipate some power. The bulk of the power will usually be radiated and, since power can only be consumed by a resistance, it is convenient to consider the radiated power as dissipated in a fictitious resistance which is called the *radiation resistance* of the antenna.

Using ordinary circuit relations, if a current I is flowing into the radiation resistance R, a power of I²R watts is being radiated. As depicted in Fig 1.2 the current distribution along a resonant antenna or indeed any standing wave antenna is not uniform but is approximately sinusoidal. It is therefore necessary to specify the point of reference for the current when formulating the value of the radiation resistance, and it is usual to assume the value of current at the anti-node or maximum point. This is known as the current loop, and hence the value of R given by this current is known as the loop radiation resistance: in practice the word 'loop' is omitted but inferred.

A half-wavelength dipole has a radiation resistance of about 73 ohms (Ω). If it is made of highly conductive material such as copper or aluminium, the loss resistance may be less than 1Ω. The conductor loss is thus relatively small and the antenna provides an efficient coupling between the transmitter and free space. However, it is important to keep the levels of resistance as low as reasonably possible to ensure the optimum efficiency. With the skin effect the actual resistance can be higher than might be expected, and therefore the use of thick wire made of copper enables these losses to be kept as low as possible.

When the antenna is *not* a resonant length, it behaves like a resistance in series with a positive (*inductive*) or negative (*capacitive*) *reactance*, shown as a figure of +*j*x or -*j*x ohms (see below). Such an antenna requires the addition of an equal but opposing reactance to bring it to resonance, so that it may be effectively supplied with power by the transmitter. The combination of resistance and reactance, which would be measured at the antenna terminals with an impedance meter, is referred to in general terms as the antenna *input impedance*. This impedance is only a pure resistance when the antenna is at one of its resonant lengths.

The input impedance of the antenna is related specifically to the input terminals, whereas the radiation resistance is usually related to the current at its loop position. It is possible to feed power into an antenna at any point along its length so that the input impedance and the loop radiation resistance even of a resonant antenna may be very different in value, although in this case both are pure resistances. Only when the feedpoint of the antenna coincides with the position of the current loop on a single wire will the two be approximately equal. If the feedpoint occurs at a position of current minimum and voltage maximum, the input impedance will be very high, but the loop radiation resistance remains unaltered. For a given power fed into the antenna, the actual feedpoint current measured on an RF ammeter will be very low, but because the input impedance is high, the power delivered to the antenna is the same. Such an antenna is described as *voltage fed*, because the feedpoint coincides with a point of maximum voltage in the distribution along the antenna. Conversely an antenna fed at a low-impedance point, usually a current maximum, is described as *current fed*.

CAPACITIVE AND INDUCTIVE REACTANCE

Articles describing the feedpoint impedance of an antenna often make reference to figures that include +*j* or -*j*, e.g. +*j*20Ω. What do the +*j* or -*j* figures mean? In 'The Doctor is IN' (*QST* January 2008), 'The Doctor' explained these terms in everyday language.

The impedance of an antenna is generally *complex*, i.e. it is not just resistive, but acts like a combination of resistance and either capacitive or inductive reactance. It can be represented as an equivalent series circuit of a resistor and a capacitor or inductor generally represented as R ±*j*X. The "*j*" part indicates that the X is the reactive component. A *plus* sign indicates *inductive* reactance while a *minus* sign indicates *capacitive* reactance.

Your antenna analyser can show the R and X, although it doesn't give the sign. You can generally tell by slightly shifting the frequency. Since the reactance of an inductor goes up as frequency increases, if the X goes up it's a plus, and if the X goes down it's a minus. Make sure you don't change the frequency very far for this test, especially don't go so far that the X value goes through 0.

Table 1.1 shows the impedance of a 102ft dipole on four bands. On 80m it is 31.9 -j326.5Ω, i.e. the antenna is acting like a termination of 31.9Ω resistance in series with a capacitance with 326.5Ω of capacitive reactance. At the stated frequency of 3.8MHz, that represents a capacitance of about 128pF. This would show up as a 24:1 SWR with 50Ω coax. One way of dealing with this impedance would be to insert an inductance with a reactance of +j326.5 (198μH) in series with the antenna. The total impedance would then be 31.9 -j326.5 +j326.5Ω, or just 31.9Ω. The two reactances have cancelled out, making the circuit resonant and leaving just the resistive part. This results in a 1.5:1 SWR.

In the particular case of a G5RV antenna, shown in **Fig 1.3**, instead of the simple single inductor 'antenna tuner' above, the trick is that by connecting about 35ft of 450Ω window line to the 31.9 -j326.5Ω, the impedance is transformed to 20.34Ω resistive, for a 2.5:1 SWR when connected to 50Ω coax. The same wire and transmission line happen to result in a relatively low SWR on parts of 40, 20 and 10m as well, thus making the G5RV a popular multiband antenna (although the SWR is often not low enough on multiple bands to allow operation without an ATU at the transceiver. Still, it does provide for coaxial cable feed to the rig and is simple and inexpensive to build). The G5RV antenna is discussed later in this book.

Band (metres)	Frequency (MHz)	Antenna Impedance (Ω)
80	3.8	31.9 -j326.5
40	7.2	558 +j1215
20	14.2	103.3 -j48.6
17	18.14	2089 +j1964

Table 1.1: Impedance of 102ft dipole.

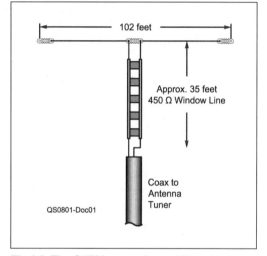

Fig 1.3: The G5RV, a popular multiband antenna that has a relatively low SWR on parts of a number of HF bands.

For practical purposes the actual sign of the reactive component is usually not that important: what matters most is the resulting SWR, which can be read directly from the antena analyser. The R and + or - X values are usually needed only if you are trying to design a custom matching network or are interested in the detailed study of the antenna operation.

RADIATION PATTERNS AND POLAR DIAGRAMS

From the point of view of effective gain it is immaterial whether this comes from horizontal directivity, vertical directivity or both, but the practical usefulness of a fixed array using horizontal collinear elements is restricted by the relatively narrow beamwidth in the horizontal plane. To illustrate the radiation pattern of an antenna, *polar diagrams* are used in the form of curves, the radius of which in any direction represents the relative strength of signals in that direction.

The radiation from an antenna occurs in three dimensions and therefore the radiation pattern is best represented by the surface of a solid object. A polar diagram is any section of the solid shape, and a large number of sections may be necessary to reduce the antenna radiation pattern to two dimensions.

In practice, it is necessary to be content with two polar diagrams taken in the principal planes, usually the horizontal and vertical, and giving the two cross-sections of the main beam.

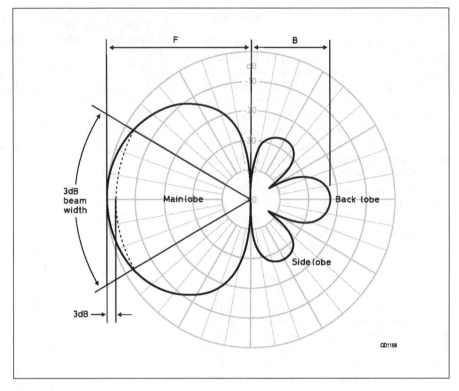

Fig 1.4: A typical polar diagram plot for a directive antenna showing the -3dB points and the beamwidth.

Where the polar diagram has a definite directional form, the angle between the directions where the power radiated is half the value at the point of maximum gain (-3dB) is called the *beamwidth* (see **Fig 1.4**).

To avoid confusion when discussing radiation, directions in the horizontal plane are referred to as *azimuth*; angles above the horizontal, in the vertical plane, are called wave angles or directions in *elevation*. Confusion often arises additionally when the expression horizontal (or vertical) polar diagram is used, unless it is made clear by a statement of the polarisation of the antenna with respect to the earth's surface. When reference is made to the polar diagram of an antenna in free space, the terms 'horizontal' and 'vertical' have no meaning, and the more precise descriptions of *E-plane* and *H-plane* polar diagrams are to be preferred. These are unambiguous, since the direction of the electric and magnetic fields around the antenna is a function only of the direction of current flow. The electric field (or E-plane) is parallel to the direction of current and therefore usually parallel to the radiating wire. The magnetic field (or H-plane) is at right angles to the current and therefore normal to the radiating wire. The polar diagram of the half-wave dipole illustrated in **Fig 1.5** is then an E-plane diagram: the H-plane diagram

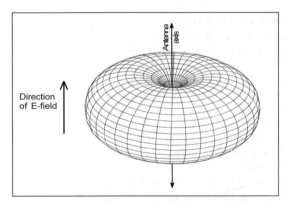

Fig 1.5: Polarisation of a dipole antenna.

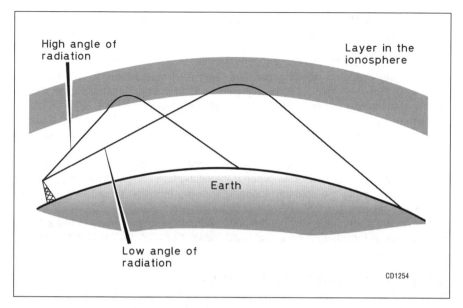

High angle of radiation

Layer in the ionosphere

Earth

Low angle of radiation

CD1254

Fig 1.6: Effect of angle of radiation and ionospheric regions on the distances achieved using ionospheric propagation.

of the dipole would be a circle. Such an antenna is then said to possess E-plane directivity, and is omni-directional in the H-plane.

No matter what name is used to describe the polar diagram, it should be remembered that these radiation patterns are for long distances and cannot be measured accurately at distances less than several wavelengths from the antenna. The greater the gain, the greater the distance required.

In terms of long distance contacts on the HF bands in particular, the angle of elevation (sometimes also called the *angle of radiation*) of the beam is of importance. The distances that can be achieved are also dependent upon the angles at which the signals travel. From basic trigonometry it can be seen that if a signal leaves the antenna at a low angle of radiation, i.e. almost parallel to the earth's surface, the distances achieved will be greater than signals leaving with a high angle of radiation, i.e. travelling at a much steeper angle upwards towards the ionosphere (**Fig 1.6**). Also, the higher the ionospheric region that is used, the greater the distances that will be achieved.

Even relatively small increases in the angle at which the signal leaves the antenna can considerably reduce the distances that can be covered. The maximum distance that can be achieved using the E layer of the ionosphere is generally considered to be 2000km (1250 miles), but this is reduced to just 400km (250 miles) if the angle is 20°. Similarly the maximum distance achievable using the F2 layer reduces from around 4000km (2500 miles) to just under 1000km (600 miles). In view of these figures, most installations where long-haul contacts are required will want to have antennas that produce low-angle radiation.

ANTENNA RECIPROCITY

One of the key features of an antenna is that it can be used both for transmitting and receiving. When being used to receive signals, electromagnetic waves are picked up and converted into electrical signals that are passed down the feeder and presented to the front end of the receiver. In the reverse mode when power is applied to the feeder from a transmitter it passes along the feeder and enters the radiating element of the antenna. Here the electrical signals are converted into electromagnetic energy that is radiated as a signal. In each case the process is the exact reversal of the other.

This means that for all practical purposes the properties of an antenna used for reception are the same as its properties used for transmission. It has the same directive pattern, impedance, efficiency, and so forth in both directions. This means that for transmitting the direction where most power is delivered is also the same direction in which the antenna has optimum 'sensitivity'. A poorly-matched antenna with a high level of VSWR on transmit will also present a poor match when used to receive.

This fact can be useful when designing antennas, because some tests are easier to make, or more accurate, when transmitting for example. In this way the test can be performed in the optimum manner, knowing the results hold for both transmitting and receiving.

Obviously parameters such as the power handling limit only apply to the antenna when it is used for transmitting as very high powers are most unlikely to be encountered when receiving.

ANTENNA PERFORMANCE FIGURES

The meaning of the antenna performance figures that are often quoted in articles about antennas, was discussed by Peter Dodd, G3LDO, in his 'Antennas' column in the July 2009 *RadCom*. The performance of an antenna is determined by comparing it with some reference antenna. Mathematical models of antennas use an isotropic radiator, a hypothetical point source antenna which radiates equally in all directions. The field strength or radiation pattern of an antenna is one of its most important characteristics and its complete description requires field intensity measurements in all directions. It follows that the field strength diagram of our isotropic antenna is a sphere, as shown in **Fig 1.7(a)**. Antenna mathematical models using this isotopic source as a reference are defined using the letters *dBi* - decibels above (or, if a negative figure, below) an isotropic radiator. Remember that this isotropic antenna is a mathematical entity; it is not possible to construct a truly isotropic antenna.

In practice, however, a full three-dimensional description is not used very often and a section through the three-dimensional space pattern will provide enough information. A useful analogy is the contour line of equal height on a map of a hill, which shows the general shape of the hill. A section through the spherical isotropic radiation pattern is a circle.

If we now consider a vertical half-wave dipole shown in **Fig 1.7(b)** it can be seen that the three dimensional polar diagram is doughnut shaped. A section through this doughnut is a figure of eight (on its side). It can be seen that the radiation pattern of this dipole is not uniform and that field strength in some directions has been increased at the expense of the field strength in other directions. This increase in field strength at area of maximum radiation is defined as power gain. The power gain of the dipole is generally considered to be 2.15dBi.

Mathematical models of antennas can be constructed using antenna modelling software such as *EZNEC* or *MIMA* and, in general, give very good indications of antenna performance, provided the methods of calculation are clearly specified.

So far we have only considered antennas in free space. Problems sometimes arise because the effect of the antenna in the real world has not been considered, or considered incorrectly. The ground under the antenna acts as a reflector. Electromagnetic waves from the antenna radiate in all directions and some of these waves are reflected by the ground. If the reflected wave is in phase or partially in phase with a direct wave, it enhances radiation and increases gain at a particular angle. Other combinations of reflected and direct waves, whose phases tend to cancel, reduce gain at other angles. This is illustrated in **Fig 1.8**, which shows that waves A and C

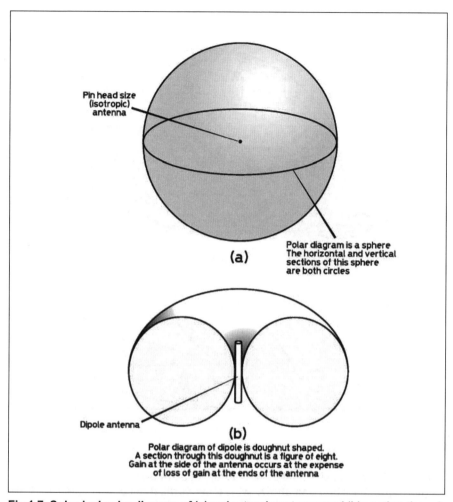

Fig 1.7: Spherical polar diagram of (a) an isotropic antenna and (b) section though a doughnut-shaped polar diagram of a vertical free-space dipole.

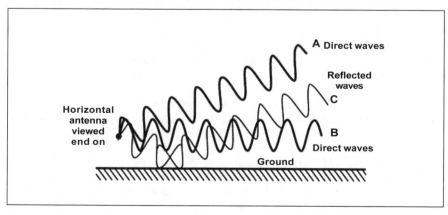

Fig 1.8: Diagram illustrating the effect of ground reflection on directly radiated waves.

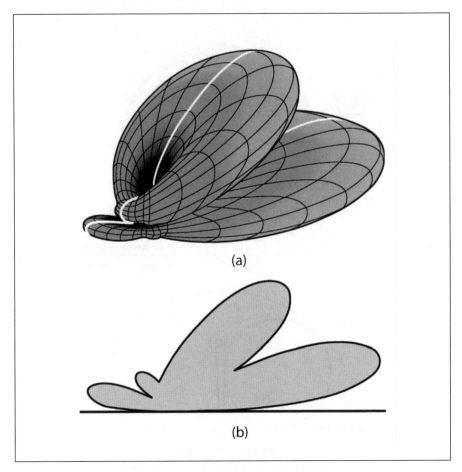

Fig 1.9: (a) Three-dimensional polar diagram of a three-element beam, one wavelength high. The white line shows where the vertical section is calculated. (b) Vertical diagram obtained from this section.

enhance gain while B and C tend to cancel and reduce the gain.

This is the cause of the familiar elevation antenna field strength diagrams. An example of a three-element beam is shown in **Fig 1.9**. The gain of the antenna in this diagram is calculated over average ground with the main lobe 13.5dBi at an angle of 14° above the horizontal. The same antenna gave a *free space gain* of 8.4dBi. The difference between these two gain figures (5.1dB) is known as *ground gain*. In the real world, almost all antennas are affected by the ground and therefore have ground gain.

Before the days of mathematical modelling the most practical method of measuring the gain of an antenna was to use an antenna testing range and compare the antenna under test (AUT) with a reference antenna such as a dipole. Because ground gain affects the both the reference antenna and the AUT it was important that the reference antenna, AUT and the signal level detection antenna were at the same height for the comparison measurements. Under these circumstances an optimised three-element Yagi gave a gain of around 8dB compared with a dipole, so the gain figure was quoted in dBd, i.e. dB above a dipole.

These days a fairly accurate estimate of the performance of most antennas can be done using a computerised mathematical model. In this case we can use a free space model of the antenna compared with the isotopic reference. Here we are dealing with mathematical entities that give proven computed antenna performance, which avoids the complications of specifying ground characteristics or antenna height above ground.

BANDWIDTH AND Q

There are no unique definitions for antenna bandwidth. Essentially the definition of the bandwidth of an antenna is the band of frequencies over which it will operate satisfactorily. Dependent upon the operational requirements of the antenna, the definitions fall into two categories: impedance bandwidth and the radiation pattern bandwidth.

Impedance bandwidth

It is more usually the impedance bandwidth that limits the operation of amateur HF antennas and it is defined as the frequency range over which the antenna impedance results in a voltage standing wave ratio (VSWR) less than some arbitrary limit. This may be typically 2:1 for amateur operation with solid-state transmitters, or higher values for other applications. Ideally, an antenna should be impedance matched to the feed line and thence to the transmitter or receiver, although this is not the case where tuned feed line antennas are used. Under these circumstances an antenna tuning and matching unit will need to be able to accommodate the high voltages that are encountered under some circumstances.

Radiation pattern bandwidth

Antenna radiation patterns are dependent upon the operating frequency and under some circumstances they may be of importance. Their sensitivity to frequency changes are in turn dependent on the degree of tuning or inherent Q required to achieve the desired characteristic. Bandwidth is defined as the frequency range over which satisfactory performance can be obtained. The criteria for defining bandwidth could be one or more of the following:

♦ Main lobe beamwidth
♦ Acceptable side lobe level
♦ Minimum gain or directivity
♦ Polarisation qualities

It should be noted that the impedance bandwidth and radiation pattern bandwidth are independent of each other. It is quite possible for the impedance bandwidth to be greater than the radiation pattern bandwidth, especially with high-gain antennas, and to be able to feed power into an antenna that is then wasted by radiating it in other than the desired direction.

POLARISATION

The polarisation of an antenna is defined in terms of the orientation of the electric field vector in the direction of maximum radiation. The maximum radiation from a dipole occurs in a plane bisecting its centre and at right angles to the dipole axis. The electric field vector in this plane lies parallel to the axis of the dipole. Thus a dipole mounted horizontally above the ground is said to radiate horizontally polarised signals, and the same dipole mounted vertically would radiate vertically polarised signals.

Radio waves comprise both electric and magnetic fields mutually coupled at right-angles to each other and at right-angles to the direction of propagation. The two principal planes used in describing radiation patterns are the E-plane, which lies parallel to the electric vector or E-field in the main lobe, and the H-plane, which lies parallel to the magnetic vector or H-field in the main lobe.

While vertical or horizontal linear polarisation is almost always used for terrestrial communications, circular polarisation may be used in some applications, often at VHF and above and for applications such as satellite communications where it is able to help to reduce the effects of propagation, ground reflections or the spinning motions of the satellites on the signals. The effect of circular polarisation can be visualised as a signal that would be radiated from a dipole that is spinning about its centre at the radiating frequency. The tip of the electric vector traces out a corkscrew as it propagates away from the antenna and, like a corkscrew, the polarisation is described as right or left-handed circular, dependent on the direction of rotation of the electric vector as seen from the transmitter.

For communication in free space, both transmitting and receiving antennas should have the same polarisation for the maximum signal to be received. Any cross polarisation will result in a degradation of the signal proportional to the cosine of the angle between them. Thus at ninety degrees, i.e. when the antennas are said to be cross-polarised, no signal should be received. In practice there are many reflections, even over short terrestrial paths, and some signal will be received. For ionospheric propagation for most purposes the signal can be thought of as being randomly polarised and cross-polarisation of antennas is not an issue.

There are, however, some advantages for choosing an antenna of a particular polarisation under some circumstances. For ground or surface wave propagation there are major benefits for using vertical polarisation, as signals may be tens of decibels higher using a vertically-polarised antenna than one that is horizontally polarised. It is for this reason that medium-wave broadcast stations use vertically-polarised antennas. This means that for local topband (160m) contacts, a loaded vertical antenna is likely to give better results than a larger horizontal one.

TYPES OF ANTENNA

There are many ways in which antennas can be categorised. Reference is often made to *Hertzian* and *Marconi* antennas. The most basic type of antenna consists of a pair of conductors which are arranged as shown in **Fig 1.10(a)**. The two wires run in opposite directions and are usually of equal length. The feedpoint is located at the centre. This is the type of antenna that Heinrich Hertz used as part of his transmitting experiments in 1887 - 88 and so these antennas, which do not require any earth connection, are known as Hertzian or Hertz antennas. Some types of loop antenna such as the quad loop are also categorised as Hertzian antennas.

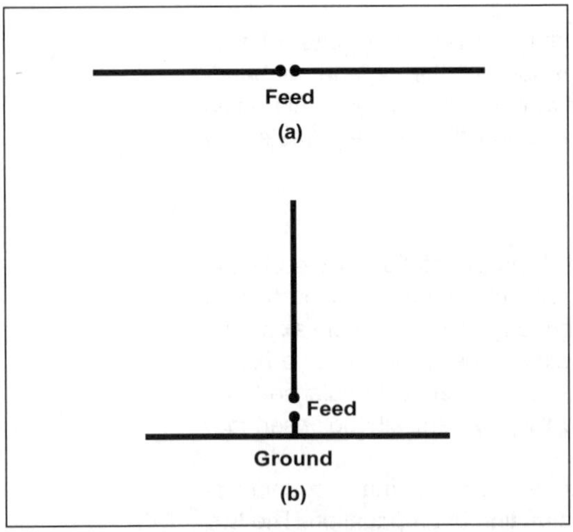

The basic Marconi antenna, shown in **Fig 1.10(b)**, is a quarter-wavelength long and is either grounded at one end or connected to a network of wires such as a ground plane or a counterpoise. The ground or counterpoise provides the equivalent of an additional quarter-wavelength which is required for the antenna to resonate. This category includes end-fed verticals (which are often referred to as ground-plane antennas or monopoles, especially if the radiating element has an electrical length of 1/4 wavelength), the inverted-L, the Marconi-T and off-centre fed antennas with a single wire feed like the Windom.

Fig 1.10: The two basic types of antenna: (a) Hertzian and (b) Marconi.

The two pioneers of radio after whom the basic types of antenna are named: left: Heinrich Hertz (1857 - 1894); right: Guglielmo Marconi (1874 - 1937).

Although there are many different interpretations, this gives a useful starting point to look at many different types of antenna.

Antennas may also be categorised according to whether they are *balanced* or *unbalanced*. Essentially a balanced antenna is one such as a dipole where there are two poles or connections to the antenna itself. An unbalanced antenna is where one of the connections of the antenna is an earth or simulated earth in the form of a counterpoise or ground plane. In order to feed an antenna, a balanced or unbalanced feeder is required, as discussed in the next chapter. However, when feeding a dipole or other balanced antenna with an unbalanced feeder such as coaxial cable, a balun (*bal*anced-to-*un*balanced transformer) is often used to accommodate the change. Further information about baluns is given in Chapter 8.

Another popular form of antenna is the *end-fed wire*. Although these antennas offer many advantages and are described later, one of their disadvantages is that the whole length of the wire radiates. Typically there is no feeder, as the antenna starts immediately it leaves the Antenna Tuning Unit (ATU). As this is often located in the vicinity of the radio equipment, i.e. in the 'shack', It means that there are likely to be high levels of RF in the shack. Not only can this give rise to difficulties with RF getting back into the equipment, particularly on audio leads, causing feedback and distortion on the audio, but also there is the potential of health hazards associated with high levels of RF. Accordingly these antennas are best used only for receiving or for low power transmitting. However, these days automatic ATUs are readily available and an end-fed wire fed through a *remote* automatic ATU can be a good all-band performer, particularly if the wire can be kept well away from buildings and other obstructions by virtue of it being fed remotely. This antenna is also discussed later in ther book.

GROUND SYSTEMS

Unbalanced antennas require a ground system for successful operation: the success or failure of the antenna system depends upon the efficiency of the earth system. In turn this is highly dependent upon the conductivity of the ground in the vicinity of the antenna. Moist land provides the best conditions, and indeed a salt marsh would be ideal. Often the underlying rock plays an important part in any ground system, so those who are living on sandstone areas will find difficulty in creating an efficient earth system. Those in more moist areas will generally find it much easier to create a good earth connection.

An earth system can have several constituents. Ground rods, radials, counterpoises; all can form part of the earth system. Not only is a good DC connection required, but a good RF one is also needed. By combining different techniques it is often possible to make a very efficient earth system.

A good DC connection is made by having a conductor in contact with the earth. As the earth has a very low conductivity it is necessary to have as much surface area in contact as possible. The importance of this is illustrated by the fact that even a good DC ground may have a resistance of several ohms and this will considerably reduce the efficiency of the antenna.

To make a DC connection to ground a variety of methods can be used. Ground rods are manufactured for electrical installations. These are typically rods with a steel centre to allow them to be driven into the ground, but with a copper surface. A clamp is then used to make a connection to the wire. These are often quite thin, and they do not present a large surface area to the ground. As a result several may be required. As an alternative, or in addition, discarded lengths of copper water pipe may be buried. As copper is soft, this normally has to be buried because if driven into the ground with a hammer it is likely to buckle and bend. If the separate earth spikes and pipes are spread out, the effect of the low conductivity of the earth itself can be reduced. A typical installation may consist of several rods and pipes connected together using copper braid to ensure a low resistance for the interconnecting wire.

Another approach that is particularly applicable when moving into a new house, or when landscaping a garden, is to bury galvanised chicken wire. This mesh comes in rolls and can be placed under a layer of earth, covered over and then a lawn can be planted over the top. By laying it under a lawn it is less likely to be disturbed. By covering a large area, as well as having a relatively large contact surface area, this method is able to provide a very efficient earth system.

A variety of approaches may be used from conductive ground rods and other conductive sheets to improve the DC connection to earth, to the use of radials of either insulated or bare copper wire to provide an RF earth with a low impedance. These radials can either be laid on the ground, or buried beneath it. In most cases the option of burying them is preferable because it means they do not then present a trip hazard. Burying radial wires can be easily achieved, even in a lawn, by simply making a narrow slit in the earth with a spade and then dropping the wire into the slit and replacing the earth. Although this will leave a mark in a lawn for a short while, it will soon grow over and will not be visible.

For broadcast stations with few limitations, grounding systems may be particularly elaborate, and this has been recognised for many years. A report from the 1930s which is still relevant today suggested that 120 radials should be used, radiating out from the base of the antenna. These radials, it suggested, should be at least half a wavelength long. This number of radials is obviously not viable for most amateur situations (120 half-wave long radials on 1.8MHz would require nearly 10 *kilometres* of wire!) and it has been suggested that at least 15 radials is a good compromise. However, even with this number of radials the earth impedance is such that the efficiency of a quarter-wavelength antenna system might fall to around 50% under average conditions.

Another option is to use a *counterpoise* system. It has been suggested that this is likely to be more efficient than an earth. A counterpoise consists of a number of radials or a grid network of wires elevated above the earth and insulated from it. A 'ground plane' consisting of radials around a vertical antenna is a form of counterpoise.

COUNTERPOISES AND RF EARTHS

A quarter-wave vertical or any end-fed antenna requires an effective and efficient RF earth or ground to radiate properly. In addition, the penalty for not having a good RF earth is that the outside of the radio equipment can be at a high RF potential. Furthermore, the microphone, key or headset leads are also 'hot' with RF, so you get RF feedback and BCI problems.

Let us consider the simple half-wave dipole. The centre of the coax is connected to one wire and the braiding to the other, as shown in **Fig 1.11**. Each wire is a quarter

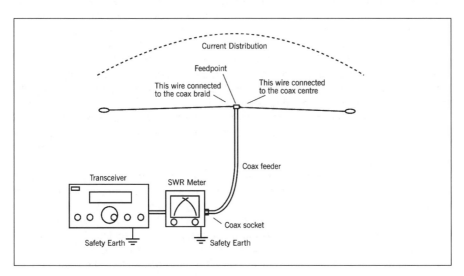

Fig 1.11: Simple dipole showing the RF current distribution. The safety earth is provided for electrical safety rather than as an RF ground.

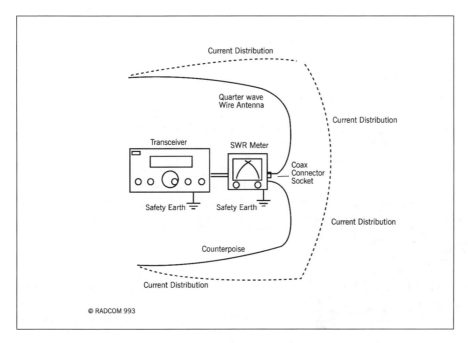

© RADCOM 993

Fig 1.12: A resonant quarter-wave end-fed wire using a counterpoise.

wavelength long and both wires radiate equally. The arrangement is good for only one band. Supposing the dipole is now orientated so that it is vertical with the right hand wire uppermost. This wire, which is connected to the centre of the coax, could now be considered as the 'antenna' and the other wire, connected to the coax braiding, as the 'counterpoise'. The current in both wires is still equal, provided they are both quarter of a wavelength long. Note that the transceiver is earthed. This is included for electrical safety reasons but it may not be a good RF earth.

Suppose we now dispense with the coax feeder and connect the 'antenna' wire to the centre pin of the antenna socket of the transceiver in the shack (via the SWR meter), as shown in **Fig 1.12**. Where is the 'counterpoise' to be connected now? In the case of the dipole it is connected to the braid of the coax but with no coax it can be connected to the outside connector of the coax socket. A more practical connection point would be the ground connector of the transceiver, which will be at the same RF potential as the outside of the coax socket. This arrangement will work only provided that the 'antenna' and the 'counterpoise' are resonant at the frequency in use, as with the case of the dipole described above.

Any conductor carrying an RF current will radiate. A counterpoise is part of the antenna system and radiates on transmit so some consideration should be given to where it is placed. Just putting the counterpoise under the shack carpet may not be such a good idea.

For multiband use, a practical solution is to use a wire that is a quarter of a wavelength long on the lowest frequency in use. This sort of antenna is often referred to as a 'random wire antenna' (or often, misleadingly, as a 'long wire' antenna). This antenna is connected to the transceiver via an ATU. This device, when correctly tuned, presents a low impedance to the transceiver antenna socket. The multiband counterpoise problem can be solved by connecting quarter-wave radials, one for each band in parallel, to the transceiver and ATU earth connector. Then run the free ends away from the transceiver, preferably outside the shack. Such an arrangement will require some experimentation to find the best position for the radials. They can be bent or even folded but the length may have to be altered to maintain resonance. The radials are best located outside the house in the horizontal plane to reduce coupling into the electrical wiring. If the radial(s) are used indoors (e.g. around the skirting board), use wire with thick insulation and an additional several layers of insulating tape at the ends, as the RF voltage at the ends can be fairly high when transmitting.

EARTH LEAD TUNER

Instead of using multiple quarter-wave long counterpoise wires, an alternative method is to use a single radial that is tuned to place a very low RF potential at the transceiver on any band. This is done by inserting an LC series tuning circuit between the transmitter and the radial - just like using an ATU with the antenna.

Such units are commercially available and the MFJ-931 is one example. These units are normally described as an 'Artificial Ground'. In addition to the LC circuit these devices usually have a through-current RF indicator which helps tuning the radial or earth lead to resonance (maximum current).

Alternatively, you can make one yourself. The unit designed by SM6AQR and shown in **Fig 1.13** uses a 200 - 300pF air-spaced tuning capacitor with at least 1mm plate spacing; the capacitor and its shaft must be insulated from the tuner cabinet. The inductor is a 28μH roller coaster. Alternatively, a

The MFJ-931 'Artificial Ground'.

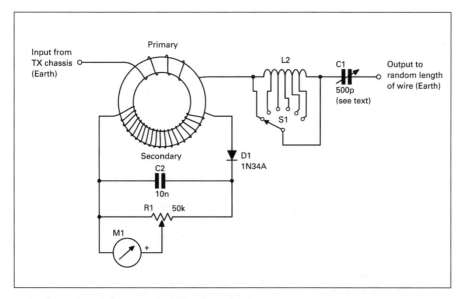

Fig 1.13: SM6AQR's earth lead tuner. T1 =Amidon T-50-43 ferrite toroid. The primary is simply the earth lead through the toroid centre; secondary = 20t small gauge enamelled wire. L = 28μH rollercoaster or multi-tapped coil with 10-position switch; see text. C1 = 200pF or more air variable, >1mm spacing, insulated from panel and case. C2, C3 = 10nF ceramic. D1 = AA119; R1 = 1kΩ; R2 = 10kΩ pot, Rx see text. M = 100μA or less.

multi-tapped fixed coil with as many taps as possible could be used. The tuning indicator consists of a current transformer, rectifier, smoothing filter, sensitivity potentiometer and DC microammeter. The 'primary' of the current transformer is the artificial earth lead itself; it simply passes through the centre of the ferrite toroid T1, on to which a secondary of 20 turns of thin enamelled wire has been wound. R_x, the resistor across the T1 secondary, should be non-inductive and between 22 and 100Ω; it is selected such that a convenient meter deflection can be set with the sensitivity control R2 on each required frequency and for the RF power used.

Just as important as setting up the ATU, the earth lead or counterpoise tuner should be adjusted on low power. The approximate settings for each band can be recorded and fine tuned on high power. It is important that the appropriate earth tuner band setting is selected as the first action to be taken when changing bands. The reason is that if the tuner was set on 40m and the band changed to 20m a situation may occur where the presented earth lead impedance could be very high. This would be the same as having no RF earth at all resulting in a high RF voltage on the transceiver case – and all the problems that entails. Using several parallel counterpoises of different lengths would eliminate this potential problem; the lengths of these counterpoises are not critical.

'REAL' EARTHS

All this messing around with counterpoises and radials seems to be a lot of trouble - would it not be possible just to use a connection to the real earth, say a ground stake, outside the shack window?

The counterpoise, described above, presents a low impedance at the frequency in use so the RF current on transmit is high. Provided that our ground stake arrangement will handle this then it is fine. In practice a good RF earth connection is hard to find and is only practicable from a ground floor shack. The problem with the earth

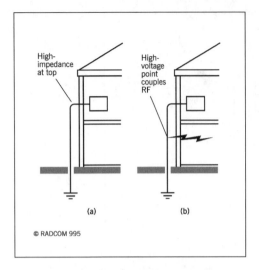

Fig 1.14: Why RF ground leads from upstairs seldom work. (a) ground lead with quarter-wave resonance (or odd multiple) is ineffective; very little current will flow into it. (b) Ground lead with half-wave resonance (or multiples) will have high-voltage points, which couple RF into house wiring.

stake is that ground has resistance and the lead connecting the earth stake radio has reactance. This ground resistance is in series with the radiation resistance of the antenna so it is important to get the ground resistance as low as possible if you want an efficient end-fed antenna.

Many ways have been tried to reduce the ground resistance. In general, the more copper you can bury in the ground the better, e.g. an old copper water tank can make a very good earth if connected to the radio with a short thick copper wire. Low-band DXers tend to use buried multiple radials: lots of wires radiating out from the earth connection and the rule is 'the more wires the better'. The length of the wires will be restricted at many stations, but nevertheless they will contribute to lowering the RF ground resistance.

If you operate from an upstairs shack, engineering a low-impedance earth connection at ground level using the method described above will probably be a waste of time. The reason for this is that the distance up to the shack is a significant fraction of a wavelength on the higher HF bands and above. Ian White, G(M)3SEK, writing in 'In Practice' in *Radio Communication* (*RadCom*) in May 1994 made the point that at frequencies where this length is near one or three quarter-wavelengths, the earth connector will act as a RF insulator, which is just the *opposite* of what is wanted, see **Fig 1.14(a)**. This is bound to happen in one or more of our nine HF bands. On the other hand, if the lead resonates as a half-wave, (a situation that is likely to arise on any band above 10MHz), it may act as a good RF earth. However, it also has a high-voltage point half-way down which may couple RF into the house wiring, see **Fig 1.14(b)**, because electrical wiring within the wall of a house is generally perpendicular.

In other words, although an earth wire from the radio in an upstairs shack to an earth stake will provide a safety earth, its usefulness as an RF earth is unpredictable.

ANTENNA WIRE CONSIDERATIONS

The type of wire used in antenna systems can be an important consideration. Any outdoor wire antenna will be subject to the action of the wind and will swing about for much of the time. Unless sensible precautions are taken when constructing such wire antennas, metal fatigue will eventually take its toll.

Single-strand, hard-drawn copper wire of 16 or 18SWG is recommended for antenna work, including particularly the fabrication of open-wire lines. It is more expensive than cheap multi-strand plastic-covered wire, but hard-drawn copper wire will last for many years.

Cheap plastic-covered wire *can* be used though, especially for antenna experimentation work when it is unlikely the antenna will be left *in situ* for long periods of time. Constant movement of the antenna may result in the conductors breaking, leaving the plastic covering undamaged. When this happens the actual break is difficult to locate and repair. Also, this type of wire often stretches by a considerable degree, leading to a lowering of the resonant frequency of the antenna.

Similarly, it must be mentioned that 75Ω twin feed is particularly prone to internal breaks if it is allowed to swing freely in the wind.

2 Feeders

ALTHOUGH NOT PART of the radiating antenna itself, the feeder, or feedline, is an integral part of the whole antenna system and its operation governs many of the parameters of the overall antenna system. In fact, there are three separate parts to an antenna system: the radiator, the feeder or feedline between transmitter and radiator, and the coupling arrangements to the transmitter. Wherever possible, the antenna itself should be placed in the best position where it can radiate the optimum signal. As these positions are generally high up and not in the optimum position for the station, it is necessary to have a feeder to connect the antenna to the transmitter or receiver with a minimum of loss due to resistance or radiation.

By the use of transmission lines or feeders, the power of the transmitter can be carried appreciable distances without much loss due to conductor resistance, insulator losses or radiation. It is thus possible to place the antenna in an advantageous position without having to suffer the effects of radiation from the connecting wires. For example, a 14MHz dipole 11m (33ft) in length can be raised 20m (60ft) high and fed with power without incurring appreciable loss. If, on the other hand, the antenna wire itself were brought down from this height to a transmitter at ground level, most of the radiation would be propagated from the down lead in a high angle direction. An arrangement of this nature would be relatively poor for long-distance communication.

OPERATION OF FEEDERS

A feeder is a transmission line along which power is transferred as an electromagnetic wave. It travels along the transmission line in fundamentally the same way as the free-space wave, although it is confined to the conductors and the field is curved about the conductors instead of being linear. In one type of feeder, which is in the form of a concentric line (coaxial cable), the current passes along the centre conductor and returns along the inside of the sheath. Due to the so-called *skin effect*, at high frequencies the currents do not penetrate more than a few thousandths of an inch into the metal, and this means there should be no current on the outside of the outer conductor. The fields are thus held inside the cable and there is no radiation, provided that current is not allowed to flow on the outside of the cable.

In another form of feeder using twin lines, the two wires carry 'forward and return' currents, producing equal and opposite fields which effectively neutralise each other away from the immediate vicinity of the wires. When the spacing between wires is a very small fraction of the wavelength, the radiation is negligible provided the line is accurately balanced. This means that, in the HF range, a separation of several centimetres may be employed, but in the VHF range a much smaller spacing is required.

CHARACTERISTIC IMPEDANCE

One of the major features of a feeder is its *characteristic impedance*. This is expressed in ohms (Ω) and just as an antenna has a value of impedance, and a receiver or transmitter has an input or output impedance, so does a feeder. This impedance is very important because it is necessary to match the feeder impedance to that of the rest of the system.

The impedance of the feeder is governed by a number of factors. The physical dimensions of the feeder have a very large bearing. Also, the dielectric constant of the material between and sometimes around the feeder can vary the impedance. These factors are easy to control and therefore all feeders are manufactured or constructed to provide a particular characteristic impedance. A match of the impedance of the receiver and / or transmitter to the feeder, and also the feeder to the antenna, is required to enable the optimum power transfer to take place, and it is for this reason that the impedance of the feeder is important. Where there is a discontinuity or change in impedance, power is reflected and standing waves are set up.

The way in which the characteristic impedance can be visualised is by looking at a travelling wave that is travelling in a certain direction without suffering any reflection or discontinuity. The same applies to transmission lines, although in this case the presence of reflections and therefore standing waves does not cause radiation if the line remains balanced or shielded.

If the line were infinitely long and free from losses, a signal applied to the input end would travel on for ever, energy being drawn away from the source of signal just as if a resistance had been connected instead of the infinite line. In both cases there is no storage of energy such as there would be if the load included inductance or capacitance and the line (as far as the generator of the signal is concerned) is strictly equivalent to a pure resistance. This resistance is known as the characteristic impedance of the line and usually denoted by the symbol Z_0.

Suppose now that at some distance from the source we cut the line; what has been removed is still an infinitely long line and equivalent to a resistance Z_0 so, if we replace it by an *actual* resistance of this value, the generator will not be aware of any change. There is still no reflection, all the power applied to the input end of the line is absorbed in the terminating resistance, and the line is said to be *matched*.

Again because no reflections occur at the end of a correctly matched line, the ratio of the travelling waves of voltage and current, V / I, is Z_0. This enables the load presented to the feeder by the antenna to be in turn presented to the transmitter, without any change in the process. This is irrespective of the length of line employed, since the value of the characteristic impedance Z_0 is independent of the length of the line.

In order to achieve maximum efficiency from a transmission line, it should be operated as close to a matched condition as possible, i.e. the load presented by the antenna should be arranged, either directly or by means of some impedance transformer, to present a good match to the line. However, the degree to which the load impedance can be permitted to depart from the characteristic impedance without introducing appreciable extra losses is quite large. On the other hand, bandwidth considerations or the need to avoid load variations which could damage transmitters may impose stringent matching requirements.

The characteristic impedance is determined by the structure of the feeder and its dimensional ratios of the cross-section of the line, and not by its absolute size.

VELOCITY FACTOR

When the medium between the conductors of a transmission line is air, the travelling waves propagate along it at the same speed as waves in free space. If a dielectric material is introduced between the conductors, for insulation or support purposes, the waves will be slowed down and will no longer travel at the free-space velocity. The velocity of the waves along any line is equal to $1 / \sqrt{(LC)}$, where L and C are the distributed capacitance and inductance values. The introduction of such material increases the capacitance without increasing the inductance because the capacitance is dependent upon the dielectric constant of the material separating the two plates in the capacitor, and consequently the characteristic impedance and the velocity are both reduced by the same factor $\sqrt{\varepsilon}$.

The ratio of the velocity of waves on the line to the velocity in free space is known as the *velocity factor*. It is as low as 0.5 for mineral or PVC insulated lines and is roughly 0.66 for solid polythene cables (ε = 2.25). Semi-air-spaced lines have a factor which varies between 0.8 and 0.95, while open-wire lines with spacers at intervals may reach 0.98.

It is important to make proper allowances for this factor in some feeder applications, particularly where the feeders are used as tuning elements or interconnecting lines in antenna arrays, or as chokes for EMC applications. For example, if the velocity factor v = 2/3, then an electrical quarter-wave line would be physically only a *sixth* of a wavelength long (2/3 x 1/4 = 1/6).

In practice, the velocity factor v can be found by short circuiting a length of cable with about 3cm of wire formed into a loop and then coupling the loop to a dip oscillator. The lowest frequency at which the cable shows resonance corresponds to an electrical length of a quarter-wave; then:

$$v = \frac{f\,(\text{MHz}) \times \text{Length (feet)}}{246}$$

and should have a value between 0.5 and unity.

The velocity factor is only of significance in certain antenna types, for example those requiring quarter-wave 'stubs'. Open-wire lines have a velocity factor of about 0.975 which means that a quarter-wavelength stub at 7MHz will be 25cm (10in) shorter than a basic electrical quarter-wavelength.

TYPES OF LINE

There are three main types of transmission line:

- ♦ The single wire feed, arranged so that there is a true travelling wave on it.
- ♦ Coaxial cable, in which there are concentric conductors, one inside the other with an insulating layer between them. The outer conductor encloses the wave.
- ♦ Parallel wire line with two conductors carrying equal but oppositely directed currents and voltages, i.e. balanced with respect to earth. Twin line and open wire feeders fall into this category.

Each of these feeders has its own advantages and disadvantages and as a result they are used in slightly different applications.

Single-wire feeders are usually connected to a point on a resonant antenna where the impedance formed by the left and right-hand portions in parallel matches the impedance of the wire. This form of feeder is now rarely used, being basically inefficient because of the losses in the return path, which is via the ground. The feeder also radiates, acting to some extent as a terminated long-wire antenna. Against this it offers the advantages of being lightweight and having a low visual impact. For short lengths (up to about half a wavelength) the losses should normally be less than 1dB.

Examples of (top) coaxial cable (Andrew LDF4-50) and (below) parallel wire line (in this case slotted twin feeder).

COAXIAL CABLE

The most common type of feeder used today is undoubtedly coaxial feeder or 'coax'. As the name suggests, the cable consists of two concentric conductors as shown in **Fig 2.1**. The centre conductor is almost universally made of copper. Sometimes it may be a single conductor whilst at other times it may consist of several strands.

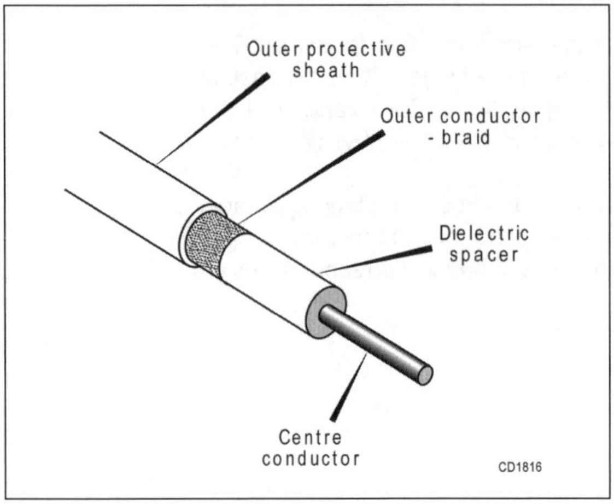

The outer conductor is normally made from a copper braid. This enables the cable to be flexible which would not be the case if the outer conductor were solid. To improve the screening, double or even triple screened cables are sometimes used. Normally this is accomplished by placing one braid directly over another, although in some instances a copper foil or tape outer may be used. By using additional layers of screening, the levels of stray pick-up and radiation are considerably reduced. More importantly for most radio amateurs this will result in lower levels of loss.

Fig 2.1: Coaxial cable feedline.

Between the two conductors there is an insulating dielectric. This holds the two conductors apart and in an ideal world would not introduce any loss. This dielectric may be solid or as in the case of many low-loss cables it may be semi-air-spaced because it is the dielectric that introduces most of the loss. This may be in the form of long 'tubes' in the dielectric, or a 'foam' construction, where air forms a major part of the material.

Finally there is the outer cover or sheath. This serves little electrical function, although it can prevent earth loops from forming. It also gives vital protection needed to prevent dirt and moisture attacking the cable. However, when burying cable it is best not to rely on the sheath. Instead use conduit or use special 'bury direct' cables that are available.

Characteristic impedance and loss

What factors affect the impedance and the loss of a coaxial cable? Ian White, GM3SEK, discussed this in his 'In Practice' column in *RadCom* (June 2007). Coax's characteristic impedance is defined by the ratio of the two conductors and the dielectric constant of the material between them. The key features of coaxial cable are shown in **Fig 2.2**. They are:

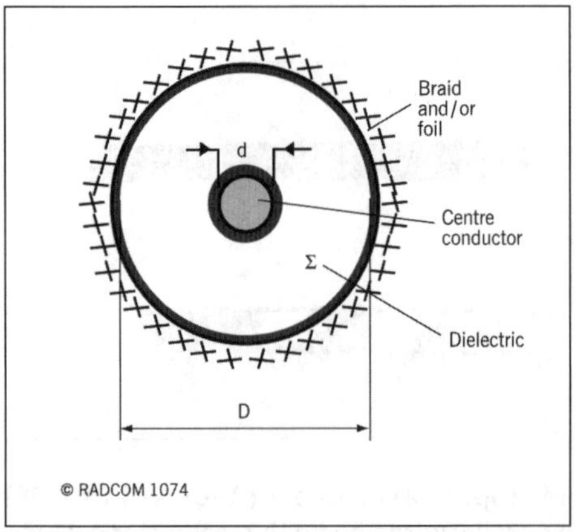

Fig 2.2: Key dimensions of coaxial cable.

♦ Z, the characteristic impedance (Ω);
♦ D (*capital D*), the inner diameter of the shield;
♦ d (*lower case d*), the outer diameter of the centre conductor (in the same units as D);
♦ ε, the dielectric constant of the insulation (for solid polyethylene $\varepsilon = 2.3$).

These are all tied together by the formula:

$$Z = (138 / \sqrt{\varepsilon}) \log_{10}(D/d)$$

RF current flows only on the surface of a conductor

due to the skin effect. This makes the RF resistance proportional to the diameter, or more strictly the circumference around the outside of the conductor, and not the cross-sectional area as you might expect.

The characteristic impedance Z does not depend on either D or d individually, but only on their ratio (D/d). If you change both D and d by the same factor, Z will remain the same. Thus we have industry-standard families of cables that differ in overall size, but all have the same dielectric and the same ratio of (D/d). In other words, they are all scale models of one another. That means they all have the same characteristic impedance, the same velocity factor, and the same capacitance per unit length. What *does* vary with overall size is the loss per unit length, which decreases as the cable gets larger. Losses are normally quoted in dB per 100m, and they also increase with frequency. These figures are all *matched* losses, i.e. when the VSWR is 1:1. Losses also increase with VSWR. On close examination of the data sheets, you can also see the difference between stranded and solid centre conductors, and the differences between bare, tinned or silver-plated copper.

For example, the industry-standard family of 50Ω cables using solid polyethylene insulation starts with RG174 (2.5mm OD, 27dB loss per 100m at 100MHz) and increases in size through RG58 (5mm, 15dB/100m at the same frequency), RG213 (10.3mm, 6.6dB/100m) and the large and heavy RG17 (22mm, 3.3dB/100m). The differences in loss can be explained almost completely by the differences in d, the outside diameter of the centre conductor.

When we talk about a 'low-loss' version of an industry-standard cable such as RG213, we generally mean a product that can physically replace the standard cable, the only difference being the lower losses. Thus the impedance *must* still be 50Ω and the new cable should have the same diameter as the standard cable, so it will fit through the same holes and can use the same connector bodies. The connector will need some minor changes to the centre pin, because a lower-loss version of the same cable must have a larger centre conductor.

But if d is increased while D remains the same, the ratio (D/d) has decreased. That means the value of Z has also been reduced, and it is no longer a 50Ω cable. The only remaining parameter is ε, the dielectric constant of the insulation. If some of the solid polyethylene (ε = 2.3) is replaced with air or some other gas with ε very close to 1, the effective value of ε is reduced and the characteristic impedance can be brought back to 50Ω. This is the reason low-loss cables use a foam or semi-air-spaced construction, as shown in **Fig 2.3**.

Good-quality foam or semi-air-spaced cable is quite difficult to manufacture: the foam in **Fig 2.3(a)** is soft and mechanically unstable, and the size and density of the bubbles can be difficult to control. The construction shown in **Fig 2.3(b)** has a polyethylene outer sleeve and a separate spiral cord spacer, but the inner conductor is able to move and, even on moderate bends, it can nudge the soft plastic cord aside to come very close to the outer sleeve. An over-sized centre conductor will still get hot when carrying high currents, and there is very little to prevent it from melting through the thin outer sleeve and touching the shield. On long vertical runs, the inner conductor can also slide slowly downwards under its own weight. In time, it can pull out the centre pin of a connector at the top of the run, or it can push the pin clear out of a plug at the bottom. **Fig 2.3(c)** shows the one-piece

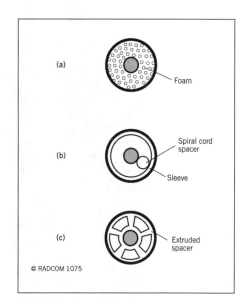

Fig 2.3: Three types of coax insulator with reduced dielectric constant: (a) foam, (b) sleeve and spiral cord, (c) extruded 'web'.

ribbed construction used in Westflex 103, which is better because it is moulded on to the centre conductor, holding it firmly in place. However, this construction is still vulnerable to overheating.

Many of these lower-loss cables also use a wrapped foil shield with an outer layer of braid, mainly to reduce unwanted pick-up and radiation levels. This doesn't do much to decrease the overall losses, because resistive losses in the outer shield are already much lower than in the centre conductor because of the difference in diameters. A continuous foil shield will have a slightly lower RF resistance than braid, but that isn't a valid reason to reduce the density of the braiding over the outside. The foil is very thin, and can easily tear when the cable is bent. For example, in rotator loops it is quite common for the foil to pull apart into several disconnected lengths. To prevent radiation losses from these breaks, it is essential to have a good coverage of outer braid as well as the foil.

Resistance loss calculated for the inner conductor accounts for about half the attenuation of new coaxial cable. The remainder is resistance loss in the outer conductor, additional resistance loss due to proximity effect arising from the close spacing between conductors, and dielectric losses in the insulating material. Radiation loss is virtually zero, provided no current flows on the outside of the cable. With most of the older types of cable there is an increase in resistance with age as a result of corrosion caused by chemicals used in the manufacture, and with cables of any age serious deterioration can result if joints are not adequately protected against moisture. A blackened inner conductor means that the cable is useless but any sign of discolouration or corrosion should be regarded with suspicion.

'RG8-X' / 'Mini-8'

These cables provide less loss than RG58, but without the inconvenience, weight and expense of a larger cable like RG213. Any improvement over RG58 has to be from a larger inner conductor, and that in turn will call for a foam dielectric to keep the

Left to right: standard RG58; a good foam 'Mini-8'; standard RG213; and semi-airspaced Belden 9913.

impedance at 50Ω. Be careful when buying these cables, because they are at the low end of the market where few standards apply.

The number '8' in the names of these cables originates from RG8, which was the old US military specification for the large 50Ω cable that we now know as RG213. When the MIL specification was revised, the designation 'RG8' fell vacant, and the number '8' was applied to all manner of unrelated products.

There are no effective standards in this volatile market, so you should look very carefully before you buy:

♦ Check the thickness of the inner conductor. It should be substantially thicker than the inner conductor of RG58, but it is never quite as thick as the inner of RG213 (see photo). This means the losses will be somewhere in between.

♦ Check the amount of copper in the braiding (a notorious area for cost cutting). Skimpy braiding may not have a large effect on the overall losses, but it's a sure sign of poor quality.

♦ Check that the foamed dielectric is reasonably rigid, and that the inner conductor is well centred. The cable should not kink as you try to bend it, and the inner conductor must not stray off centre. (At VHF and UHF the inner conductor can get pretty hot, so avoid any combination of high power, high frequencies and tight bends.)

♦ Roll the cable between your fingers and thumb, and check that it feels firm and solid, very much like a good MIL-spec RG58. If it feels loose, the outer jacket is not holding the shield firmly on to the inner dielectric. This is another sign of poor quality, and can cause bewildering variations in VSWR, especially at VHF and UHF.

These 'mini' low-loss cables definitely have their place, and there are some good ones around. . . you just need to be careful.

50Ω or 75Ω coax cable?

If you are feeding a dipole, which has an impedance of around 73Ω, with coaxial cable, should you not use 75Ω coax instead of the more usual 50Ω variety? Well, as

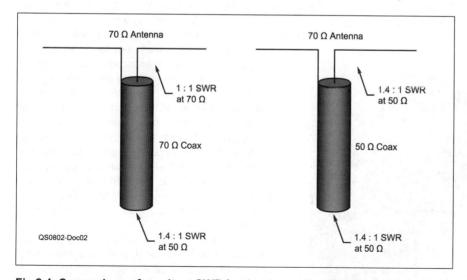

Fig 2.4: Comparison of resultant SWR for the cases of a 70Ω antenna fed with 70 or 50Ω coaxial cable. As indicated, there is not much difference as seen at the transmitter end (reprinted with permission of the American Radio Relay League).

'The Doctor' explained ('The Doctor is IN', *QST*, February 2008) at HF it usually makes little or no difference.

If we connect a 70Ω antenna to a 50Ω transceiver through 70Ω coax, the coax will have an SWR of 70/70, or a perfect 1:1. The radio will see an SWR of 70/50 or 1.4:1. Most radios will be quite happy with that. On the other hand, if we use the same antenna with 50Ω coax as shown in **Fig 2.4**, the SWR at the connection to the antenna will be 70/50 or 1.4:1. The SWR in the coax will be 1.4:1 and that is almost what the radio will see (reduced just a bit by the cable loss in either case), so there's not much difference at the radio (the loss in the coax will be slightly higher in the second case).

Let's take the lossiest 50Ω coax likely to be used, RG58, and assume 100ft on 10m. It will have a 'matched loss' of about 2.0dB. The SWR of 1.4:1 will result in an additional 0.1dB; hence, that's not too much of an issue either.

For most real antennas, the change in impedance as we change frequencies within a band will result in a larger difference. The height of a dipole will play a role in its impedance as well. At low heights, say 0.1 to 0.15λ, depending on ground conditions, it will have an impedance close to 50Ω at resonance. At heights between there and below 0.5λ, *EZNEC* predicts it will be around 80Ω, returning to 70Ω by 0.5λ.

Waterproofing coaxial cable

The trouble with water from an engineering point of view is that it reacts chemically with practically everything. This means that it is necessary to keep it out of areas where such a reaction will cause a problem. One particular area is coaxial cable, where water getting in will tend to oxidise the outer braid and considerably reduce its conductivity, thus increasing its loss. This means that every time coaxial cable is used outside it is necessary to give some thought to how to stop water getting in. With good quality cable being expensive, it is imperative to ensure that it remains in top condition as long as possible. John Nelson, G(W)4FRX, in an article in the January 1989 *RadCom* gives some useful ideas.

Waterproofing is required for any coaxial connector that is to be used on outdoor antennas. The simplest and best way is to use self-amalgamating tape. This is made by a number of companies and is available from antenna and general amateur radio stockists. It comes in the form of a roll that looks like thick insulating tape, but with a thin backing strip on one side. Peel off the backing strip and wrap around whatever it is to be waterproofed, overlapping each winding by about 50% of its width to ensure a good seal. Stretch the tape as it is being wound, so that it goes on under tension. It is best to start from the thinner end of the job, so that if an in-line connector joining two pieces of coaxial cable is to be waterproofed, start the tape on one piece of the cable, take it over the connector and on to the other piece. It is good practice to make the joint 'half-lapped', meaning that when the thickest part of the job (such as the connector) is reached, the tape is cut and then started again from the other piece of cable, overwinding the second tape run on to the first so that the connector is completely covered. This will ensure that there are no 'voids' in the join in which water could condense.

What happens then is a little miracle of industrial chemistry. In a short time the separate layers of tape which have been wound on start to fuse together, so that ultimately the connector is completely covered with what amounts to a fully waterproof 'boot'.

A roll of self-amalgamating tape, showing the peel-off backing.

Self-amalgamating tape is a plastic substance called polyisobutylene, which is one of a class of thermoplastics that is affected by the ultra-violet content of sunlight, so it tends to go brittle and crack after a year or two. All that needs to be done is to cover it with a layer of ordinary PVC insulating tape.

Using this technique should ensure that no water enters the cable. Self-amalgamating tape is amazingly tough, and nothing short of a Stanley knife with a new blade will make any impression on it (so when moving house and taking down the antennas, allow a little extra time for dismantling).

A final note on waterproofing: it is tempting to assume that the outer plastic sheath of coaxial cable is completely watertight, especially with a brand new drum of cable. This is not necessarily correct. It does not appear to be uncommon to find that drums of brand new cable, even from reputable manufacturers, have the occasional little nick or hole in the outer sheath. Presumably this arises from a problem somewhere in manufacture, or maybe when the cable is wound on to the drum. It is always worth closely inspecting a new run of coaxial cable (or multi-core rotator or preamp control cable) before installing it. If the odd flaw is found in the outer, the self amalgamating and insulating tape routine will soon deal with it.

TWIN LINE FEEDER

The third type of feeder used at HF is parallel wire line. This may be in a number of forms. It is possible to buy manufactured versions of this line having impedances between 75 and 300Ω: the most common is 300Ω line. This is a flat construction having the two wires covered in a plastic insulation and dielectric that is also used to space them apart, as shown in **Fig 2.5**.

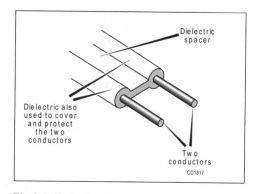

Fig 2.5: Twin feeder.

A version of this feeder with a light opaque plastic is widely used for commercially-manufactured temporary VHF / FM antennas. This feeder can obviously be bought separately and can be used in a number of applications. This type does have some drawbacks though, as it tends to absorb moisture when used externally; this naturally alters its characteristics and the loss rises. Another type, with black insulation that is slotted between the conductors, is far more suitable.

Open wire feeder, as the name suggests, is made up from wire with spacers at suitable intervals along the wire. As the spacing is greater this generally has a higher characteristic impedance.

In just the same way that the characteristic impedance of coaxial feeder was governed by the ratio of the diameters of the conductors and the dielectric between them, the equivalent is also true for twin wire feeders. However, the measurements that govern the impedance of the twin wire feeder are the diameters of the wires and the distance between them. In this way the formula used to calculate the impedance of a feeder diameter d and centre spacing S is given by the approximate formula:

$$Z_0 \text{ (ohms)} = 276 \log_{10} (2S/d)$$

Feeder losses

The losses in tuned lines include any loss by radiation (which is normally very small), and any resistive loss in the conductor wires. Assuming that the feedline is made from 18 to 14SWG copper wires, the resistive losses are insignificant and those that exist are mostly related to the dielectric properties of the material used for the spacers.

At VHF and UHF spacers are seldom used, the wires being held taut and parallel with just air as the dielectric. Open-wire matched lines with spacers arranged at

45cm (15in) intervals will show an attenuation of 0.03dB per 30m (100ft) at 3.5MHz, rising to 0.25dB at 144MHz. This means that a 3dB power loss (half power) will only occur when the feed line is about 3km (10,000 feet) long at a frequency of 3.5MHz. Tuned lines will exhibit higher losses.

For convenience, 300Ω ribbon feeder may be used as tuned line, especially the slotted variety. The finest available ribbon feeder will have a greater loss than open-wire line, but this will still be relatively insignificant. The older type of flat 300Ω ribbon feeder, when used as a matched line, has an attenuation of 0.18dB per 30m (100ft) at 3.5MHz, rising to 1.55dB at 144MHz. However, this older ribbon detunes badly in wet weather, with the plastic dielectric absorbing moisture to give a significant increase in loss as well as a change in dielectric constant and hence the velocity factor. It has also been found that the absorbed moisture gives rise to corrosion in the wires, further worsening the performance over a period of time. The black plastic slotted variety has a better performance and its 'semi air' spacing and water-shedding characteristics make it ideal. Its use also avoids the tedium of making up a long run of open-wire feeder.

Unscreened twin-wire feeder must not be buried or its nominal impedance may be affected, and there will then be a high SWR on the line. The twin feeder is, however, less susceptible to dampness effects than some of the 300Ω ribbon cables available, for most of the electrical field between the conductors is confined within the solid black polyethylene insulating material into which they are embedded. The black colouring helps to reduce UV damage (caused by sunlight) to the plastic, so avoid light coloured or transparent cable varieties.

Reactance

Tuned feeders can exhibit reactance at their feed point, and this reactance may be either inductive or capacitive depending upon the frequency, the feeder length and the length of the antenna top. With any given antenna which uses tuned feeders, the reactance will be different on each frequency band, and it can be that on one or more bands there will only be resistive impedance which is much easier to cope with when using an ATU.

The use of an ATU is essential when using an antenna with a tuned feedline. In most cases the ATU will be able to 'tune out' the reactance present, but unfortunately there is no ATU design which will cope with an infinite range of impedance or reactance, so in practice certain combinations of antenna and feeder lengths must be avoided. An antenna which appears almost impossible to match on just one amateur band may have this corrected by the addition or subtraction of feet, or tens of feet, of feedline.

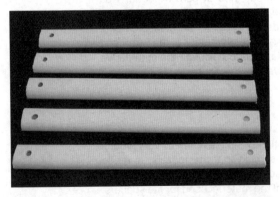

'Homebrew' open wire feeder spreaders made from 170mm lengths of 16mm electrical conduit.

Open-wire feeder construction

Apart from the advantages of very low levels of feeder loss, open-wire feeder has the advantage that it can be made at very little cost, a considerable advantage compared with the investment that has to be made when any significant length of low-loss coaxial feeder is installed.

Sourcing the spacing spreaders always seem to present the greatest challenge. Almost any insulator, from plastic hair curlers to coat hangers, is suitable. One solution is to use Perspex strips measuring approximately 13cm (5in) by 18mm (0.75in) wide, and cut from the scrap off cuts available at

The garden wall can be used as an anchor point when making open-wire feeder.

'give away' prices at local glassworks. Eamon Skelton, EI9GQ, used 170mm lengths of 16mm electrical conduit, available from DIY shops such as B&Q, for his open wire feeder spreaders. Each length of conduit was drilled 10mm from the end, giving a wire spacing of 150mm (see photo).

The number of spreaders required depends on a number of factors including the thickness of the wire. Using very thin wire will mean the use of many more spreaders, and this will raise the dielectric losses of the line. 18SWG or, better still, 16SWG enamelled or hard-drawn bare copper wire is ideal. Fewer spreaders will also reduce the weight of the feed line and its pull on the antenna.

Construction needs to be undertaken with a little thought to ensure the best end result. One method is to take two equal lengths of wire. These can be tied to an outside feature such as a garden wall, fence post or railing, and then pulled out tightly towards another tie point. The spacers can then all be threaded on to the wires, after which the wire ends are secured to the second tie point. The spacers must then be equally spaced along the feeder at intervals of about 45cm (18in). The holes in the spreaders near their ends must be just large enough to allow the wires to be pushed through. To ensure that the feeders will not slip out of position with the passage of time, some short lengths of wire can be twisted on to the feeder wires just above

A small diameter wire can be used to fix the spreaders to the wire and prevent them slipping.

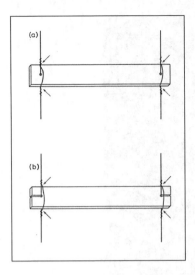

Fig 2.6: (a) An open-wire feeder line spacer with drilled holes for the wires, and wire 'retainers' to prevent slip. Spacers of this type have to be threaded on to the feeder wires before they are set into their final positions. (b) A spacer with slotted ends which can be easily fixed at any point along a completed length of feeder.

and below each spreader. These are indicated by the arrows in **Fig 2.6(a)**.

Instead of drilling holes in the spacers, they may be slotted as shown in **Fig 2.6(b)**. This method allows additional spreaders to be added after the line is completed.

It is often sensible to anchor an open-wire feedline to stop excessive swaying, and this can be done with the help of nylon fishing line. This line is often stained blue, and is invisible from more than a few metres. Any bends in the feedline must be of as large a radius as possible, and there must be no sudden and sharp bends. The line must be kept as far as possible from walls, down-pipes, gutters etc, and it should also drop down from the antenna centre at a right angle for at least a quarter-wavelength at the lowest frequency to be used. If the feeder runs under one leg of the antenna top the system will become unbalanced.

Homebrewing 600Ω feeder

The precise impedance of open-wire feeder is often not critical if the antenna system is matched using an ATU. However, some antenna designs call for open-wire line to have an impedance of close to 600Ω and this can be home made easily enough.

First, determine the size of wire being used and then determine the distance apart the wires must be using the formula for the characteristic impedance (Z_0) of a balanced line with air dielectric:

$$Z_0 = 276 \, \text{Log}_{10} \, (2S/d),$$

where S is the centre-to-centre spacing between the conductors, and d is the diameter of the wire used (in the same units as the spacing).

Using this formula, two 16SWG (14AWG) gauge (1.63mm / 0.064in diameter) wires spaced 4.8in apart will have a characteristic impedance of approximately 600Ω.

Larger diameter wire could be used for high-power use and would have even less loss, but the spacing may be too great for use on the 10m band: the spacing should be held to less than 0.01λ for the highest frequency used. Larger spacing may cause the feedline to start to radiate and become more like an antenna than a feedline. For portable use or low power, smaller diameter wire can be used without appreciable loss.

FITTING PL259 CONNECTORS

There are several types of connector frequently used with coaxial cable, including BNC, N-type and the 'UHF' or PL259 connector. Roger Blackwell, G4PMK, wrote a good article about fitting such connectors in the May 1988 *RadCom*. Despite being nearly a quarter of a century old, his advice is as relevant today as it was then. Since the PL259 is by far the most common connector used with wire antennas, and since virtually 100% of HF transceivers use the mating SO239 antenna socket, here we look only at fitting the PL259 connector. The 1988 article also describes how to fit BNC and N-type connectors.

First a word about the different designations of cable. Cables are commonly of one of two families: the American 'RG' (Radio Guide MIL specification) types and the British 'UR' (UniRadio) series. URM67 is equivalent to RG213, is 10.5mm diameter and is the most common feeder used with PL259 (as well as N-type) connectors. URM43 (5mm OD) is one usually used with BNC connectors, although these also fit RG58 cable since both have similar dimensions. In order to fit a PL259 connector to URM43 or RG58 cable, a reducer must be used. Note that 'RG8' is an obsolete designation - the modern equivalent is RG213, or URM67.

Despite also being call a 'UHF' connector, the PL259 is actually not much good beyond about 200MHz, because the impedance through the plug-socket junction is not maintained at 50Ω. They are, however, very widely used at HF. Beware of any PL259 plugs that do not have PTFE insulation: many cheap types are lossy and poorly made. The plating should be good quality: silver solders best, although some proprietary plated finishes are just about as good and there should be two or more solder holes in the body for soldering to the braid. There should be two small tags on the outer mating edge of the plug, which locate in the serrated ring of the socket and stop the body rotating. If small diameter cable is to be used, obtain the correct reducer. Often two types are available: for 75Ω and 50Ω cable. The 50Ω type is often called UG175. It is necessary to buy the plugs and reducers at the same time because some manufacturers use different reducer threads.

Tools for the job

Firstly, a good soldering iron is a necessity. A small iron may have insufficient heat output to solder the coax braid to the outer of the plug. A sharp knife is another essential. A Stanley-type is needed for larger cables, provided that the blade is sharp. For smaller cables, a scalpel or very sharp penknife can be used. Model shops have a good range of craft knives which will also do an excellent job. *Safety warning:* use sharp blades, cut away from you, and keep the object you're cutting on the bench, not in your hand. Although sharp, steel blades are brittle and will shatter if you apply excessive force or bend them, with bits of sharp blade shooting all over the place. Dispose of used blades in a box or plastic jar.

A pair of sharp small scissors is needed for cutting braids, and a blunt darning needle is useful for unweaving the braid. A small vice a great help as well. A junior

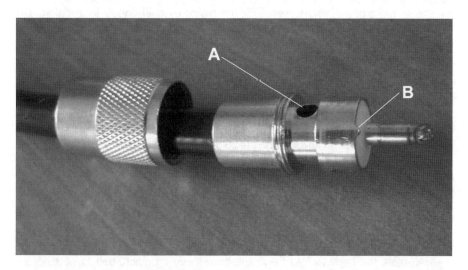

A PL259 plug fitted to URM67 coaxial cable. The cable braid should be soldered through the hole at 'A'. At 'B' is one of the small tags that slot into the serrated ring of the SO239 socket, in order to stop the plug from rotating.

hacksaw is needed to cut larger cables such as URM67. Finally, for putting heat shrink sleeves over the ends of plugs for outdoor use, some form of heat gun helps, although the shaft of a soldering iron may work. A hot air paint stripper can work well for this job.

Preparing cables

Fitting a plug requires the removal of various bits of outer sheath, braid and inner dielectric. The important knack to acquire is that of removing one at a time, without damaging what lies underneath. To remove the outer sheath, use a sharp knife or scalpel. Place the knife across the cable and rotate the cable while applying gentle pressure. The object of doing this is to score right round the cable sheath. Now score a line from the ring you just made up to the cable end. If you have cut it just enough, it should be possible to peel away the outer sheath leaving the braid intact underneath. Before trying this on a real piece of cable, practice on a surplus or scrap section first. For some connectors, it is important that this edge of the sheath is a smooth edge at right angles to the cable, so it really is worth getting right.

Braid removal usually just requires a bit of combing out and a pair of scissors. Removal of the inner dielectric is most difficult with large diameter cables with laid multi-strand inner conductors like URM67. Again, it is important that the end is a clean, smooth cut at right angles to the cable. This is best achieved by removing the bulk of the dielectric to length. There is a limit to how much dielectric that can be removed at one time. Between one and two centimetres is about as much as can be attempted without damaging the lay of the inner. For the larger cables, it is best to pare down the bulk of the unwanted material before trying to pull the remainder off the inner. One trick that helps when making up short cables is to fit one plug on the free end before cutting the cable to length. This helps to prevent the inner sliding about when stripping the dielectric.

Fitting the plug
(a) Without reducer (URM67 / RG213 cable)

The first step is to make a clean end. For this large cable, the best way is to use a junior hacksaw. Chopping with cutters or a knife just spoils the whole thing. Having obtained a clean end, refer to **Fig 2.7(a)** for the stripping dimensions. First, remove the sheath braid and dielectric, revealing the length of inner conductor required. Do this by cutting right through the sheath and braid, scoring the dielectric, then removing the dielectric afterwards. Next carefully remove the sheath back to the dimension indicated, without disturbing the braid. Examine the braid; it should be shiny and smooth. If it has been disturbed or it looks tarnished, start again a little further down. Now the tricky bit: with a hot iron, tin the braid carefully. The idea is to do it with as little solder as possible. Lightly tin the inner conductor also at this stage.

Now slide the coupling piece on to the cable (threaded end towards the free end). Examine the plug body. If it is not silver plated, or it looks as if it will not solder easily, apply a file around and through the solder holes. Now screw the body on to the cable, hard. When you've finished, the sheath should have gone into the threaded end of the connector, the inner should be poking out through the hollow pin, and the end of the exposed dielectric should be hard up against the inside shoulder of the plug. Look at the braid through the solder holes. It should not have broken up into a mass of strands; that's why it was tinned. If it has, it is best to start again.

If all is well, lightly clamp the cable in the vice. Then apply the iron to the solder holes. Heat it up and apply the solder. It should flow into the holes; if it stays there as a sullen blob, the body isn't hot enough. Now leave it undisturbed to cool before soldering the inner by heating the pin and feeding solder down the inner. Finally, when it is cool, cut any excess protruding inner conductor and file flush with the pin, then screw down the coupling ring. Merely as a confidence check (of course), test for

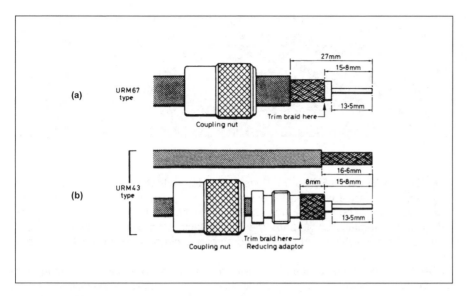

Fig 2.7: PL259 plug assembly (a) for URM67 / RG213 type cable, (b) with a reducer for URM43 / RG58 cable.

continuity on both inner and outer from one end of the cable to the other, and check that the inner is not shorted to the braid.

(b) With reducer (URM43 / RG58 cable)

First, slide the outer coupler and the reducer on to the cable. Referring to **Fig 2.7(b)**, remove the outer sheath, without nicking the braid. Now, using a blunt needle, gently unweave the braid a bit at a time until it is all straight and sticking out like a ruff around the cable.

Remove the inner dielectric, without nicking the inner conductor, to leave the specified amount of dielectric. Tin the inner conductor. Bring up the reducer until the end of the reducer is flush with the end of the outer sheath. Fold the braid back so it lies evenly over the shank of the reducer, then cut off the excess braid with scissors so that it is not in danger of getting trapped in the threads. Smooth it down once more, then offer up the plug body and, while holding the reducer and cable still, screw on the plug body until it is fully home. The only really good way of doing this is with two pairs of pliers. Now hold the assembly in the vice and ready the soldering iron. There has been a spirited discussion from time to time about the advisability of soldering the braid through the holes; the best information is that it *should* be soldered. If it is not soldered, the cable will ultimately fail. So with a *big* iron, solder the braid through the holes. See the section above for advice. Finally, solder and trim the inner conductor and test the assembly as described earlier.

Re-using connectors

It would be nice to use new connectors every time, but often there are several in or around the shack that can be reused and give further excellent service without the expense of having to buy new connectors each time. Tarnished silver-plated connectors can be made to shine by dipping the metal parts in silver cleaner.

To waterproof a connector-cable joint and to provide added strength where flexing of the cable will occur, heat shrink a piece of adhesive-lined heat shrink sleeving over the plug body and cable or use the self-amalgamating tape method described earlier.

3 Dipoles

THE WIRE DIPOLE is a very effective antenna that can be constructed and installed very easily and for only a small cost. The half-wave version of the dipole has become the standard against which other radiating systems are judged and it remains as perhaps the most effective, yet simple, single-band antenna, and one which can virtually be guaranteed to perform well even when used in far-from-ideal situations.

As the name suggests, it contains two legs or 'poles'. The most common form is the *half-wave* dipole, which (not surprisingly) is an electrical half-wavelength long. The basic format for a half-wave dipole along with the voltage and current waveforms can be seen in **Fig 3.1**. The voltage rises to a maximum at either end and falls to a minimum at the centre, whereas the current is at its minimum at the end and its maximum in the centre. Its feedpoint in the centre forms a low impedance point suitable for many sorts of feeder.

A dipole does not have to be a half-wavelength long. A three half-wavelength version can be seen in **Fig 3.2**. Again the points of voltage maximum are at either end and at a minimum in the centre. Likewise the current is at its minimum at either end and maximum in the centre.

DIPOLE LENGTHS

A resonant half-wavelength of wire will be somewhat shorter than its name implies. RF energy in free space (electromagnetic radiation) can travel at the speed of light, but when moving along a conductor it travels more slowly. At HF (between 3 and 30MHz) wires exhibit *skin effect*, i.e. most of the RF energy flows along the outer surface of the conductor. A practical half-wave antenna made from wire needs end supports; each end usually being terminated with an insulator. The capacitance between the ends of dipole and its supports, even when the supporting material is non-metallic, gives rise to *end effect*. This effect additionally loads the wire capacitively and contributes towards its shortening from the theoretical half-wavelength.

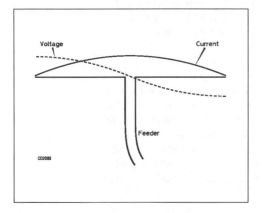

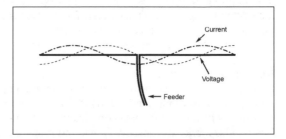

(Left) **Fig 3.1: A basic half-wavelength dipole antenna with the voltage and current waveforms.**

(Above) **Fig 3.2: A three half-wavelength dipole.**

Frequency	Length				
	With insulators			Without insulators	
(kHz)	(feet)	(metres)		(feet)	(metres)
1850	252' 11"	77.29		258' 5"	78.75
1950	240' 0"	73.33		245' 1"	74.71
3550	131' 10"	40.28		134' 8"	41.04
3750	124' 9"	38.13		127' 5"	38.85
7050	66' 4"	20.28		67' 10"	20.66
10100	46' 4"	14.15		47' 4"	14.42
14100	33' 2"	10.14		33' 11"	10.33
14250	32' 10"	10.03		33' 6"	10.22
18100	25' 10"	7.90		26' 5"	8.04
21100	22' 2"	6.77		22' 8"	6.90
21300	21' 11"	6.71		22' 5"	6.84
24940	18' 9"	5.73		19' 2"	5.84
28100	16' 8"	5.08		17' 0"	5.18
28500	16' 5"	5.01		16' 9"	5.11
29000	16' 1"	4.93		16' 6"	5.02
29500	15' 10"	4.84		16' 2"	4.93

Table 3.1: Lengths of half-wave dipoles.

The theoretical half-wavelength may be calculated from the expression:

Theoretical half wavelength (metres) = 150 / f (MHz)

or

Theoretical half-wavelength (feet) = 492 / f (MHz)

To take account of the end effect and the use of insulators, the length may be calculated by using either:

Antenna length (metres) = 143 / f (MHz)

or

Antenna length (feet) = 468 / f (MHz).

When using nylon rope it has been suggested that no insulators are required. In his book *HF Antennas for All Locations* (published by the RSGB), Les Moxon, G6XN, suggests that when no insulators are used a half-wavelength can be found by using either 478 / f (MHz) feet or 145.7 / f (MHz) metres.

A further factor which influences antenna resonant length is the diameter of the wire used for that antenna. The formulas above are for typical wire dimensions. Typical antenna lengths for the amateur bands from 160 - 10m, both when using insulators or nylon rope, are shown in **Table 3.1** above.

DIPOLE IMPEDANCES

A half-wave transmitting antenna, when energised and resonant, will have high RF voltages at its ends with theoretically zero RF currents there. This means that the ends of a half-wave dipole in free space will have an infinitely high impedance, but in practice in the real world there will always be some leakage from its ends and into the supporting insulators. This means that in reality the impedance at the dipole ends is close to 100,000Ω, a value which depends upon the wire or element thickness. At a distance of approximately one-sixteenth wavelength from either end it is 1000Ω, and at the dipole centre, where the current is greatest and the RF voltage is low, the impedance is also low.

If it were made from an infinitely thin conductor wire, our theoretical dipole in free space would have an impedance of about 73Ω at its centre. Such an antenna is impossible in the material world, and a practical half-wave dipole made from wire will have an impedance at its centre at resonance close to 65Ω. Antennas fabricated from tubing have lower values at their centres, of between 55 and 60Ω. These impedance values also depend upon the height of the antenna above ground, as will be shown later.

The very high values of self-impedance at the ends of a half-wave wire makes end-feeding difficult, and this is why breaking the wire at its centre and connecting the inner ends so formed to a low-impedance feedline makes a convenient and efficient coupling and match. Suitable feeder is available in the form of twin-lead or coaxial cable, which both have design impedances lying between 50 and 75Ω. These present a good match to dipole centres.

At exact resonance the impedance at the centre of a half-wave dipole is like a pure resistance. At any other frequencies the same dipole will have either inductive or capacitive reactance at its feedpoint. If the dipole is too short to be resonant the reactance is capacitive and when it is too long the reactance becomes inductive. In either case there will be problems in matching the 50 or 70Ω feeder to the dipole and if the reactances are great, there will be a high SWR on the feeder and considerable power loss.

ANTENNA Q

A half-wave antenna is something like a conventional tuned circuit where the Q, or 'Quality factor', is largely determined by the resistance of the coil. Losses in the capacitor used in the circuit are generally small and are not so significant in the determination of Q. A high-Q tuned circuit exhibits very sharp tuning (selectivity) and this is also the case when an antenna has a high Q.

Using thin wires lowers the bandwidth of a half-wave antenna, but not dramatically. However, short wires that are brought into resonance will exhibit high Q. The shorter the wire in terms of wavelength, the higher the Q. Small changes in the transmitting frequency away from the antenna resonances will give rise to a rapid rise in the reactance at the feedpoint.

Thicker wire will lower the Q, reduce resistive loss and make the half-wave dipole less frequency conscious. It is therefore best to ensure that such an antenna is made from the thickest possible wire consistent with such factors as the pull on the antenna supports, windage and sag.

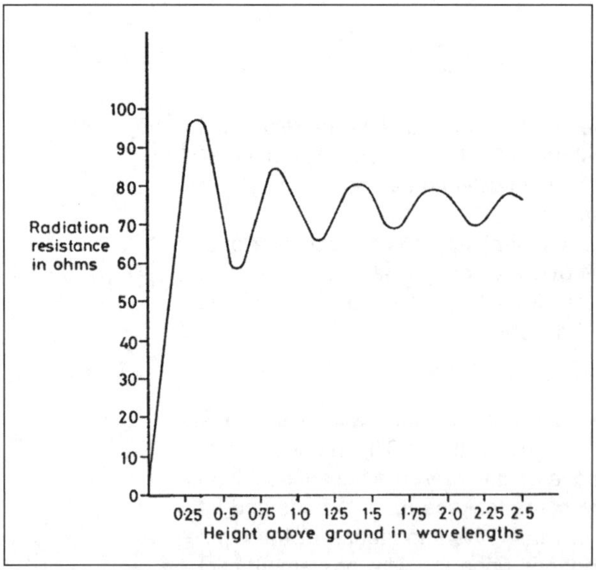

DIPOLE HEIGHT

The height of a horizontal dipole above the ground as a ratio of its design frequency is important (see the standard curves of feed impedance against height in **Fig 3.3**). When below about half a wavelength high the radiation resistance at the feedpoint will be reduced, and down at a height of just one-tenth of a wavelength it will only be 25Ω. This means that a dipole fed

Fig 3.3: Radiation resistance of a half-wave dipole as a function of height above the ground (reprinted with permission of the American Radio Relay League).

from a standard type of low-impedance feeder will suffer a considerable mismatch when near the ground. One-tenth of a wavelength is about 15m (50ft) on 1.8MHz and as little as a metre (3ft) on 28MHz. This helps to explain why low dipoles on the lower frequency bands are far from efficient radiators.

A horizontal half-wave antenna, if at least a half-wavelength above ground, will radiate most of its applied power at right angles to the line or axis of the wire. Its radiation pattern may be visualised as having the shape of a torus or doughnut, with the wire running through the centre hole (**Fig 3.4**). About 40° on either side of the broadside maxima of radiation the power falls to half, i.e. -3dB, and it will fall rapidly as the angle increases.

Theoretically, there should be little or no radiation off the wire ends, but in practice there will remain some radiation at high angles to the horizon from both ends, which might prove useful for short-range work. The horizontal radiation pattern at both 30° and the low angle of 9° may be seen in **Fig 3.5**. The 30° high-angle radiation from a half-wave dipole at a height of half a wavelength will tend to be from one to two S-points greater than the low-angle radiation needed for DX working in most directions (i.e. about 5 to 10dB better), and emphasises the fact that a half-wave dipole is a general-purpose, 'all-round' antenna type, good for both semi-local and distant working.

From the ends, however, there is little low-angle radiation, and here it is as much as three to four S-points down from the maxima at right angles to the wire. This explains why a dipole is best arranged to be at right angles to the areas to be worked, especially for long-distance communication.

When lower than a half-wavelength from the ground, a greater proportion of the transmitted power will leave the antenna at high angles. This makes it ideal for short-haul communications.

Although in theory a dipole at a height less than half a wavelength is not ideal, in practice it is still possible to use it for long-haul communications. For example, a dipole for 160m at a height of 30m would make a highly effective antenna as it will be well clear of any obstructions. Even though much of the power will be radiated upwards, the power that is radiated at a low angle will be subject to less absorption by local objects than that radiated by many other antennas such as a vertical at a lower height. Thus even though antennas for the low frequency bands are unlikely to be

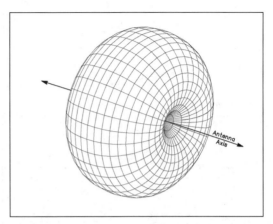

Fig 3.4: Representation of the radiation from a half-wave dipole antenna in free space. Practical antenna systems are, however, influenced by ground reflection and their radiation patterns are much modified (diagram reprinted from The ARRL Antenna Book).

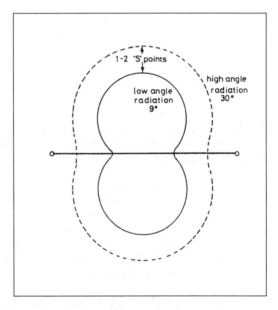

Fig 3.5: The horizontal polar diagram of a half-wave dipole at a height of half a wavelength above the ground, showing the considerable high-angle radiation (at 30°) off the ends of the wire. The low-angle radiation is mainly at right angles to the wire and is from 5 to 10dB down relative to the 30° radiation.

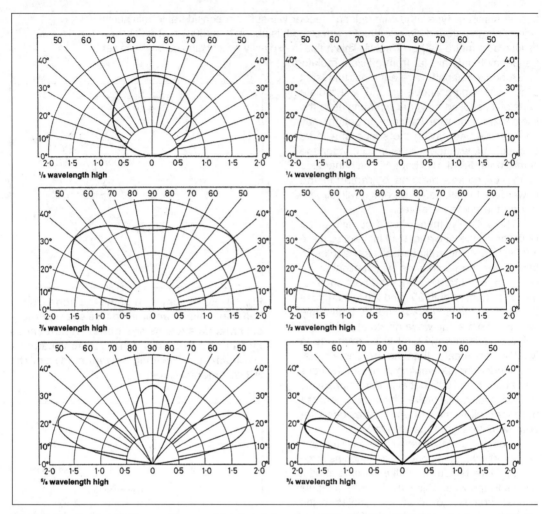

Fig 3.6 : Vertical radiation patterns of horizontal antenna at differing heights above a perfectly conducting ground (from *The ARRL Antenna Book*, reprinted with permission of the American Radio Relay League).

raised to heights that are theoretically required, nevertheless they are able to provide excellent service.

The vertical radiation patterns of horizontal antennas at different heights above the ground ranging from one eighth of a wavelength to two wavelengths can be seen in **Fig 3.6**. In all these examples it is assumed that the antennas are above a perfectly conducting ground.

A PRACTICAL DIPOLE ANTENNA

There is no doubt that the dipole is the simplest and yet most effective all-purpose, single-band antenna for the amateur, so long as it conforms to the basic design parameters and is correctly adjusted and trimmed.

The top length of this antenna may either be calculated or taken from **Table 3.1**, and almost any kind of copper wire can be used. For permanent or semi-permanent installations 16 or 18SWG hard-drawn copper is to be preferred, and for experimental and temporary antennas most types of stranded and plastic-covered wire can be

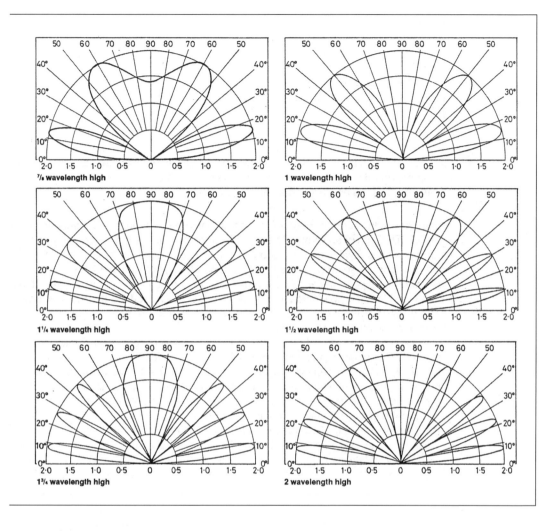

used. The resonant frequency of an antenna made from this wire is said to fall by 3 to 5% but the author has never noticed such an effect. This lowering of frequency may, however, become noticeable when making and testing wire beams, especially those with quad loops as driven and parasitic elements.

If any antenna end insulators are to be used, those made from Pyrex glass are perhaps the best, and when the antenna ends are close to a metal mast more than one insulator at each end is to be preferred. Nylon or Terylene cords may be tied directly to the antenna wire ends (knotted), and they will make effective insulators if more than about 2m in length.

The antenna maker must bear in mind the change in resonant lengths which are induced by this technique (see Table 3.1), and cut his dipole longer than it would be if normal end insulators were to be used. Without end insulators the suggested 2m or more of cord between the antenna and the fixing point will present a very low leakage path even in wet weather. Although ultra-violet energy (present in sunlight) can bring on a deterioration in the structure of non-organic ropes, the author has had nylon cords in use for many years with no apparent ill effects [*editorial note:* this is certainly more of a problem in the tropics - *9M6DXX*.]

If antenna insulators are used the length of the resonant top of the antenna must

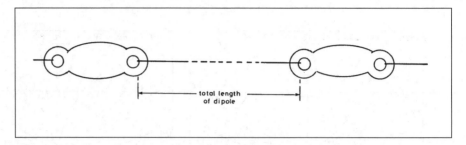

Fig 3.7: The end insulators of a dipole antenna, showing that the total length of the antenna includes the wrap-round at the tie points. Although small, such additions could detune the antenna on 21MHz and higher.

also include the furthest ends of the loops which pass through the insulators - see **Fig 3.7**. The inch or so involved here can be important on the higher frequency bands, but of course is nothing to worry about on 1.8 or 3.5MHz. If joins are required in the top wire it is best to solder and then weatherproof them. Try to avoid joins towards the centre of the dipole, because here the levels of current increase and any resistance introduced in a join will increase the resistive losses and reduce the radiated power. Further away from the centre, as the impedance rises, the effect of any introduced resistance is much less critical.

The dipole top is broken at the half-way point and here an insulator must be inserted. This point is at low RF potential and low impedance so the insulation need not be high. Using expensive glazed ceramic or glass centre insulators is a waste of money and most plastics such as Perspex, acetate or similar insulating material may be used. The centre blocks are best fabricated in the shape of a 'T' (**Fig 3.8**) or 'Y' so that there is some way to anchor securely the top few inches of feeder. When using either twin-wire 75Ω feeder or heavier coaxial cable there must not be any strain put on to the connections to the dipole wires. All antennas will sway or swing even during relatively calm weather conditions; this can easily induce metal fatigue and an early demise of feeders high up where they cannot be observed. Fig 3.8

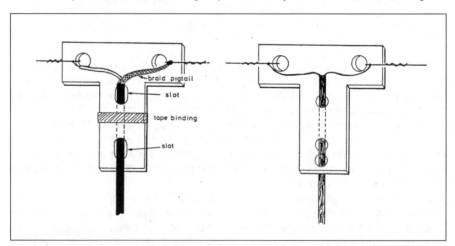

Fig 3.8: Centre 'T' blocks of an insulating material which may be used at the centre of a dipole antenna. Coaxial cable feeder, being heavier, will require more support than the twin-wire 75Ω type of feeder. Almost any insulating material which is weatherproofed may be employed for the centre blocks. No strain must be put on the soldered connections to the dipole halves.

shows suggested anchoring methods for both types of feeder.

If possible the dipole feeder should run down vertically for at least a quarter of a wavelength before it bends to run to the house or shack, although this is clearly impractical in most cases for 160m or 80m dipoles, as it would imply they are to be mounted more than 130ft or 65ft above ground respectively. If possible the feeder should avoid running below and in line with the antenna top as a feeder beneath the leg of a dipole will unbalance the system and will lower feedpoint impedance. A useful and tidy way to arrange a coaxial feeder is to run it vertically down from the antenna to the ground and then bury it a few inches down on its run to the shack (although obviously if twin or open-wire feeder is used it cannot be buried).

When coaxial cable is used to feed the dipole some extra care is needed where it connects to the antenna. The outer jacket of the cable should be stripped for about 10cm (4in) and then just above the new termination of the outer sleeve a hole is made through the copper braid. The insulated 'inner' may then be pulled out through this hole. In this way the braid 'pigtail' will be strong and unlikely to fray away or weaken, especially if its end is tinned with solder. The feeders must be soldered to the antenna wires and then the joints effectively weatherproofed.

Fig 3.9 shows the theoretical radiation pattern of a half-wave dipole in free space. Where there is no restriction in the location of the antenna and the use of only one dipole is contemplated, in the UK it is best to run it roughly from north to south. In this way most of the world will be covered - there are comparatively few populated areas directly north and south of the UK. (Similar analyses can be carried out for other countries where antennas are to be erected. An examination of a great circle map for the required country will give a quick summary of the optimum direction for the antenna.) An small extra dividend is available when a dipole is cut for the 7MHz band, for then it will also work fairly well as a centre-fed 1.5λ wire on the 21MHz band. It will, however, have quite a different radiation pattern to a standard dipole, but show a little gain over a dipole cut for 21MHz in its preferred directions of radiation. The three half-waves dipole is covered in more detail later in this chapter.

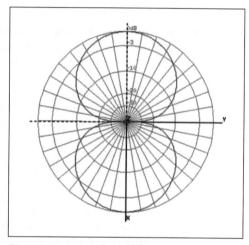

Fig 3.9: Theoretical radiation pattern of a half-wave dipole in free space.

TO BALUN OR NOT TO BALUN, THAT IS THE QUESTION...

If a dipole is fed with coaxial cable, an unbalanced feeder, the question of whether or not to use a 1:1 balun arises. Although coax has a number of advantages when used with any antenna, there are also some disadvantages that need to be noted:

♦ There may be RF currents induced on to the outer braid of the cable if no balun is used.
♦ The outer shield may radiate if no balun is used and this may cause interference to televisions or other equipment under some circumstances.
♦ Similarly the coaxial feeder may pick up interference. As the feeder is likely to pass near to the house, there could be additional levels of electrical interference picked up.
♦ There is a greater sensitivity to nearby objects such as masts, telephone and other overhead wires, buildings or trees.
♦ Losses can be high if the cable weathers badly and inside corrosion begins.
♦ Coaxial cable is heavy and can pull the top wire down considerably, so inducing tension strains.

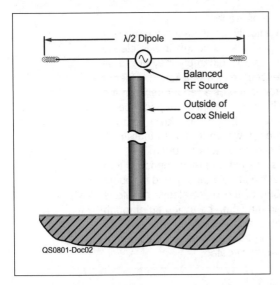

λ/2 Dipole

Balanced RF Source

Outside of Coax Shield

QS0801-Doc02

Fig 3.10: Electrical equivalent of a dipole fed with coaxial cable without a balun (reprinted with permission of the American Radio Relay League).

However, the dipole *will* work, and work well, in practice without the use of a balun. So do you actually *need* to use one? In 'The Doctor is IN' (*QST* January 2008), 'The Doctor' said that most people find that it doesn't usually make much difference either way, but crucially *sometimes* it does. Coaxial cable is designed to keep signals on the inside, between the outside of the centre conductor and the inside of the braid, or shield. Because of the skin effect, the outside of the shield acts like a separate wire for RF current. A dipole has one conductor on each side of the centre insulator. If there is a current balun there, the currents are forced into the dipole wires and kept off the outside of the shield. Without a balun, it acts as if there is an additional wire (the outside of the coax shield) connected to the shield side of the dipole and going to your transceiver.

Fig 3.10 shows a simplified diagram of this. All current that goes into the dipole wires will be radiated. If you add an extra wire, what happens? If it has a high impedance, very little current will flow down it. If it has a low impedance, though, the current on the shield side of the dipole will split between the dipole wire and the outside of the shield of the coax. What determines the impedance of the outside of the shield is its length and the impedance to ground at the bottom of the coax.

If the physical length of the coax is near to a half wave (or multiple of half waves), the outer of the coax at the antenna end will be at low impedance because the outside of the sheath is always at low impedance (earth potential) when connected to the transceiver - if we assume the body of the transceiver is connected to earth, as it should be. A half wave along the coax from the transceiver (with reference to the outside of the outer sheath) a low impedance will again be seen.

If the impedance of the outside of the shield is low it will take significant current, perhaps as much as (or even more than) the dipole wire itself. The current running down the outside of the coax can get into your equipment and cause feedback into your mic wires, or sometimes lock your transmitter into transmit. The current will also radiate. This is not *necessarily* bad - if it is outside. It usually adds some vertically polarised signal, which can sometimes even be beneficial. Your resulting pattern won't be quite what you expect from the dipole - this too can be good or bad. But it will also radiate into anything else that it encounters - TV cable, stereo speaker wires, phone lines, alarm systems and anything else nearby.

So the answer is - 'it depends'. If you have no such problems without a balun, you probably do not need one. If you do have a problem, a balun can be helpful. Note that the property of a balun most important here is the 'common-mode choke' part of what a balun does. You can get this effect by just coiling up some coax at the centre insulator. A coil of half a dozen turns of 6 to 8in in diameter will usually provide a good choke for the upper HF region. Another one just before the coax comes into the shack will help eliminate any current that is coupled from the dipole to the coax shield, which happens if the coax is not perpendicular to the antenna during its run. These coils add inductance to the outside of the shield, not to the inside.

Much more on the use of baluns can be found in Chapter 8, 'Impedance Matching and Baluns'.

MATCHING

Mention was made earlier of the use of an ATU when twin-wire feeder is used. The use of an ATU brings many advantages and when properly adjusted will ensure that a good match is obtained and a low value of VSWR is seen by the transceiver - an essential requirement for most modern units. In addition to this, an ATU provides an additional tuned circuit on the transmitting or receiving frequency which aids selectivity, possibly reducing cross-modulation effects from strong off-frequency signals and, most importantly, cutting down any radiation of harmonics or spurious signals.

Most solid-state transceivers automatically reduce power output when used with a VSWR of more than about 2.5:1 or 3:1. The use of an ATU can help to prevent such problems arising, especially when a dipole is being used away from its design frequency and when therefore it does not match its feeder. Such a mismatch to the antenna cannot be avoided and there will be of course some loss of power radiated, but the use of an ATU in such a situation will ensure that the transceiver will be 'fooled' into behaving as if all is unchanged despite the mismatch. An ATU should of course also be used in conjunction with an SWR meter, and if this instrument is connected between the end of the feeder and the ATU, any mismatch which occurs when the dipole is used on either side of its design frequency will be very noticeable. At best, even on the dipole's resonant frequency, it is unlikely that the SWR reading will be perfect unity, for it is very difficult to achieve a perfect match to either 50 or 75Ω at the dipole centre. This is because the nominal antenna impedance is dependent upon such factors as height, the type of ground beneath the antenna, nearby objects and so on.

Although it is necessary to keep the SWR as low as reasonably possible to enable modern transceivers to operate satisfactorily, as far as the antenna itself is concerned, it can operate with a much higher SWR without its performance being unduly degraded. It needs an SWR reading of 3.7:1 to double feedline losses and it is unlikely that even the most ill-fashioned or awkwardly positioned dipole would present such a high mismatch. If the SWR reading lies between unity and 1.5:1 any mismatch loss will be negligible. At such an SWR reading the total line losses will then only be the cable losses multiplied by a factor of 1.1.

Before leaving the topic of SWR on feedlines it must also be stressed that a feeder connecting to a half-wave dipole antenna can be of any length, so long as its nominal impedance equals the impedance at the dipole centre. If any addition or subtraction of feedline greatly affects the SWR present, it means that there must be a serious mismatch at the antenna connection.

INCREASING THE BANDWIDTH OF A DIPOLE

It has already been stated that a low-Q half-wave wire will have a wider bandwidth than a high-Q one which has been made with very thin conductor wire. One way to ensure that a dipole covers an entire band (especially on the 3.5MHz and 1.8MHz bands) is to use a very thick wire for the antenna. Two or three thinner wires can be put in parallel to achieve this, but a better way is to use a 'fantail' or 'bow tie' arrangement (see **Fig 3.11**), which will provide a low SWR right across the band. This technique will allow a single antenna to be used on the 3.5MHz band. A half-wave dipole cut to resonate at the LF end of this band will be 2.13m (7ft) too long at the HF end. On the higher-frequency bands the width of the band relative to the frequency is small, and the antenna wire is thicker in terms of wavelength, therefore the antenna Q will be lower. A single dipole cut to mid-band will normally suffice; despite this, those who intend CW operation at the LF end of the 28MHz band, together with some working on FM or satellite reception above 29MHz, might find they need to increase the bandwidth of the antenna. A half-wave wire cut for 29MHz is around a third of a metre shorter than one for 28MHz, a difference of about 6%.

When using a 'fantail' arrangement, a separation of about a metre between the

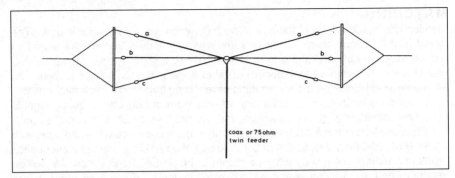

Fig 3.11: How a broadbanded 'bow-tie' or 'fantail' dipole can be constructed. The three dipoles 'a', 'b' and 'c' are cut to resonate at the band edges and centre band frequency.

wires is adequate, and they may either go to different end tie points or more conveniently attach to plastic or wooden spreaders (via insulators). Table 3.1 can be used for determining the wire lengths of broadband multi-dipoles.

USING A COAX STUB TO MOVE DIPOLE RESONANCE

An alternative method of providing a low SWR at both ends of the 80m band is to use a coaxial stub, as shown in **Fig 3.12**. Bob Raffaele, W2XM, presented an article on the

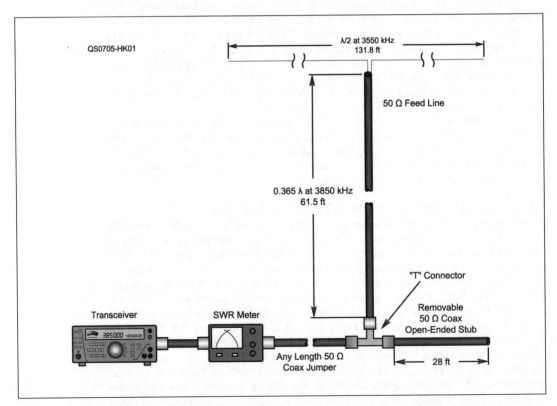

Fig 3.12: An 80m dipole resonant at 3550kHz connected to a transceiver through an SWR meter. For operation at 3850kHz the open-ended stub is added at the T connector (reprinted with permission of the American Radio Relay League).

use of a coax stub to shift the antenna system resonance in the May 2007 *QST*. Those who use both CW and SSB on 80m will know that a dipole designed for the CW end of the band - close to 3500kHz - will have a high SWR around 3800kHz, and *vice versa*.

The technique for achieving two dipole 'resonances' within a band requires that the antenna be cut for the lower frequency. In this example figures are given for 3550kHz and 3850kHz (the latter in the US phone part of the 80m band, which is often referred to as "75 metres" in the USA).

Using the well-known formula:

Length (in feet) = 468 / f (in MHz)

the length of the dipole at 3.550MHz is 468 / 3.550 = 131.8ft. Cut the wire a bit longer, and then build your dipole to be 131.8ft long. The feedpoint impedance at resonance will be near the theoretical free-space value of 73Ω. At 3550kHz, the SWR is 1.3:1. With any length of feedline, the installation works well at 3550kHz.

Making no changes to our system, we might observe a 5:1 SWR at 3850kHz. An open-ended stub, cut to a particular length and connected at the right place along the feedline, will act as our antenna tuner, and will reduce the SWR at the transmitter to 1:1.

In his *QST* article, W2XM explains how a Smith chart may be used to calculate the length of the stub required to shift the resonance of the antenna system to 3850kHz. (Those interested to know how the stub length is calculated are advised to refer to the original article: 'More on Using a Coaxial Stub to Shift Antenna-System Reso-nance', by Bob Raffaele, W2XM (in 'Hints & Kinks', edited by ARRL Senior Assistant Technical Editor Larry D Wolfgang, WR1B), *QST*, May 2007, pp61-62.) The calcula-tions indicate that a 28ft-long open stub will provide the capacitive reactance which, when connected as shown in the diagram, will cancel the inductive reactance. Look-ing into that junction, a 3850kHz signal sees a 50Ω resistance.

The capacitive stub acts as an antenna tuner, providing the transmitter with a 50Ω resistive load. The feedline between the stub and the antenna is characterised by a high SWR; the SWR-related losses may be considered significant.

The stub can be left coiled up while in use. There may be a high voltage at the open end of the stub so it should be insulated and kept out of reach.

THE INVERTED-V DIPOLE

The maximum radiation from any antenna is from the points of high RF current, and a half-wave dipole has this maximum at its centre and for a few feet on either side of the feeder connections. Therefore it is best to make the centre of the dipole as high as possible. If it is only possible to have one high support, an inverted-V arrange-ment is obviously ideal. In this way it is possible to use one fairly high mast in the centre of a garden or plot in locations where the erection of a pair of similar supports with their attendant guy wires would be difficult. A roof-mounted or chimney-mounted mast may also serve as the centre support for a 'V', and the two ends of the dipole can then drop down on either side of a house or bungalow roof. Such chimney mounting will allow the feeder to be dropped to the shack quite easily if it is located in the house.

Although an inverted-V has its greatest degree of radiation at right angles to the axis of the antenna, its radiation pattern is more omni-directional than that of a horizontal dipole as a result of the fact that the legs are angled downwards.

The inverted-V has a reputation (possibly somewhat exaggerated) for being a good DX antenna on the lower-frequency amateur bands, where the erection of large verticals or high horizontal dipoles is not practicable. There are, however, some design features concerning this antenna which must be considered when contem-plating making one.

The angle between the sloping wires must be at least 90° and preferably 120° or

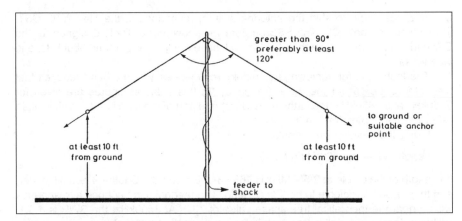

Fig 3.13: A half-wave inverted-V dipole with the angle between the top wires at 120°. This angle must never fall below 90°. The centre support mast puts the high RF current section of the antenna at the highest point and also carries the weight of the antenna and the feeder.

more, as shown in **Fig 3.13**. This angle dictates the centre support height as well as the length of ground needed to accommodate the antenna. For example, when designed for the 3.5MHz band, an inverted-V will need a centre support at least 14m (45ft) high and a garden length of around 34m (110ft). By contrast, a horizontal dipole needs at least 40m of garden and that is without taking into account guys to the rear of the end support masts. The inverted-V is also ideal for portable operation because one for operation on 20m (14MHz) only needs a lightweight 5m (15ft) pole to hold up its centre.

The sloping of the dipole wires causes a reduction of the resonant frequency for a given dipole length, so about 5% must be subtracted from standard dipole dimensions. One reason for this is the increased self-capacitance of the antenna when its ends are brought closer together and also towards the ground. The calculated wire lengths for inverted-V dipoles on the amateur bands are given in **Table 3.2**.

A further consequence arising from sloping the dipole wires is a change in its radiation resistance. The centre feed impedance falls from the nominal 75Ω of a horizontal dipole to just 50Ω, which is, of course, ideal for matching the antenna to standard 50Ω coax. An inverted-V antenna has a higher Q than a simple dipole so it tends to have a narrower bandwidth.

It is not recommended that the ends of an inverted-V are allowed closer to the ground than about 3m (10ft), even on the higher-frequency bands, because there can be a possible danger to people, especially children, or animals touching the wire ends which will be at a high RF potential when energised. The effect could be a shock or nasty RF burn.

Coaxial feed is recommended with an inverted-V, and the low-loss heavier varieties of cable can be used to advantage, for there are no sag problems when the feeder is fastened up at the top and also down the length of the mast. The feeder will impose no strain upon the antenna or the soldered connections at its feedpoint. As with an ordinary horizontal dipole, a balun may be used, although they may operate satisfactorily without one.

Frequency	Length	
(kHz)	(ft)	(m)
3600	123' 6"	37.74
7050	63' 1"	19.27
10100	44' 0"	13.45
14200	31' 4"	9.57
18100	24' 7"	7.69
21200	20' 11"	6.41
24940	17' 10"	5.45
28200	15' 9"	4.82
29200	15' 3"	4.65

Table 3.2: Suggested lengths for inverted-V dipoles.

THE SLOPING DIPOLE

Horizontal half-wave dipoles require two end supports and it is not always possible to provide these in some awkward locations. In such situations a single support, preferably a non-metallic mast or a high point on a building, will suffice, and then the antenna can be arranged to slope down towards the ground at an angle lying somewhere between 30° and 60° (**Fig 3.14**). The sloping half-wave dipole should have its lower end at least one-sixth of a wavelength above ground, and its feeder should ideally come away from the radiator at 90° for at least a quarter of a wavelength. If coaxial feeder is used the braid should connect to the lower half of the antenna.

The performance of a sloping dipole is quite different from one of the horizontal variety and it can be good for long distance work. The radiation from a sloping dipole shows slant polarisation with both vertical and horizontal components according to the amount of slope. Its lower angle of radiation to the horizon can result in a little low angle gain over a horizontal dipole. This kind of gain is difficult to realise on the low bands in other ways, where for most amateurs multi-element Yagi beams are out of the question.

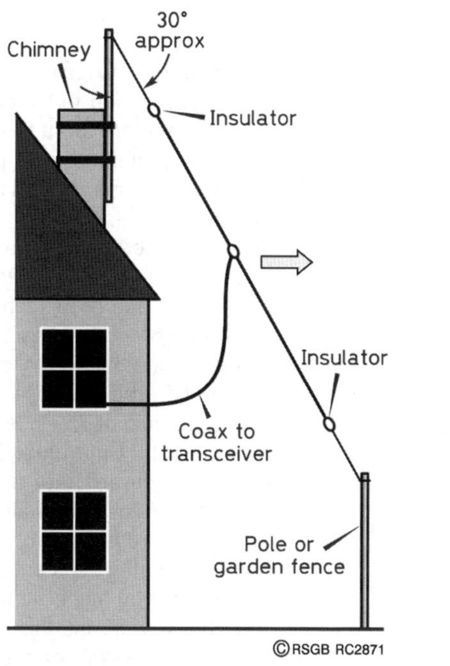

There is some high-angle radiation from the sides of the sloping dipole but very little radiation from its high end. An actual plan of the horizontal radiation pattern resembles a heart with a null between its two upper lobes. This null corresponds with the high end of the sloping dipole. A disadvantage is of course that long-distance working will only be possible towards one direction, but this may be overcome by having a group of three or four 'slopers' suspended from a common central support, each with its individual feedline which may be selectively switched to the transceiver. (There are designs which involve the unused dipoles in such arrangements as reflectors to improve forward gain and front-to-back ratios, but their correct adjustment can be complicated.)

Slopers are ideal in many applications where a single support is available. Many people who have beams and towers, mount a sloper on the tower for one of the lower frequency bands, ensuring that the direction of maximum radiation is arranged towards the areas of the globe they want to contact, sometimes having two or more around the tower.

Fig 3.14: A half-wave sloping dipole which can be put up in a small space and which will be useful for long-distance working. Most of its low-angle radiation is towards the low end of the antenna but there is also considerable radiation at high angles in other directions.

THE VERTICAL DIPOLE

A vertical half-wave dipole will radiate vertically-polarised signals all round, and much of the radiation will be at the low angles favourable for DX working. If a feed impedance of around 70Ω is required, the centre of this antenna must be around 0.45λ above the ground and so it is usually more convenient to arrange for a vertical *quarter-wave* antenna to be used, which can then have its feedpoint at or near ground level. A vertical dipole cannot be hung down from a metal mast or tower, and it should have its feeder come away from the radiator wire at right angles if the radiation pattern is to be preserved, which may present some problems. As a result, vertical half-waves are not often used by amateurs, although they can be practical on the higher-frequency HF bands. A practical design for vertical dipoles is given in the chapter on vertical antennas.

A 3λ/2 DIPOLE: THE 40M DIPOLE ON 15M

The dipole, when fed with coaxial cable, is basically a single band antenna. While this is true, there are a few ways that dipoles can be made to work on more than one band. One method is to parallel two or more dipoles for different bands together; another is to use traps. We will look at both of these methods later in this chapter. The simplest way, though, is to take advantage of the fact that the low impedance at the centre feedpoint of a dipole occurs not only when it is one half-wave long, but also when it is three half-waves long (and in fact all odd numbers of half-waves). We can take advantage of this where amateur bands have this same harmonic relationship, i.e. where one band has three times the frequency (or five or seven times, etc), and therefore one third (or one fifth or one seventh) of the wavelength of another band.

On HF, the best example of this is the relationship between 40m and 15m: the third harmonic of 7MHz is 21MHz. What this means is that a 40m dipole *should* also work on 15m. Unfortunately, life isn't quite that simple. As we have already seen, the end effect means that a half-wave dipole is physically about 5% shorter than its theoretical (electrical) half-wave length. However, when the same antenna is operating on its third harmonic, it becomes *fifteen* per cent shorter than the electrical length of a three half-waves antenna. What this means in practice is that it is actually resonant quite a bit higher in frequency than you might expect.

The way around this problem is to resonate the 40m dipole at the very bottom of the band, 7000kHz, or even make it somewhat longer still, so that the minimum SWR point is actually *below* the bottom of the band on, say, 6980kHz. On 21MHz you will find the minimum SWR point is nevertheless at the *top* of the band, around 21400 or 21450kHz.

Furthermore, *QST* Technical Editor Joel Hallas, W1ZR, points out (in the July 2009 *QST*) that the resonant impedance of a 3λ/2 dipole is above 100Ω, so it's not as good a match to 50Ω coax as is the λ/2 case.

The good news is that an external ATU or the internal automatic ATU in your rig should be able to reduce the

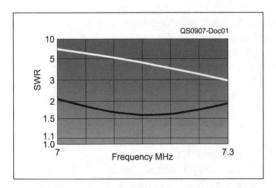

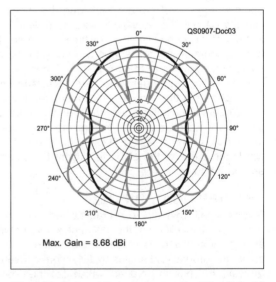

Fig 3.15: Comparison between the 40m (black) and 15m (white) *EZNEC* SWR plots of a 66ft high, 67.2ft long, 40m dipole (diagrams reprinted with permission of the American Radio Relay League).

Fig 3.16: Comparison between the 40m (black) and 15m (grey) azimuth patterns of a 40m λ/2 dipole.

SWR to close to 1:1 at your operating frequency of choice in both the 40m and 15m bands.

Fig 3.15 shows a comparison between the 40m and 15m *EZNEC* SWR plots of a 66ft high, 67.2ft long, 40m dipole made of 14 gauge bare wire. In **Fig 3.16** note that the azimuth pattern of a 3λ/2 dipole is not the same as the usual λ/2 case. While different, the pattern can be useful and provides a bit of additional gain in its prime directions.

On HF there are a few other combinations of bands that have an odd harmonic relationship, for example an 80m half-wave dipole cut for the lower-frequency end of the band is five half-waves long on the 17m band, and seven half-waves long on the 12m band. (However, if the 80m dipole is cut for the SSB DX end of the band, around 3800kHz, its five and seven half-wave resonances will be well above the top end of the 18MHz and 24MHz bands respectively, and the SWR is likely to be very high on both bands.)

MOUNTING A WIRE DIPOLE ABOVE A ROTATOR

Most amateurs with masts and towers suspend their HF wire dipole or inverted-V dipole from a point below the rotator, leaving the beam free to rotate above. However, mounting a dipole on a mast extension *above* the beam is a much better option, provided the inverted-V angle can be made shallow enough to clear the beam as it rotates underneath. Another strong reason for mounting low-band dipoles above the beam is the extra height above ground, which makes them more effective – undoubt-edly for DX, and often for more local QSOs as well. The problem with this 'over the top' approach is that the centre of the dipole must be able to pivot on the top of the mast, so that the mast and beams can rotate beneath it.

One successful solution to this problem was designed by Jan Fisher, G0IVZ, and taken up by Ian White, GM3SEK, in his 'In Practice' column in the April 2009 *RadCom*. The rotating mast for the HF beam is made from scaffold tubing, extended by a 1.5in fibreglass pole (an aluminium pole of that diameter probably couldn't handle the bending forces). The top of the extension pole is filled by a close-fitting

80m dipole over the top of a small HF beam.

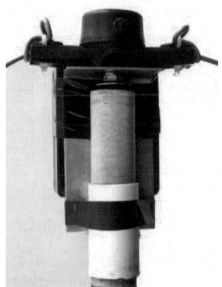

Close-up of the rotating dipole centre with balun box to the rear.

hardwood plug, drilled 8mm through the centre and secured with epoxy.

G0IVZ's idea was to use a ready-made centre insulator that was originally de-signed for mounting a tubular dipole on the boom of a Yagi. The plastic moulding is strong enough to support a much longer wire dipole, simply tied on through the fixing holes as shown in the photograph. G0IVZ used the built-in terminal box to connect the dipole to the coax feedline, while GM3SEK, who has adopted a similar set-up, connected the two wire ends to the terminals on the balun box.

The main mounting hole of the centre insulator is drilled 8mm for an M8x100mm stainless steel screw which is the pivot pin for the whole assembly. In GM3SEK's version, the balun bracket is fixed to the bottom of the insulator with a nut, so those two parts rotate together. A large washer is added to spread the down-thrust, and the free end of the screw simply drops into the hole in the wooden plug. A later addition was a piece of white PVC waste pipe, taped to the bracket to prevent the bottom edge scratching the fibreglass. Below this fitting there has to be a rotation loop in the coax and of course there's the usual loop around the rotator itself.

THE FOLDED DIPOLE

Another form of dipole is the folded dipole, shown in **Fig 3.17**. It is often used as a part of more complex antennas such as Yagis, but it can also be a useful antenna on its own. It has the advantages that it has a higher impedance and a wider bandwidth than an ordinary dipole.

The 300Ω feed impedance is an important feature of a folded dipole. The power supplied to a folded dipole is evenly shared between the two conductors which make up the antenna, so therefore the RF current, I, in each conductor is reduced to I/2. This is a half of the current value (assuming that the same power is applied) at the centre of the common half-wave dipole, so the impedance is raised. By halving the current at the feedpoint yet still maintaining the same power level, the impedance at that point will be four times greater. This means that a two-conductor folded dipole will have a feed impedance of 280Ω, which is close to the impedance of 300Ω twin feeder. It can therefore be satisfactorily matched and fed with this feeder, and have a low SWR along the feedline.

If a third conductor is added to the folded dipole (**Fig 3.18**), the antenna current will be evenly split three ways and the impedance at the feedpoint will be nine times greater than the nominal 70Ω impedance of a simple dipole. Such a three-wire dipole with its feed impedance of 630Ω will make a good match to a 600Ω feeder. This feeder may be made from 18SWG wires which are spaced at 75mm (3in).

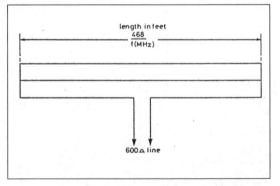

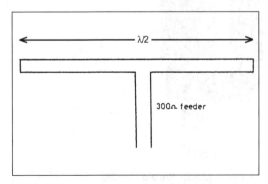

Fig 3.17: The basic two-wire folded dipole.

Fig 3.18: A three-wire folded dipole. If each wire is of equal diameter the total current will be shared equally between the three wires and the impedance at the feedpoint will be nine times that of a conventional half-wave dipole (9 x 70Ω = 630Ω), a close match to a 600Ω feedline.

Similarly, a four-wire folded dipole will have a feed impedance of 1120Ω, which is 16 times the impedance of a simple dipole antenna. The feed impedances of the folded dipoles so far considered will only apply when their conductor wires are of equal diameter, and are in the same plane (a wide range of step-up ratios may be achieved when tubing elements of differing diameters and spacings are used, but the calculations involved in respect of such arrangements are outside the scope of this book).

The fact that the feed impedance of a folded dipole is increased is used in the design of Yagi and other beam antennas that use parasitic elements, i.e. elements that pick up and re-radiate the power and are not directly driven by a feedline. The fact that the elements are placed close together in these designs means that the feed impedance of the driven element falls, often to very low values. A figure between 10 and 15Ω is not unusual. By using a folded dipole the feed impedance can be multiplied by four to bring it back up to a value which presents a good match to 50Ω coax.

Resonant length

A folded dipole which is made with two wires spaced several inches apart will have a resonant length which is equal to that of a simple half-wave dipole: **Fig 3.19(a)**, i.e. 468 / f (MHz) feet. However, if the antenna top is fashioned from 300Ω ribbon or a similar solid dielectric line, the velocity factor of such a line must be taken into account. The older unslotted 300Ω ribbon has a velocity factor, K, of 0.8 whereas the new slotted variety has a K of 0.87. The resonant half-wave length of 468 / f (MHz) feet must be multiplied by the value of K to determine the length of a folded dipole when it is made with 300Ω ribbon.

This will be shorter than the normal dipole length and it is brought up to resonance by the addition of short wire extensions at the dipole ends: see **Fig 3.19(b)**.

A useful 'spin-off' from the use of a folded dipole is its inherent lower Q and its

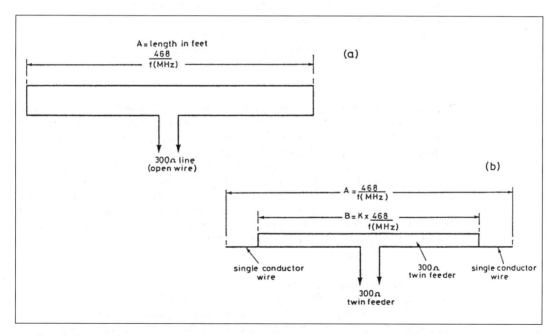

Fig 3.19: (a) The dimensions of a folded-dipole antenna using wires spaced between 6 and 12in apart. (b) When 300Ω ribbon is used to make a folded dipole, the velocity factor of this material must be taken into consideration when calculating its length. Small end wires are used to make up the full half-wavelength of the folded-dipole top.

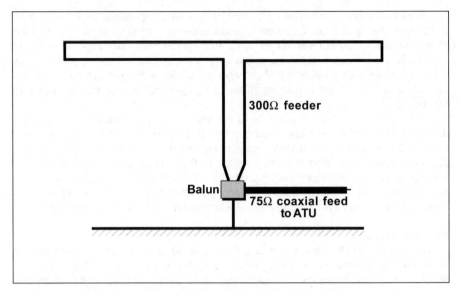

Fig 3.20: The 300Ω impedance of the feeder to a folded dipole can be reduced to a value of 75Ω (unbalanced) by using a 4:1 balun.

flatter impedance / frequency characteristics, which produces a better bandwidth than that of a simple dipole.

Like the basic dipole, a folded dipole cannot be used at twice its fundamental frequency or at any even multiple of that frequency, as the currents in the two conductors will be out of phase and will cancel. If used on these frequencies it will behave like a continuation of the feedline and the RF currents will be out of phase. On its third and other odd multiples of its resonant frequency, however, a folded dipole will have the proper current distribution and phasing to give effective radiation, and additionally its feed impedance will be close to 300Ω, although the radiation pattern will become that of a centre-fed wire three or more half-wavelengths long.

Feeding a folded dipole

The simplest way to feed a folded dipole is with a 300Ω impedance balanced line. This can be either of the solid dielectric 'ribbon' type or instead made up in the open wire 'ladder' manner as described in Chapter 2. At the bottom end of this feedline a suitable ATU must be used to provide a match to 50Ω.

It is often inconvenient to arrange for a long run of balanced feeder, and in this case the feed method which is illustrated in **Fig 3.20** may be adopted. Here the 300Ω line drops vertically from the centre of the antenna to almost ground level, where it connects to a 4:1 balun, B, providing an unbalanced output impedance of 75Ω. A length of 75Ω coaxial cable can then be led from the balun to the operating position. An ATU can be used in order to match the 75Ω impedance of the cable to the 50Ω output of the transceiver.

Folded dipole construction

The best and most mechanically sound way to construct a half-wave folded wire dipole is to use a single length of wire (preferably single-strand copper) to make up the two parts of the dipole, as shown in **Fig 3.21**. The two parts can be held apart by the use of a few spreaders made from a weatherproof insulating material. The RF voltages towards the ends of folded dipoles are not very high so there is little likelihood of large losses from the use of such spreaders.

The fact that the top and the bottom dipole sections are not exactly parallel will

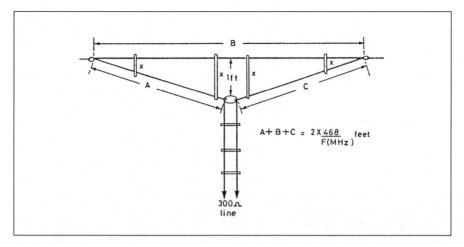

Fig 3.21: An 'all-wire' folded dipole. The feeder can be the open-wire type or a length of 300Ω ribbon. A disadvantage of ribbon feeder is that its characteristics can change when it is wet.

have almost no effect upon the performance or the feed impedance of such an antenna. Instead of using end insulators such as those shown in the diagram, lengths of nylon or similar cord can be used as both insulators and supports. A folded dipole has no power gain advantage over a basic half-wave dipole.

THE HALO

Popular back in the 1970s as a horizontally-polarised mobile antenna for use on 2m SSB (when it was made of aluminium tubing and sometimes called a 'squalo'), the halo is basically a half-wave dipole folded into a square shape, or originally a circle - hence the name. On HF, a square dipole made of wire can be a useful antenna for those who do not have enough horizontal space to put up a full-size half-wave dipole.

In the September 2009 *QST*, Joel Hallas, W1ZR, discussed the antenna and a few ways the halo can be fed.

Figs 3.22 and **3.23** show the *EZNEC* model results of the elevation and azimuth patterns of a

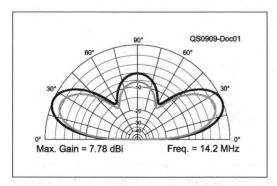

Fig 3.22: Elevation plots of the straight (black) and square (grey) dipoles for 20m. Each is at a height of 40ft (diagrams reprinted with permission of the American Radio Relay League).

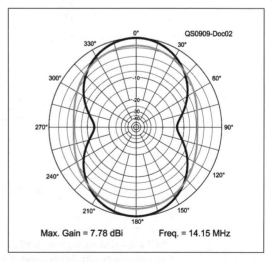

Fig 3.23: Azimuth plots of the straight (black) and square (grey) dipoles for 20m. Each is at the 24° peak of the elevation response.

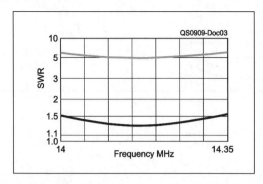

Fig 3.24: SWR of the straight (black) and square (grey) 20m dipoles. This provides the only challenge to using the square configuration, but it can easily be overcome (see text).

20m standard dipole at 40ft over typical ground, along with the patterns of the same antenna built into a square. A side length of 8.4ft with a 5in gap opposite the feedpoint was used as the model. The gap will be a high voltage point, so you should use a good insulator here when making the antenna. The square antenna tends to fill in what would be the nulls off the ends of the straight dipole. The directivity is thus less dramatic with the square much closer to omnidirectional, being just 3.7dB down on the 'ends'. The result is slightly less gain in the forward directions, down about 1.6dB, a small price to pay for the reducxed size and the added azimuth coverage if you only have one antenna for the band.

As with most shortened antennas, the square has a lower impedance at resonance than the stand-

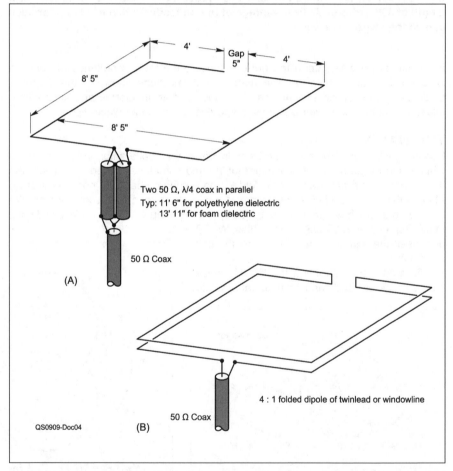

Fig 3.25: (a) Dimensions and details of the square dipole or 'halo' for 20m with λ/4 matching section for use with 50Ω coax. The dimensions assume 14 gauge bare wire. For insulated wire, the wire lengths should be reduced 2 to 4% depending on thickness and type. (b) A folded dipole version for direct coax connection. Both solutions are best for a single band.

ard dipole. The impedance at resonance is about 10Ω - this will vary with height, but is likely to be about 15 to 20% of the impedance of a standard dipole at the same height. The SWR is therefore likely to be around 5:1, as shown in **Fig 3.24**. If you have a very short run of low loss coax, you could feed it directly to your ATU (50ft of low loss LMR400 coax, for example, would have a loss of about 0.5dB at 14MHz with a 5:1 SWR, while window line would have a loss of 0.9dB for the same length).

Alternately, you could use a λ/4 matching section. For the matching section, you would want a line with a Z_0 of 22.3Ω, not too easy to find. Fortunately, you can hook two λ/4 sections of 50Ω coax in parallel for 25Ω and end up with an SWR of about 1.25:1 at the other side of the section - see **Fig 3.25(a)** for the details. Don't forget to reduce the matching section length by the velocity factor of the line, typically 0.66 for regular coax, or around 0.85 for foam (check the manufacturer's data sheet on the Internet to get the exact value for your cable).

Another possibility for single band use would be to use a two-wire folded dipole (**Fig 3.25(b)**). It should raise the impedance to about 40Ω, close enough for direct use of 50Ω coax.

The use of the λ/4 transformer or the folded dipole limits the use of the antenna with coax feed to a single band. For multiband use one possibility is a 1:4 (*not* 4:1) balun. While these are not generally commercially available, Jerry Sevick, W2FMI, describes their construction in his book *Transmission Line Transformers*. If you use the balun (or direct coax feed), you could try parallel square dipoles on the other bands. In each case, the coax should include a common-mode choke at or near the feedpoint for best results.

If you do use ladder line and an ATU, you will find that the single 20m halo should work well on 20m and all higher HF bands - on 17 and 15m it is almost omnidirectional, while on 12 and 10m it starts to look more like a dipole pattern - all with dipole or higher gain.

Incidentally, the halo has made a reappearance in the form of the well-known G3TPW CobWebb antenna (www.g3tpw.co.uk), a commercially-made multiband version of this antenna, with five separate dipole elements (for 14, 18, 21, 24 and 28MHz) each bent into a square.

MULTIBAND PARALLEL DIPOLES

With the exception of the use of the 40m dipole on 15m, all the dipoles discussed so far have been monoband antennas. However, it is possible to enable these antennas to operate on several bands. One technique is to feed several dipoles resonant on different frequencies from the same feeder. Each will present a feed impedance of between 50 and 70Ω at its own particular resonant frequency. On all other frequencies its impedance will rise, and it will not accept power from the feeder, and will therefore not affect the performance of the resonant dipole.

A multi-band antenna using a number of horizontal dipoles can be devised in the way suggested, but the extra weight over that of a single dipole will cause considerable sag and a fall

A practical installation of a multiband dipole constructed from drop feed telephone wire and plastic high-pressure water pipe as spacing insulators. The spacing between each of the elements should be about 6cm.

Close-up of the centre of 9M6DXX's 12/17m parallel dipoles. The whole arrangement is sloping and the ends are tied off at different angles. It works!

in the effective height of all the dipoles. However, it is possible to make an effective multi-band system using the inverted-V configuration with its central high point where the feeder and the combined weight of the dipole wires may be anchored.

This method of connecting together two or more dipoles for different frequency bands is well known. The co-editor of this book, Steve Telenius-Lowe, 9M6DXX, being fortunate enough to have a beam antenna for 10, 15 and 20m, uses separate pairs of parallel wire dipoles on 12 / 17m and on 40 / 80m. In each case the two dipoles are simply connected together at the centre, using a ferrite current balun, and the ends of the wires are fanned out and tied off to suitable supports. This method works very well, with no obvious interaction between the two bands in either case.

However, many years ago I tried to make a six-band version, for 40, 20, 17, 15, 12 and 10m, but found that adjusting the length of one dipole had a marked effect on the resonant frequency of the others. When the resonant frequency was at the required

The three-band dipole at 5X1NH in Uganda.

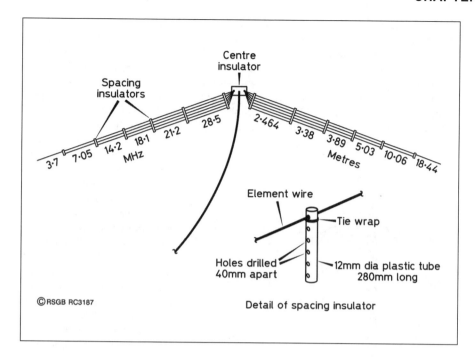

Centre insulator

Spacing insulators

3·7 7·05 14·2 18·1 21·2 28·5 2·464 3·38 3·89 5·03 10·06 18·44
MHz   Metres

Element wire

Tie wrap

Holes drilled 40mm apart

12mm dia plastic tube 280mm long

© RSGB RC3187

Detail of spacing insulator

Fig 3.26: Multiband arrangement using parallel dipoles in an inverted-V configuration. It will work just as well with the elements horizontal or sloping.

place in one band, or perhaps two, all the others were well out. Correcting those caused the original dipoles' resonant frequencies to shift, sometimes in a completely unexpected fashion. After much pruning, cutting and cursing, I gave it up as a bad job.

It was therefore interesting to read the comments of Peter Dodd, G3LDO, in his 'Antennas' column in the March 2011 *RadCom*. Peter said, "I used to think that connecting them [the dipoles] at single points and just fanning out the separate elements would do the trick but my attempt at that sort of structure was not successful." It seems likely that two, or perhaps three, dipoles can be connected together in this way but, if you wish to have more bands on the same feeder, another method is required. G3LDO goes on to say that the elements are best spaced apart in a parallel manner with insulated spacers and brought to the feedpoint over, say, the last 25cm (10in), as shown in **Fig 3.26**. The spacing between each of the elements should be about 6cm (just over 2in).

A practical installation is shown in the photograph on page 63, which uses drop feed telephone wire for the elements and plastic high-pressure water pipe as spacing insulators. Another practical installation is shown in the photograph opposite. This is the three-band antenna of Nick Henwood, G3RWF, at his 5X1NH station in Uganda.

G3LDO modelled the multiband dipole arrangement using *EZNEC* by creating a basic dipole (the 'main dipole') and testing its performance. He then added an extra band element and made a further check before connecting it to the main dipole and found that the antenna already exhibited a dual-band characteristic. He then added a further band element, again without connecting it to the main dipole. The antenna then had a tri-band characteristic. In reality this is nothing new and the resulting antenna is known as the coupled-resonator antenna. This antenna is described later in this chapter.

THE 'TEE PEE V' 20 AND 40M ANTENNA

Robert Giuliano, KB8RCO, described another practical implementation of the use of multiband parallel dipoles in the June 2008 *QST*. His local radio group enjoys setting up portable stations for special events and public service use. The antenna described here developed after an inverted-V dipole was used on a 22ft guyed telescopic pole at a field day event. The question was asked why four guys were needed as well as the dipole wires. Couldn't parallel dipoles with a common feedpoint be used as two inverted-Vs, with the wires also acting as guys for the pole?

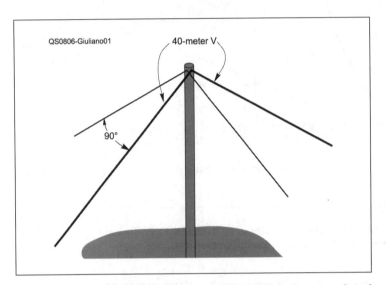

Fig 3.27: Layout of the 'Tee Pee V' antenna (illustrations reprinted with permission of the American Radio Relay League).

Combined 20m and 40m inverted-V dipoles were made as shown in **Fig 3.27**. The details of the connections are shown in **Fig 3.28**. The origin of the name should be clear from the drawings.

Because the two antennas are perpendicular to each other, the coupling that can cause problems with multiband parallel wire dipoles is minimised. A balun was not used at the feedpoint, but if you experience the effects of common-mode currents on the outside of the coax you may want to add a choke consisting of half a dozen turns of coax, about 8in in diameter.

The element lengths are approximately 17ft for 20m and 33ft for 40m; the total wire required is therefore about 100ft. A little geometry was used to keep the angle with respect to the pole at 56.75°. This allows each guy stake to be the same distance from the pole and makes setup easy. The distance the stakes need to be from the pole was calculated by multiplying the height by the tangent of the included angle (56.75°) and that came out to be about 33.5ft. The 56.75° angle of each wire to the pole results in the angle between the antenna wires of 113.5°, nicely larger than the design goal for inverted-Vs of being greater than 90° according to most dipole documentation.

A couple of checks with the antenna analyser showed the antenna to have the predicted flat SWR across both bands. Checks on the air received 59 reports from a local net on

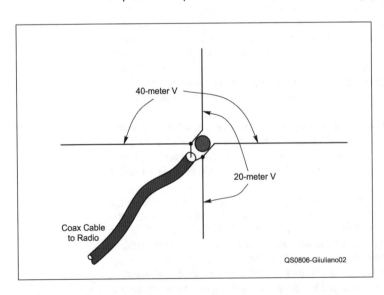

Fig 3.28: Details of the feedpoint connection arrangements.

The 'Tee Pee V' in use.

40m and from a more distant station on 20m: no DX, but it was clear the antenna was usable. Compared with a Mosley vertical, signals were pretty close.

The Tee Pee V is a simple dual-band antenna that can be set-up by a single person and will get you a decent signal on the design bands. If you trim it properly, it doesn't need a tuner. This antenna has been set up in many locations now, and it appears to give a good consistent SWR reading in each location.

THE COUPLED-RESONATOR ANTENNA

This is another way of getting dual-band performance from a single antenna. It was described by Joel Hallas, W1ZR, in an article called 'A Folded Skeleton Sleeve Dipole for 40 and 20 Meters' in the May 2011 *QST*. The skeleton sleeve dipole has been around for many years and has a parasitic element for the higher frequency on each

The W1ZR coupled-resonator antenna for 40 and 20m.

side of a lower frequency directly-fed element, in order to achieve dual band resonances. In fact, the antenna built and described by W1ZR is a simplified version of the skeleton sleeve which uses a *single* close-coupled wire to achieve the same result. The concept of coupling to a single conductor, rather than the two or more of the traditional skeleton sleeve, was first described by Gary Breed, K9AY, in 'The Coupled-Resonator Principle: A Flexible Method for Multiband Antennas', published in *The ARRL Antenna Compendium, Vol 5*.

This design is for a compact antenna with performance similar to a full size dipole on two bands, 40 and 20m, and is unusual in two regards:

♦ It uses the parasitic skeleton sleeve coupling from a single driven 40m dipole to a single higher frequency element to provide the second band, rather than the more common parallel connection.

♦ The ends of the lower frequency dipole are bent back to almost reach the higher frequency one. This results in an antenna about 10ft shorter than the usual 40m dipole. This is independent of the sleeve coupling method.

The folding of the lower band dipole is not fundamental to the design, and it will provide just a bit better performance on the lower band if it is unfolded and made full size: the objective was to make a compact dual-band antenna.

The antenna can be constructed from a single piece of nominal 450Ω window line, as shown in **Fig 3.29**. The coupled-resonator / parasitic skeleton sleeve coupling eliminates the narrow bandwidth usually encountered in closely-spaced parallel wire dipoles. Note that it is critical that the coax feedline is connected to the longer

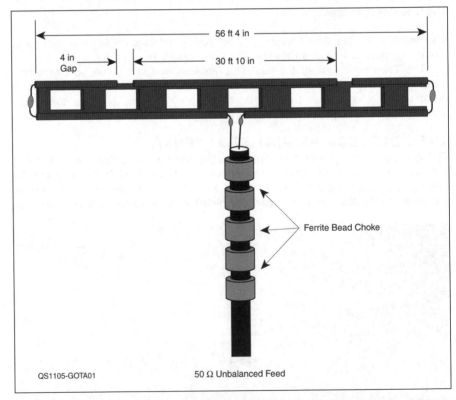

Fig 3.29: Dimensions of the folded sleeve dipole for 40 and 20m (illustrations reprinted with permission of the American Radio Relay League).

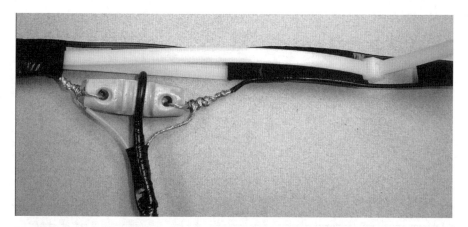

Detail of centre insulator and common-mode choke. The RG58 coax is wrapped around the centre insulator and taped to provide strain relief and to seal the end. The tape also holds the ferrite beads prior to application of heat shrink tubing.

40m wire (there is a mode in which it can be made to work the other way, feeding the shorter dipole instead, but the dimensions will be different and the system will not match to 50Ω).

W1ZR formed a common-mode choke by wrapping eight turns of the coax feed line through an FT-240-43 ferrite toroid. A better approach, particularly if foam coax is used, would be to use five 43 mix ferrite beads, with their inner diameter selected to fit snugly on the coax just below the feedpoint. They could be secured with shrink tubing or PVC pipe, if desired.

Unlike the case with close spaced parallel dipoles, there is almost no interaction between the bands. Changing the overall length of the antenna by 1in moves the 40m resonance about 130kHz: keep in mind that, because it is folded on 40m, it changes more rapidly than might be expected. The same adjustment in overall length makes a change to the 20m resonance by only about 10kHz. Changing the length of the 20m dipole by 1in (by making a change to the inner edge of the 4in gap) results in a change of about 50kHz on 20m, with virtually no change to the 40m resonance - so start with the 40m adjustment, if needed. As expected, making either portion shorter results in a higher resonant frequency.

This antenna provides gain and directivity comparable with a full size dipole on both 40 and 20m. See **Fig 3.30** for the *EZNEC* elevation patterns. On 20m, *EZNEC*

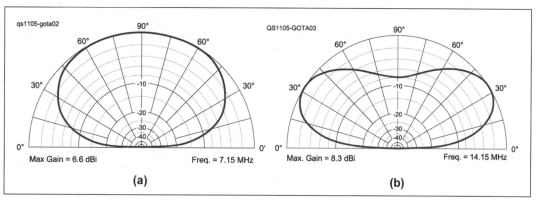

Fig 3.30: *EZNEC* **predicted elevation pattern of two-band dipole at a height of 30ft, (a) on 40m, and (b) on 20m.**

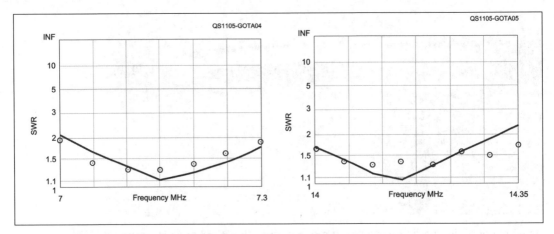

Fig 3.31: *EZNEC* **predicted SWR sweep of the two-band dipole on 40 and 20m. The 'O's indicate** *measured* **SWR at the end of 45ft of RG8X with a height of 25ft.**

predicts about 1.5dB gain over a half-wave dipole, as a result of narrowing the main beams by 4 - 5°. This is likely the effect of radiation from each side of the 40m antenna acting as 20m half waves in phase: a small bonus at no extra cost.

In use
At its design height of 30ft, the SWR across both bands is 2:1 or less to 50Ω coax, as shown in **Fig 3.31**. There is a small variation in resonance predicted at heights from 20 to 50ft.

W1ZR used the antenna to make many contacts on each band with good results compared with other antennas. With the antenna just below his second storey roofline, his first contact was from Connecticut to Australia with 100W on 20m CW. The station was stronger on this dipole than on a single element rotary about 10ft higher, in the clear and pointed at VK. On 40m, stations were just a bit lower in level than on a 100ft doublet fed with window line. This was expected since the doublet is about twice as high and also provides some gain over a full-size half-wave dipole on 40m.

ARRL Test Engineer Bob Allison, WB1GCM, also made a 40 / 20m coupled resonator antenna and found that it was more effective on 40m than his inverted-L, with much less noise pick-up. It was also quieter on 20m, with similar signal levels from most directions as a ground plane at the same height. His first contact on 20m SSB was also with Australia!

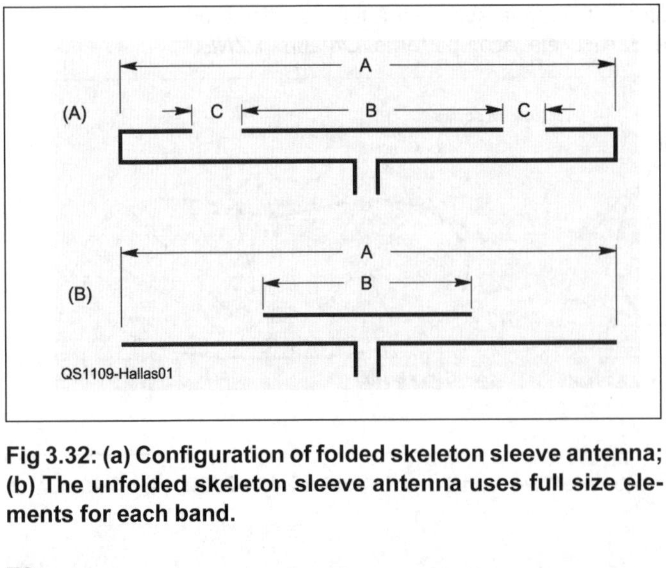

Other bands
W1ZR has not make a version of this antenna for other bands, although he did try modelling other band combinations with *EZNEC*. There is nothing magic about the 2:1 frequency relationship. For example, a model for 20 and 17m seems to work fine, although the

Fig 3.32: (a) Configuration of folded skeleton sleeve antenna; (b) The unfolded skeleton sleeve antenna uses full size elements for each band.

Bands (Metres)	Dimensions - Folded		
	A (Feet)	B (Feet)	C (Inches)
80/40	111.4	61.5	12.0
80/10	96.0	15.4	9.6
75/40	107.0	60.8	7.2
40/30	58.0	43.0	6.0
40/20	56.3	30.8	4.0
30/20	42.0	30.7	7.8
30/17	40.8	24.1	5.5
20/17	30.6	24.0	4.2
20/15	29.6	20.5	9.1
20/10	27.6	15.4	3.6
17/15	24.3	20.5	9.0
17/12	23.6	17.4	9.6
15/10	10.0	7.7	4.2
10/6	14.4	8.3	5.6

Bands (Metres)	Dimensions - Unfolded	
	A (Feet)	B (Feet)
40/20	63.4	30.8
20/17	32.0	24.0
15/10	10.65	7.65

Table 3.3: Suggested dimensions for both folded and unfolded versions of the skeleton sleeve / coupled-resonator antenna.

extra bit of gain on the higher band is not predicted for this case.

Rather than folding the dipole for the lower frequency band, if size is not an issue both dipoles can be made full size and the unfolded version will have a slight edge on both bandwidth and gain on the lower band. This configuration is shown in **Fig 3.32** with some suggested dimensions in **Table 3.3**.

LOADED DIPOLES

Not everyone has room for a full-sized dipole. Although those for the higher frequency bands are smaller, even these can be difficult to fit into some locations. By their very nature, dipoles for the low bands are very much larger and need large plots if full-sized antennas are to be installed. Fortunately it is possible to reduce the physical length of many antennas, with just a small degradation to the performance of the antenna. The reason for this is that the middle section of a dipole radiates most of the power: 71% of the total radiation occurs from the central half of a dipole's length.

One method is to bend the legs of the antenna, thereby enabling it to fit into a small plot. The ends can be dropped down to ensure that the centre remains as high as possible, or the antenna can be arranged in a zig-zag fashion. This can often work reasonably well.

An alternative is to use inductive loading in each dipole leg. Using this approach it is possible to achieve resonance and have little loss with a dipole only half the normal length for the frequency used. Off-centre loading can be achieved by inserting an inductor at a pre-determined position along each of the dipole legs. However,

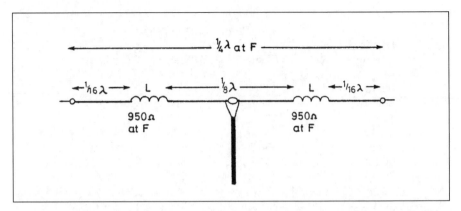

Fig 3.33: An inductively loaded half-size dipole. The lengths of each wire section may be calculated from the half-wave dimensions given in Table 3.1. The radiation pattern of a normal full-size dipole will also apply in the case of a shortened version, but its efficiency will be reduced. Coils made from very thick wire or tube, and wound on a high-grade former, will increase the efficiency by reducing resistive and other losses.

Band (MHz)	Inductance (μH)	Frequency when tuned with 100pF in parallel (MHz)
3.6	40	2.6
7.0	25	3.2
14.0	12	4.5
21.0	8	5.6
28.0	6	6.6

Table 3.4: Loading inductors for half-wave dipoles.

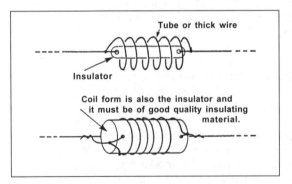

Fig 3.34: Two ways to insert the loading coils along the dipole wires. Self-supporting inductors can easily be adjusted by squeezing the turns together or apart. The loading coils can be set to the correct inductance before they are used in the antenna, and any final trimming to resonance will only involve the length of the end wires.

there are several considerations to be noted when deciding which is the most useful point for the loading coils.

The greater the distance they are from the antenna centre the more efficient the system will be but, when that distance is increased, larger values of inductance are needed. An increase in inductance results in an increase in the resistive loss, a narrower antenna bandwidth, and a heavy coil. The coil adds weight to the antenna increasing the strain and the degree of droop at the centre. If a dipole is halved in length (i.e. the top is only a quarter-wavelength long overall) and a loading inductance is put at the half-way point along each shortened leg, the inductors required must each have a reactance of approximately 950Ω at the operating frequency (see **Fig 3.33**).

By using this information it is possible to determine the actual inductance needed on each amateur band. **Table 3.4** gives these inductance values. It also gives the resonant frequency of the inductor when it is placed in parallel with a 100pF capacitor for testing and adjustment purpose. Winding coils to a specific inductance is not an easy task for amateurs because there are so many variables to consider: coil diameter, turns per inch, wire thickness and the coil length to diameter ratio. The coils must either be wound on a high-grade insulating material or be stout enough to be self-supporting using thick wire or tubing (**Fig 3.34**). By adding the parallel capacitor when testing and adjusting the coil it is relatively easy to determine the inductance. The coils can be trimmed with some accuracy. This can be done by squeezing or opening out the turns of the self-supporting types, or removing or adding turns to those coils which are wound on formers. It is suggested that a dip oscillator coupled to a frequency counter be used when adjusting the coils. This is done without any kind of connection to the antenna wires.

An insulator can be inserted half-way along each of the short dipole legs, and the coils (without the 100pF capacitors) may be soldered into place across them. Those coils wound on formers can be fully weatherproofed by giving them a liberal coating of silicone-rubber sealant. Insulation problems are not great, because the RF voltages will be low where the coils are positioned along the wires at their half-way points.

The finished loaded short dipole may not resonate at exactly the desired frequency at first test, so some adjustments can be made to the lengths of the dipole end sections. A dip oscillator / frequency counter arrangement can be coupled to a single-turn link across the dipole centre (the antenna may be lowered to about 3m (10ft) above ground to do this, or instead a check on the SWR should be made as the transmitted frequency is moved across the band. The lowest SWR normally indicates antenna resonance. An antenna analyser can also be used to check for dipole resonance.

Even a properly resonated, loaded half-size dipole will not be as effective as a full-sized antenna, but it will still prove to be a very useful radiator and show the same directional characteristics. The shortened loaded dipole must not be confused with a *trap dipole*, a type which is little shorter than a normal half-wave on the lowest band covered (see later in this chapter).

ZL1VL LOADED DIPOLE FOR 40 AND 80M

This design by Vince Lear, G3TKN / ZL1VL, appeared in the October 2004 issue of *RadCom*. In this design the antenna uses loading coils in place of more conventional traps to obtain two-band operation. The idea of using loading coils in this way was described over 50 years ago in an article entitled 'Multi-band Antenna Using Loading Coils' by W J Lattin, W4JRW, that appeared in the April 1961 issue of *QST*. The concept offers the advantage of simplicity (compared with construction of traps), and also results in considerable shortening of the antenna, which now takes up less space than the popular G5RV with its 31.09m (102ft) top, or the standard 33.53m (110ft) trap dipole.

The inductive reactance of a coil increases as the frequency applied to it increases. In the 40 / 80m loaded dipole (**Fig 3.35**), the coils are sufficiently large that they show a high impedance on 40m, and provide inductive loading on 80m. Lattin

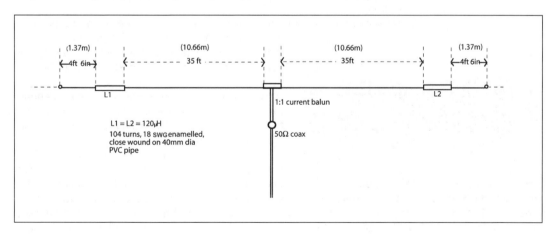

Fig 3.35: Dimensions of the 80 / 40m dipole.

found that values between 80µH to 120µH gave good results when used in this way, the larger values of inductance requiring less wire on the outer sections for 80m resonance. However, Lattin acknowledged that no exact formulas have been found to determine the relationship between coil size, wire lengths and the two frequencies for dual-band resonance. Therefore, the published design may be regarded as a starting point for experimentation.

It should be appreciated that when an antenna is inductively loaded several things happen. The most noticeable is the reduction in bandwidth of the system: the greater the loading, the smaller the bandwidth. The efficiency of the antenna also decreases. However, this decrease in efficiency is dependent on where in the antenna the loading coils are placed and, more importantly, on the construction of the loading coils. In a loaded wire antenna, the size and weight of the loading coils have to be important considerations, so to some extent there will always be some compromise between efficiency and what is practical.

As the loading is increased and the antenna becomes shorter, the feedpoint impedance decreases. With a very heavily-loaded antenna, it may not be possible to feed it with 50Ω coax, and some extra matching circuitry may need to be employed.

Using loading coils to achieve two-band resonance does mean that one has no choice but to place the coils a quarter-wavelength out either side of the feed-point on the higher frequency. The advantage is that, on 80m, the radiation resistance is kept at a higher level in this configuration than if the coils were placed close-in to the feedpoint. The disadvantage is that it results in a narrower operating bandwidth when the antenna is used on 80m. A good match is obtained to a 50Ω feeder on both 40 and 80m, although the bandwidth on 80m is restricted to about 60kHz between the 2:1 SWR points. No such problem occurs on 40m, where an SWR of about 1.5:1 was achieved across most of the band.

In this antenna the 120µH coils were constructed by close-winding 104 turns of 1.25mm (18SWG) enamelled copper wire on to a 17.8cm (7in) length of white PVC pipe of 40mm (1.6in) diameter. The winding length was 14cm (5.5in). Note that the total length of wire needed to construct these coils is a little more than that available from a standard 250g reel of wire. A 1kg reel of wire was used for the design antenna (available from Wires.co.uk, a division of the Scientific Wire Company, Unit 3 Zone A, Chelmsford Road Industrial Estate, Great Dunmow, Essex CM6 1HD, England; tel: +44 (0)1371 238013; fax: +44 (0)1371 871882; website: www.wires.co.uk; e-mail: dan@wires.co.uk). An alternative, although this has not been tried, could be to divide the wire from a 250g reel into two equal lengths and use these to wind as many turns as possible on to the two formers, making sure that they have the same number of turns.

With care, it should be possible to achieve about 92 close-wound turns which will yield around 106µH. The dimensions of the antenna will be affected, but those given for the 120µH version should make a good starting point for experimentation.

As always, when experimenting with antennas, make them longer than expected and then trim down for resonance. The PVC piping is obtainable from most DIY outlets in 1.8m (6ft) lengths.

The antenna wire was fixed to each end of the loading coil via holes drilled in the PVC pipe. The ends of the coil were anchored through small holes in the coil, and soldered to the antenna wire.

A short section of the PVC piping was checked out in a microwave oven to examine for any heating effect. None was found, so it was therefore as-

The coil used in the 40 / 80m dipole is made from standard 40mm (1.6in) diameter PVC pipe. It is 17.8cm (7in) long, with a winding length of 14cm (5.5in). Holes are drilled at each end to secure the antenna wire.

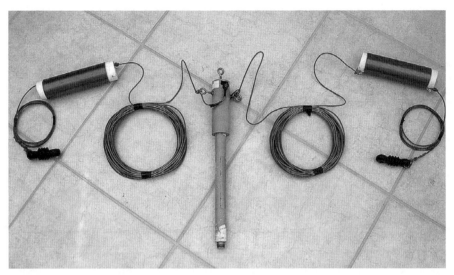

The 40 / 80m loaded dipole is made from flexible grey plastic-covered 14 strand copper wire.

sumed that the material was quite suitable for use in this application. Care should be exercised in the use of some PVC piping which may be quite lossy if it is carbon-filled. The whole coil assembly was given two coats of marine yacht varnish. The operation of the antenna was not affected during periods of heavy rain, so the weatherproofing provided by the varnish appeared quite adequate.

The antenna handled 400W from a linear amplifier without any problems, although this was only done where the SWR was no greater than 1.5:1. The photos show the coil construction and the antenna components, together with the current-mode balun. Losses are greater in a voltage-mode balun if used off resonance where reactive components are present. A current-mode balun can easily be constructed by winding 5 to 8 turns of RG58 coax (5mm diameter) around a pair of stacked ferrite rings.

The 40m section needed to be 10.66m (35ft) per leg as opposed to 10.05m (33ft) for resonance. This was the same length as found by W4JRW. If an antenna has end capacity-loading (as would be the case for a top-loaded vertical with a large capacity hat of wires fanning out from its top), its length can be reduced due to the end capacity. However, in the case of the 40m section in the 40 / 80m loaded dipole, inductive loading is seen at the end, and hence the opposite occurs with a resulting increase required for resonance at 7MHz. This effect should not be confused with inductive loading in series with an antenna rather than at its end. In the former case, the antenna will be electrically lengthened, and hence a shorter length of wire will be required for resonance.

The trimming of the end sections is very critical. It was found that 1.27m (4ft 2in) gave resonance on 3774kHz with a resulting 1:1 SWR, the 2:1 SWR points occurring at 3805kHz and 3742kHz. The antenna should, of course, be trimmed for one's favourite part of the band. The use of the auto ATU allowed for some limited excursion outside of the 2:1 SWR points on 80m. However, it should be appreciated that this in no way reduces mismatched line loss on the coaxial feeder.

As the coils also offer a high impedance on 15m, the inner section can be used as a near $3\lambda/2$ dipole on that band. The actual resonance in this mode was found to be 20.2MHz but, using an ATU, it was able to deliver full power across all of the 15m band on this design.

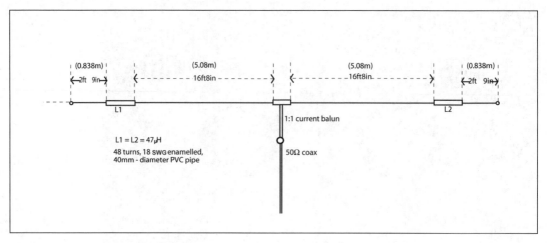

Fig 3.36: The 20 / 40m loaded dipole.

The antenna may be used on 160m instead of 80m by extending the wires on the outside of the loading coils from around 1.22m (4ft) to 7.62m (25ft). This gave a 1:1 SWR on 1840kHz. The bandwidth between the 2:1 SWR points is in the region of 35kHz on 160m. The antenna will now function on 40 and 160m.

A very successful 20 / 40m version was also constructed (**Fig 3.36**) using the same principles as used for 40 and 80m. This had an overall length of 11.89m (39ft) and used coils of 47µH. The coils were again made of 1.25mm (18SWG) enamelled copper wire, close-wound with 48 turns on standard 40mm (1.6in) diameter PVC pipe. Coil formers of 10cm (4in) length were used. The antenna had 5.08m (16ft 8in) inner sections with 0.83m (2ft 9in) outer ends.

The SWR on 20m was less than 1.5:1 across most of the band, and the antenna showed a 1:1 SWR on 7072kHz with a 2:1 SWR bandwidth of 96kHz. Typical dipole performance resulted on 20m, with good all-round reports on 7MHz.

If the standard 40 / 80m design is fed with open-wire line (or 450Ω ladder-line) coupled into the transceiver via a balanced ATU, the antenna could be operated efficiently on both 17m and 20m. The inner section will operate as two half-waves in phase on 20m, and as a double extended Zepp on 17m with theoretical broadside gain figures of 1.6dBd and 3dBd respectively. On 21MHz and above, a multi-lobe pattern will result.

W8NX SIX-BAND LOADED DIPOLE

This design, by Al Buxton, W8NX, was featured in the August 2007 *QST* and is for an antenna that covers the 160, 80, 40, 30, 17 and 12m bands. It is thus ideal for those amateurs fortunate enough already to possess a 10, 15 and 20m triband beam and,

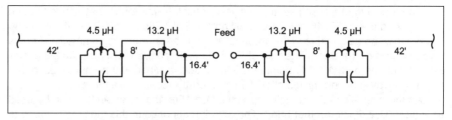

Fig 3.37: The W8NX six-band loaded dipole (illustrations reprinted with permission of the American Radio Relay League).

W8NX six-band loaded dipole mounted at 47ft on tower used to hold triband Yagi.

with the beam, will allow for all MF / HF bands coverage with just two antennas.

The antenna is based on the highly efficient 'dominant element' principle, requiring only *two* pairs of load elements to give six bands of operation. The radiation patterns have a single pair of broadside lobes on the 160, 80 and 40m bands but are similar to those of long wire antennas on the 30, 17 and 12m bands.

Radiation takes place along the entire length of the antenna on all bands, providing small but useful gains. Good bandwidth is provided on all bands when used in conjunction with an ATU. With the exception of the 160m band, full band coverage is provided on all bands. On 160m the effective working bandwidth is typically limited by the size of the capacitors in the antenna tuner.

The antenna length is 134ft and the one at W8NX was installed as an inverted-V dipole, with the apex at 47ft and drooping to a height of 20ft at each end. Some bending and folding at the ends of the dipole is permissible to accommodate installation in a small garden.

Fig 3.37 is a diagram of the antenna: it looks the same as a standard three-band trap dipole, however, the loads do not use the truncating capability of tuned parallel resonant traps. This type of load acts as either a pair of inductors or capacitors to supply the necessary reactance to bring the antenna into resonance with a low feed-point impedance on both fundamental and odd-order harmonic modes. This makes the antenna suitable for feeding via a 1:1 current balun with either 50Ω or 75Ω coaxial cable: 75Ω is advised because it makes a typical ATU more

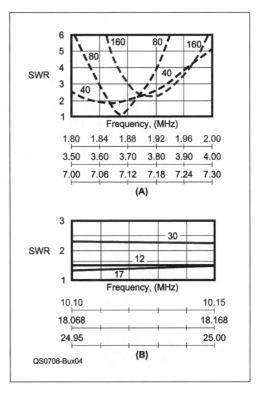

Fig 3.38 (a): SWR curves for 160 / 80 /40m; (b) SWR curves for 30 / 17 / 12m.

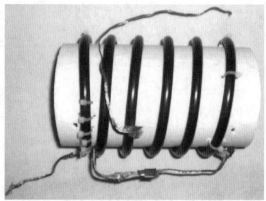

Construction techniques for 160/80m load element (above) and 40/30m load element (right).

effective especially on 160m where the size and cost of the large high voltage capacitors is the limiting factor in the effectiveness of a tuner.

The innermost pairs of loads create fundamental resonance on both 160 and 80m. The outermost pairs create fundamental resonance on 40m and third harmonic resonance on 30m. The overall antenna gives fifth harmonic resonance on 17m and seventh harmonic resonance on 12m.

The loads are necessarily physically large to achieve high Q, low loss performance, and have significant stray capacitance.

Wide air gaps between turns of the load windings and the use of thin walled PVC coil forms minimise dielectric losses in the load elements. The use of RG8U (RG213) coax cable with large diameter stranded wire centre conductors minimises skin effect I^2R losses.

The Q of each 160 / 80m load is 260, and the Q of the 40 / 30m loads is 325. Load losses on 80 to 12m are less than 0.5dB, but on 160m the loss approaches 3dB. On 160m the radiation resistance of the antenna is low because of the relatively short length of the antenna, reducing the overall radiation efficiency to about 50%.

The radiation patterns have a single pair of broadside lobes on 160, 80 and 40m. The patterns on the higher frequencies display numerous lobes, characteristic of long wire types of antennas. The peak gain on 40m is 3dB above an ordinary dipole. As is the case with an ordinary dipole this has only two lobes. The gain on 12m is about the same as on 40m but the pattern has 10 lobes. The measured SWR curves for the 160, 80 and 40m bands are shown in **Fig 3.38(a)** and those for 30, 17 and 12m are shown in **Fig 3.38(b)** (as measured at the rig end of an 80ft long, 75Ω RG59 feedline).

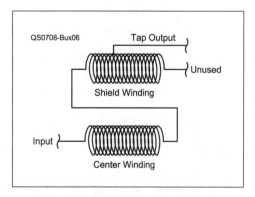

Fig 3.39: The RG8U (RG213) load element.

Construction

The photos above show the 160 / 80 and 40 / 30m load elements. A diagram of the load element is shown in **Fig 3.39**. Note how the pigtail at the output end of the centre winding is fed backwards to the pigtail of the input end of the shield winding. The loads are made of R-G8U coaxial cable (Belden 8237) wound on a former made of 4.188in outside diameter PVC drain pipe.

Fig 3.40 shows details of the coax used for the loads. **Fig 3.41** shows the load forms, the critical ones being the lengths and diameters of the forms and the 1in edge margins of the windings on the forms. Dimensions A and B fix the output tap location, with the

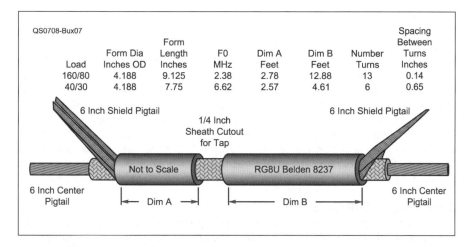

		Form					Spacing Between
	Form Dia	Length	F0	Dim A	Dim B	Number	Turns
Load	Inches OD	Inches	MHz	Feet	Feet	Turns	Inches
160/80	4.188	9.125	2.38	2.78	12.88	13	0.14
40/30	4.188	7.75	6.62	2.57	4.61	6	0.65

Fig 3.40: Details of the load element coax.

RG8U / RG213 laid out flat and straight on a table. The tap is a 15in length of silvered braided shield (braid) wire cannibalised from RG58 coax cable. The tap requires two turns tightly wrapped around the RG8U / RG213 wire at the quarter-inch break cut in the PVC sheath. Cover this break with anti-corrosion 'gunk' (such as Penetrox) to prevent resistance developing at the tap.

Care is required in making the output tap to hold the two turn wrap around the RG8U / RG213 permanently in tension using a crimp connector. **Fig 3.42** shows the details of the 15in output tap of the loads. Unfortunately, soldering at the tap would weaken the electrical properties of the RG8U / RG213 coax cable so a mechanical-only connection is necessary. The input terminal of any load is the near end (nearest the feedline) of the centre conductor winding of the coax cable. The far end of the centre conductor is fed back to the near end of the shield winding. The output of the load is taken at the tap on the outer shield winding.

The output tap acts as an auto transformer, giving the needed L/C ratio for the load. You should fine tune the loads to within 1% of the specified frequency by using a

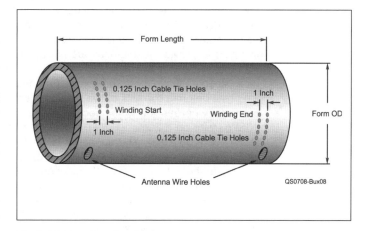

Fig 3.41: Details of coil form.

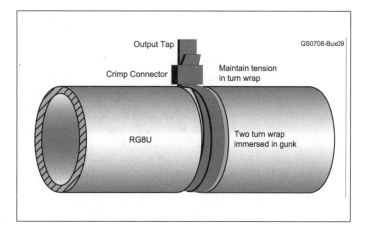

Fig 3.42: Output tap detail.

dip meter and an accurately calibrated receiver.

Air gap spacing between the turns of each load reduces dielectric load losses and permits fine tuning of the load resonant frequency. Expanding the air gap increases the load resonant frequency; reducing the gap lowers the frequency. Do not hesitate to increase the gap between turns as much as necessary to achieve the resonant frequency of the load, even though you may distort the appearance of the load. After completion of the fine tuning, the location of the turns must be stabilised by cable ties, as shown in the photographs. More cable ties are actually required than are shown, especially around the first and last turns of the load winding. Stabilising the interior turns is not as critical, as they have less effect on the load's resonant frequency than the outermost first and last turns. Although making the loads for this antenna may seem like a challenging task, your efforts will be well rewarded!

THE TRAP DIPOLE

Over the years a number of designs have appeared for multi-band trap dipoles covering the 80, 40, 20, 15 and 10m bands. The original design was by C L Buchanan, W3DZZ, in 1955 and consequently the trap dipole is often called a 'W3DZZ' antenna. In the UK, the late Rowley Shears, G8KW, marketed the G8KW trap dipole which was very popular in the 1970 and 1980s, while in Germany the Fritzel W3-2000 was a similar design. The design, with a single trap in each leg, was from many years before amateurs were granted the 30, 17 and 12m bands so there was never any intention to provide resonances around these frequencies.

The 'traditional' five-band (80, 40, 20, 15 and 10m) trap dipole can be installed as a 'straight' dipole, or in the inverted-V configuration, as shown in **Fig 3.43**. Each leg of the antenna consists of two lengths of wire, the one closest to the centre is 32ft 6in long, whereas the outer section is 21ft 6in. The traps comprise 23 turns of 18SWG wire on a 30mm (1.25in) diameter former with a winding length of approximately 65mm (2.5in). The capacitor is 50pF and must be a high voltage type to withstand the antenna end voltage when used with a transmitter. Before connecting the trap to the antenna it is made resonant at 7.1MHz.

The antenna forms a half-wave on 80m. On 40m it uses the trap and is similarly a half-wave antenna. On the higher frequency bands it acts as a multiple half-wave antenna and, although it will radiate on each of the five bands, it can sometimes be difficult to obtain a low SWR on the three higher-frequency bands. The design is optimum on 80 and 40m only and on the higher-frequency bands the radiation pattern splits up into many lobes.

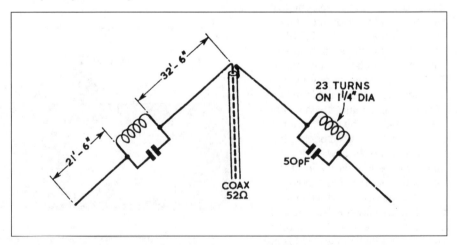

Fig 3.43: The inverted-V trap dipole.

WB2EZG FIVE-BAND TRAP DIPOLE

Can a wire antenna using only two basic traps work well over the five 'traditional' amateur bands, from 10 to 80m? Yes, it can, and Vincent Biancomano, WB2EZG, writing in the ARRL's magazine for technical experimenters, *QEX* (September / October 2010), presented an entirely new design. His work addresses the various drawbacks of the original W3DZZ antenna. Specifically, it:

♦ Offers broad response - at least 200kHz at 80, 20 and 10m and a practical bandwidth of 100kHz on 40 and 15m (3:1 SWR or better with 75Ω feed);
♦ Lifts the resonant frequency of the traps (more correctly, 'loading elements'), usually at 7MHz for this class of antenna, out of the band to cut power losses and trap rating requirements;
♦ Does away with special trap arrangements and configurations, matching sections and 'add-on' compensating elements; and
♦ Minimises the time for in-the-field pruning.

WB2EZG's article uses a lot of mathematics (which he describes as "basic math"); what is presented here is a much shortened version that concentrates on the practical implementation of the new design of antenna. Those who are interested in learning how the antenna was developed are advised to obtain a copy of the original article (it is available, for example, from ARRL on a compilation CD that includes all 2010 issues of *QST*, *QEX*, and *NCJ*, the *National Contest Journal*).

The W3DZZ antenna's signature configuration centres on the 40m band; i.e. two traps tuned to 7MHz or so that are placed at each end of a centre-fed wire about 65ft long with the antenna having a total length of about 110ft. That antenna is designed to work as essentially a half-wave dipole on 80 and 40m, three half-waves on 20m, five half-waves on 15m, and seven half-waves on 10m. In practice, the W3DZZ can be made to work over two bands without much difficulty and three bands with a bit of cut-and-try. Adjusting the antenna to work on four bands is significantly more difficult, however, and five bands presents the ultimate challenge.

The success of the new design (**Fig 3.44**) springs from a 'top-down' approach, i.e. it is focused on the *highest* frequency of operation. The antenna has a physical length that's resonant at the highest frequency of operation (28MHz): a little over 120ft. Indeed, operation at 28MHz in a traditional two-trap design isn't otherwise easily secured with a shorter antenna, given the fixed placement and component values of the L and C elements. Moreover, the values of L and C used in a traditional trap dipole have little effect on antenna response at 10m. The maths tells us the length of the antenna should be essentially 7/2-λ at 28MHz.

One possible solution for the new five-band dipole, designed for the CW ends of the bands is that shown in Fig 3.44. The antenna wire used was 14 gauge bare solid

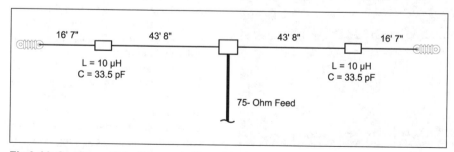

Fig 3.44: Configuration of one solution of the WB2EZG five-band dipole, as tweaked for the CW bands (illustrations reprinted with permission of the American Radio Relay League).

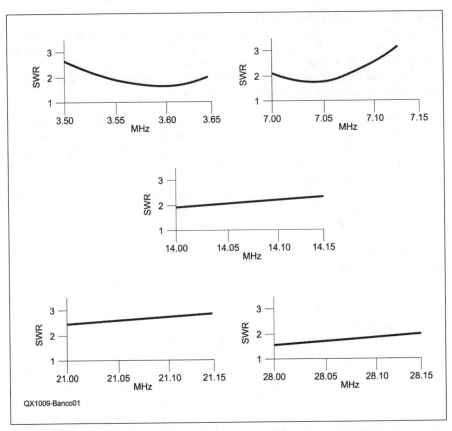

QX1009-Banco01

Fig 3.45: SWR curves for one solution of the WB2EZG five-band dipole at a height of 28ft, as tweaked for the CW bands. SWR measured at the transmitter end of an 85ft section of RG6 (75Ω) coax.

copper. With the overall length of 120ft 6in as shown, the mathematical analysis calls for the traps to be made up of an inductance of approximately 10μH and a capacitance of 33.5pF. At a height of about 35ft above ground the SWR curves shown in **Fig 3.45** are obtained.

Antenna 'pruning' for your particular installation should require no more than a few iterations: place the antenna between two supports such that the dipole's centre is at least 15ft above ground. Then resonate the flat top to the lower end of 28MHz. The traps should be inserted between 13 and 14% from each end of the 121ft flat top. Install suitable insulators at these points for wire support and to allow adjustment of wire lengths as well as for easy attachment and removal of the traps in the pruning process. The LC components are housed in a pop-open plastic enclosure measuring approximately 1.75 x 2.5 x 5in for protection from the weather. Adjust the trap capacitance and wire lengths as re-

One of the prototype traps used with this antenna. It is comprised of a 10μH B&W miniductor coil and a Johnson 158-5-23 air variable capacitor set to 33.5pF.

A more robust trap than that shown opposite. It is made in the true amateur radio spirit, using whatever was on hand! The 2in diameter coil is constructed from 16 gauge insulated wire to provide about 10.8μH. The capacitor consists of two sections of copper tubing, a 3/4in diameter section placed within a 1in diameter section and adjusted to yield a capacitance of about 31.3pF.

quired (take care to ensure symmetry on each side of the dipole) for the lowest SWR on each band. You may find it more effective to cut or add wire from both the inner and outer sections of the flat top. For best results, though, maintain each trap at a distance of 13 to 14% from each end of the flat top.

Fixed-value transmitting mica capacitors or a homebrew alternative might serve better than the typical close-spaced, transmitting air variable to maintain antenna characteristics and also to allow for high-power operation. Fixed-value transmitting ceramic caps, if used, might best be suited to moderate climates where there's no great swings in seasonal temperatures or environmental conditions.

The antenna is fed by RG6 75Ω coax and a choke balun should be installed at the feedpoint: slip 12 F-50B toroid cores (Palomar Engineers) over the feedline before making measurements. Apply heat shrink tubing to keep the cores in place.

The new antenna's comparative band-to-band response, versus that of many previous trap designs, is relatively insensitive to small changes in antenna length and the exact placement of the loading elements - issues that usually create insurmountable tuning difficulties in a traditional trap dipole as the designer struggles to redress the resonance requirements for each band simultaneously. The main operating trade-off with the new antenna is a bit less bandwidth on 40m.

THE TERMINATED TILTED FOLDED DIPOLE (T2FD)

The T2FD covers a frequency ratio of 4:1 or more and is only a third of a wavelength long at its lowest frequency of operation. It bears a superficial resemblance to an ordinary folded dipole, but its dimensions, the use of a non-inductive terminating resistor, R, and the 20° to 40° tilt result in an aperiodic or non-resonant vertically-

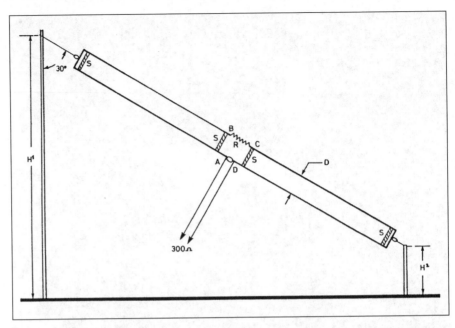

Fig 3.46: The T2FD antenna. The version of the antenna shown is designed for operation down to 7MHz. The high support H1 need only be 11m (36ft) high and the lower support H2 need only be 2m (6ft).

polarised radiator. **Fig 3.46** shows the principal features of a T2FD. If designed for 7MHz it will work up to at least 30MHz and will also work to a degree on half its design frequency (3.5MHz). It can be fed with 300Ω impedance untuned line.

When set up at its optimum slope angle of 30°, the T2FD displays an almost omni-directional, low-angle radiation pattern similar to that of a quarter-wave vertical. There is, however, some reduction in field strength compared with a quarter-wave vertical.

The antenna is useful in cramped locations, for on its design frequency it is somewhat shorter than an equivalent half-wave antenna. On 7MHz a half-wave is

The terminated tilted folded dipole in use.

about 20m (66ft) long from end to end but a T2FD will only be about 14.33m (47ft) in length. Also, the T2FD only needs a single support 11m (36ft) high and an additional short 1.8m (6ft) pole at its low end.

The length of each leg (when measuring from the centre of the wires across the end spreaders to the feed point or the terminating resistor) should be 50,000 / f (kHz) metres (or 50,000 / f (kHz) x 3.28 feet). The total top length in Fig 3.46 will be twice this calculated length. The frequency is the lowest operating frequency of the antenna although, as has been mentioned, a T2FD will work with reduced efficiency at half this frequency. The spacing between the two radiator wires D in metres can be found by dividing 3000 by the frequency in kilohertz.

The terminating resistor must be non-inductive for the antenna to operate satisfactorily. If an inductive resistor is used the antenna resonates on some frequencies and then the feeder must then be used as a tuned line, and the flat 300Ω impedance at the feedpoint is lost.

The terminating resistor value is to some extent determined by the impedance of the feedline used. When using 300Ω twin lead to feed the antenna, the optimum resistor value is about 400Ω, although any resistance value between 375 and 425Ω will work well. With 450Ω open wire feed line a 500Ω resistor is satisfactory, and the use of 600Ω line requires a 650Ω resistor.

Some experimenters have fed the T2FD antenna with low-impedance line (including coaxial cable), but then the terminating resistor value becomes very critical and must be within 5Ω of optimum. The terminating resistor must dissipate about 35% of the transmitter output power. This may seem to be a serious power loss, but in fact it only represents a signal loss of from 1.5 to 2dB (below half an S-point).

A T2FD antenna can be assembled by using two wires of equal length, each wire making up one of the sections A-B and C-D as shown in the diagram. Their lengths for each band are given in **Table 3.5**, where the spacing distances D are also shown. The heights of the antenna supports on different bands may be interpolated from the mast height of 11m (36ft) for a T2FD designed for the 7MHz band.

Trees or buildings can also be used as end supports, but when buildings are used there will be some additional attenuation of the radiation from that end of the antenna. A 2m (6ft) anchor point at the low end of the antenna can be used for all antenna lengths, its main purpose being to safeguard the wires from children or animals.

It has been found that when the antenna is pulled tight, it only needs a centre spreader and a spreader at each end. However, there is no reason why additional spreaders cannot be used towards the centre of each leg of the antenna. If the end spreaders are fashioned from a material like Perspex, the antenna wires can be threaded through the spreaders and no additional antenna insulators will be needed.

A correctly designed T2FD using a non-inductive terminating resistor presents a uniform feed impedance right across its frequency range. The antenna described should have a 300Ω feeder which may be taken right to the shack and the ATU. As an alternative, when long feeder runs are used that may run through the house or near other objects, the feeder may be connected to a 4:1 balun which will bring down the impedance to 75Ω (unbalanced) and then allow the use of coaxial cable.

Frequency (kHz)	Length A-B and C-D (also top length)	Spacing D
1800	55.54m (182' 2")	1.66m (5' 5")
3600	27.76m (91' 1")	0.83m (2' 8")
7000	14.28m (46' 10")	0.42m (1' 5")
10100	9.9m (32' 6")	0.30m (1' 0")
14150	7.06m (23' 2")	0.21m (0' 8")
21200	4.7m (15' 6")	0.14m (0' 5")
29000	3.44m (11' 4")	0.10m (0' 4")

Table 3.5: Dimensions for T2FD antenna.

4 Doublets

ONE CLASS OF antenna that is not as widely used as it might be is that of tuned feeder antennas. Using an open-wire tuned feedline as part of the overall antenna system enables multi-band operation to be achieved, although such an antenna - often called a *doublet* - does require the use of an ATU to ensure that there is a good match to the transceiver.

The key to tuned feedline antennas is naturally the feeder. As discussed in Chapter 2, these open-wire feedlines have a characteristic impedance which relates to the diameter of the wire used and the spacing between the feed wires. This impedance is important in many applications, but note that it is of no consequence when considering centre-fed antennas which use tuned lines exclusively.

Tuned feedlines operate on the principle that they are really a part of the antenna and have 'standing waves' along their lengths. Standing waves are a feature of most radiating wires but, if two such wires of equal length are closely spaced (in terms of wavelength) and fed in anti-phase, in theory they will not radiate (in practice they will radiate a very small proportion of the RF power applied).

THE BASIC DOUBLET ANTENNA

The basic doublet (**Fig 4.1**) is a probably the most useful simple multi-band antenna for amateur use. It is simple and yet effective, and requires no special earth or counterpoise arrangements. The only drawbacks are the requirement to use an ATU

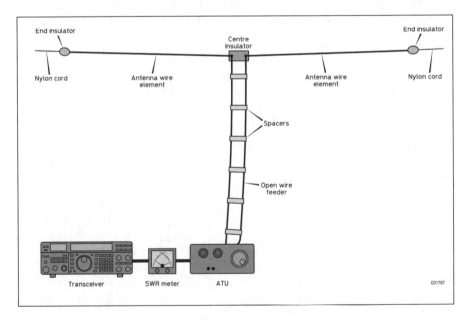

Fig 4.1: The basic doublet antenna.

and that the balanced feeder cannot be routed through the house.

The doublet is essentially a balanced system and each half of the top, plus each wire in the feedline, must be equal in length. The antenna top is not cut to resonate at any particular frequency (unlike the half-wave dipole), and almost any length may be chosen to suit an individual location.

The doublet can be used over a wide range of frequencies although as the frequency changes so the radiation pattern of the antenna will alter. A half-wavelength antenna has the maximum radiation at right angles to the axis or line of the antenna. As the electrical length of the antenna increases the phasing of the radiation from the antenna wire means that new lobes appear and grow. Examples of polar diagrams of a half-wave and a three half-wave radiator are shown in **Fig 4.2**.

When erecting an antenna of this nature there are no particular precautions to observe except that, due to possible problems with reactance making a good match difficult to achieve, certain combinations of feeder / top leg length should be avoided. These are summarised in **Table 4.1**. The table shows that when using doublet legs of 15.2m (50ft) together with 16.4m (54ft) of feeder there ought to be little difficulty with reactance on most amateur bands. There are of course many other combinations of top length and

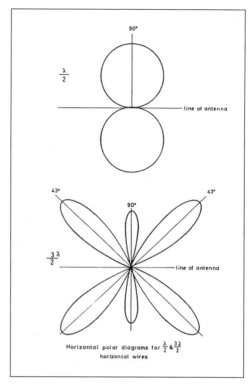

Fig 4.2: Horizontal polar diagrams for half-wave and three half-wave horizontal wires.

Band (MHz)	Lengths to be avoided (metres) (half the total top length plus feeder length)					
1.8 / 1.9	56.4m	93.7m	131m			
3.6	29.26m	48.8m	68.3m			
7	15m	25.14m	35.2m	45.26m		
10.1	10.5m	17.52m	24.53m	31.54m		
14.15	7.5m	12.6m	17.6m	24.2m	27.7m	32.7m
18.1	5.9m 29.7m	9.9m 33.7m	13.86m	17.83m	21.8m	25.8m
21.2	4.9m 24.7m	8.2m 28.0m	11.6m 31.4m	14.9m 34.8m	18.1m	21.5m
24.94	4.3m 21.3m	7.1m 24.1m	10m 27.1m	12.8m 29.9m	15.6m	18.5m
29	3.7m 18.3m	6.1m 20.7m	8.5m 23.2m	11m 25.6m	13.4m 28m	15.8m 30.5m

Table 4.1: Lengths to avoid when designing multi-band doublets with tuned feeders.

feeder length which can be chosen, either the feeder or the top being adjusted to suit individual locations.

One advantage of the doublet over a resonant dipole is that the tuned feeder type of transmission line has the advantage of low loss, even with a high SWR and long runs. Open wire feeder or any commercial 300 or 450Ω ladder-line can be used. An ATU with a balanced feed is used to take care of the wide variations of feed impedance on the different bands. The traditional T-match with a balun at the output for balanced feeders is the most popular.

Most information available indicates that the doublet should be at least half a wavelength long at the lowest frequency of use. However, Peter Dodd, G3LDO, writing in *RadCom* in May 2008, commented that he had found that the doublet can be reduced to 3/8-λ on the lowest frequency and still have an effectiveness greater than 98% relative to a half-wave dipole, with impedance values that are reasonably easy to match. A 3/8-λ dipole at 3.5MHz is approximately 30m (100ft) long, which means that any length from 27m (90ft) to 30m will make an excellent radiator on all HF amateur bands from 80 to 10m, including the 12, 17 and 30m bands.

Alternatively, if you don't have room for a 30m length of straight wire for operation on 80m, a 3m to 5m (10 to 16ft) portion of each end may be dropped vertically from each end support. There will be no significant change in radiation pattern on 80 and 40m. There will, however, be a minor change in polarisation in the radiation at higher frequencies, but the effect will be negligible.

Where a total top length of 30m (100ft) is possible, the doublet will work well on all the bands 3.5MHz to 28MHz and, if the feeders are strapped at their lower end and tuned against ground, it will also work on 1.8MHz. The radiation pattern in the horizontal plane will be similar to that of a half-wave dipole when it is used on 3.5MHz; as two half-waves in phase on 7MHz; as a 1.5-wavelength antenna on 14MHz with a six-lobed pattern of radiation; and progressively like a long wire on the higher-frequency bands with the lobes tending to align with the direction of the wire of the antenna.

This antenna can also be supported using a single pole to form an inverted-V, although the ends should be fixed as high as possible. If you are willing to forgo the

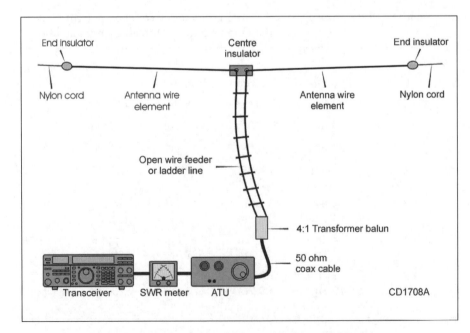

Fig 4.3: The 'Comudipole' arrangement. Compare this with Fig 4.1.

use of 80m, a centre-fed wire half the length quoted above will work on all the bands from 7 to 29MHz. And remember, the dimensions of this antenna are not critical, unlike those of the resonant dipole or the G5RV.

While the open-wire tuned doublet is a very good antenna there are problems in many locations of bringing open wire feeder into the shack. This is because twin feeder must not be allowed to come close to metal objects such as metal window frames, guttering or flashing and particularly electrical wiring. Metal objects close to the line can cause the currents in the line to be unbalanced. On the other hand, coax cable is fully screened and can be allowed close to metal objects, but it has greater losses. The solution, if you do not have a clear run from the antenna to the ATU, is to use part balanced feeder and part coax (**Fig 4.3**). This method was described by Dick Rollema, PA0SE, in 1993 and termed the 'Comudipole', meaning 'COax-fed MUltiband Dipole'. All this arrangement does is to move the balun, normally located inside the ATU, to a place outside the ATU and the shack, making a more convenient connecting point for open line feeder. It is connected to the coax output socket of the ATU. Although the position of the balun is not critical, the coax section should be kept as short as possible to keep the losses down. You don't have to remove the balun physically from your ATU! You can buy one, or make one as described below.

Many published and commercial T-match ATU designs use a 4:1 transformer balun to provide a balanced input for impedances in the range 150 to 600Ω. However, under certain circumstances a low impedance is presented to the balun on some bands, depending on the length of the antenna and the length of the feeder. It is very easy to expand the design of the balun to include a 1:1 ratio which can be selected from 4:1 by a selector switch or coax connector. This will expand the range of balanced inputs from about 45 to 600Ω without introducing any noticeable losses into the system.

Balun construction

A suitable balun transformer is shown in **Fig 4.4**. It is wound on a single Amidon T200-2 powdered-iron core, colour coded red. For sustained high-power operation, 400W plus, two such cores can be taped together by using plumbers' PTFE tape, which can also be used to provide an added layer of insulation between the core and the windings. T200-2 cores can be obtained from JAB Electronic Components (see www.jabdog.com).

The design of the balun and the construction description is by Mike Grierson, G3TSO: "Balun construction is simple, but a little cumbersome; some 14 turns of 16SWG (1.6mm) enamelled copper wire have to be wound trifilar fashion on to the toroidal core. That is to say, three identical windings are wound on together. Care

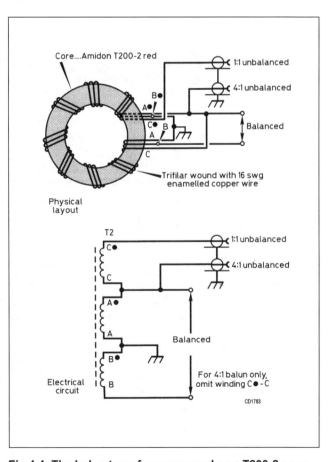

Fig 4.4: The balun transformer wound on a T200-2 core.

must be taken to ensure that the windings do not overlap or cross one another and that neither the core nor enamel covering is badly scratched during construction.

"Fourteen turns will require approximately 97cm (38in) of 16SWG wire, so cut three equal lengths of 16SWG wire slightly longer than required and pass all three wires through the core until they have reached about half way. This now becomes the centre of the winding and it is easier to wind from the centre to either end, rather than from one end to the other, which involves passing long lengths of wire through the toroid. The T200 size core will accommodate 14 turns trifilar without any overlapping of the start and finish of the winding. Close spacing will occur at the inside of the core, and a regular spacing interval should be set up on the outside. A small gap should be left where the two ends of the winding come close together.

"Connection of the balun requires care and it is necessary to identify opposite ends of the same windings, which can be done with a continuity meter, with some form of tagging or colour coding being worthwhile. On the circuit diagram a dot is used to signify the same end for separate windings. It is essential that the various windings are correctly connected if the balun is to work properly."

Construction of a 4:1 balun only is slightly simpler and only requires two (bifilar) windings. More on baluns can be found in the 'Antenna Matching Systems' chapter.

GAIN AND IMPEDANCE OF A DOUBLET

Fig 4.5 shows a *NEC2* plot of the gain, front-to-back (FB) ratio, SWR and impedance seen at the feedpoint of a centre-fed doublet. The total length of the doublet is 39m and the wire diameter is 2mm. The *NEC2* software has been configured to calculate

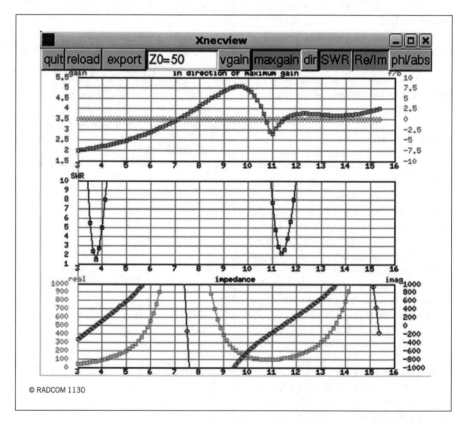

© RADCOM 1130

Fig 4.5: *NEC2* plot of gain, front to back ratio, SWR, resistive (real) impedance and reactive impedance of 39m long doublet antenna vs frequency.

the gain and impedance at 100 different frequencies starting at 3.0MHz and ending at 15.5MHz. Since the doublet is a bidirectional antenna, the F/B ratio is always 0dB. The centre graph shows the SWR that would appear on a 50Ω feeder connected to the feedpoint.

If you look at the left side of the impedance graph, you will see that the reactance plot crosses the zero line at about 3.75MHz. This is the half-wave resonant frequency of the doublet and coincides with the lowest point on the SWR plot. Note that a negative value of reactance signifies a capacitive reactance and a positive value signifies an inductive reactance. You will also notice that the gain is approximately 2.15dBi at this frequency. All of these figures are in the expected range and it seems that our *NEC2* model is reasonably accurate. Apart from the half-wave resonant frequency, there are several other points of interest on the graphs. The full-wave resonance can be seen at around 7.5MHz where the antena operates as a collinear pair of half-wave dipoles. The maximum gain broadside to the doublet is 3.5dBi (1.36dBd) at 7.1MHz. The feedpoint resistance at 7.1MHz is very high and because the reactance changes very rapidly with frequency near the full-wave resonance, there is considerable reactance at 7.1MHz.

If we were to use a 50 or 75Ω coax feeder, the SWR on 40m would be about 90:1. This would result in very inefficient operation because of the very high feeder losses. The next point of interest is the peak in maximum gain at about 9.5MHz. At this frequency, each side of the doublet is 5/8-λ. This is the length that provides maximum gain broadside to the doublet. If we increase the frequency much beyond this point, the two main lobes of the radiation pattern will start to break up into several smaller lobes. (A 2 x 5/8-λ doublet is an 'extended double Zepp' and has a maximum gain of just over 5dBi: this antenna is described in more detail in the next section.)

The next point of interest is around 11.25MHz where the doublet is 1.5λ long. Like the half-wave resonance the feedpoint is at a low voltage, high current (voltage node) point and the impedance is a reasonably good match to 50 or 75Ω. Note the sharp dip in the SWR at this point. At four times the half-wave resonant frequency, the doublet is two wavelengths long and the feedpoint impedance is very high. This point can be seen at just over 15MHz on the impedance graph. The doublet can be considered as four half-wave dipoles split into two pairs. At 15MHz, the current in each pair of dipoles is not in phase so the doublet will not operate as a collinear array. The radiation pattern splits up into four lobes and resembles a four leaf clover (see **Fig 4.6**).

The feedpoint impedance will be low at the half-wave resonant frequency and at odd multiples of this frequency. The feedpoint impedance will be high at even multiples of the half-wave resonance. One significant point to note is that the maximum gain at every frequency above 3.75MHz is greater than the 2.15dBi gain of a half-wave dipole. This tends to support the general principle that bigger is better (at least in some directions) as far as antennas are concerned.

The gain graph in Fig 4.5 shows clearly that this doublet would make an excellent multi-band antenna. It would work very efficiently on 80m as a simple dipole. It offers gain over a dipole on 40m and considerable gain on 30m where it is just over 2 x 5/8λ. On 20, 17, 15, 12 and 10m the radiation pattern breaks up into multiple lobes, offering useful gain in several directions.

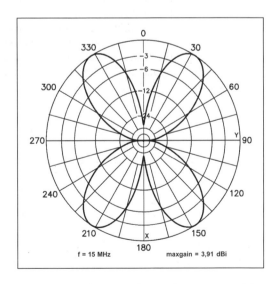

Fig 4.6: The clover-leaf radiation pattern of the doublet at 15MHz.

THE EXTENDED DOUBLE ZEPP ('EDZ')

If the top of a doublet is made from a pair of half-wavelength wires the antenna becomes a simple collinear with some gain over a dipole (although due to its high impedance it may be difficult to match with some ATUs). The radiation pattern will be similar to that of a dipole but it will more nearly resemble a narrowed figure 8, having a reduced radiation towards the ends of the wires. Its theoretical gain over a half-wave dipole is 1.9dB.

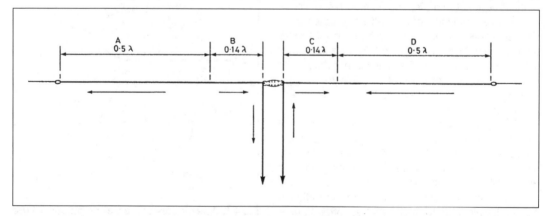

To achieve a greater gain when using two half-waves in phase, the spacing between the adjacent ends of the two half-wavelength wires must be about 0.45λ. This spacing is easy to arrange when using separately fed, individual half-wave dipoles in phase, when the gain over a single dipole becomes 3.3dB. To do this involves a pair of feedlines equal in length and a considerable space, at least 30m (100ft) on 14MHz. Fortunately there is a very effective and simpler substitute which has almost the same gain; this antenna is known as the Extended Double Zepp or 'EDZ'. (The original 'Zepp' antenna was a single half-wave long end-fed antenna fed with open wire feeder that was used by Zeppelin airships in the early part of the 20th century. The EDZ is simply a pair of these, which have been extended in length to produce additional gain.)

The *ZR-3 USS Los Angeles* airship over Manhatten in the late 1920s.

By lengthening both the elements of a doublet consisting of two half-waves in phase, the effective spacing between the inner ends of the half-wave sections becomes greater. With an antenna top made from two 0.64λ wires, the effective spacing between the two half-waves becomes 0.28λ. This spacing gives a gain of about 3dB over a single half-wave dipole antenna: equivalent to a doubling of the transmitted power. **Fig 4.7** shows the extended double Zepp arrangement, and it will be noticed that the antenna currents in the added sections B and C, although in phase with each other, are opposed to the currents in the two longer half-wave sections of the top. The power radiated by the centre sections contributes towards four weak lobes, each of which lies approximately 35° from the line of the wire top.

An added bonus to be gained with the EDZ is that it will also radiate well on other bands. For example, the 14MHz version will have a total top length of about 25.4m (83ft) and will behave as a long dipole on 7MHz. Even on 3.5 MHz, where each leg is about 8m (25ft) short of a quarter-wavelength, the antenna will still radiate effectively.

Fig 4.7: The design criteria for the extended double Zepp antenna.

A PRACTICAL EDZ

In an article in the September 2006 *QST* ('The Extended Double Zepp Revisited'), Jerry Haigwood, W5JH, gave a design for the EDZ which has the advantage of being able to be fed with 50Ω coaxial cable. The basic layout can be seen in **Fig 4.8**.

The EDZ is the longest doublet that will yield a pattern with the major lobe broadside to the antenna. Longer lengths will start to produce a 'butterfly wing' pattern. Even longer lengths will produce multiple lobes broadside with the largest lobes approaching the ends of the antenna. The azimuth plot of the EDZ is shown in **Fig 4.9** and the elevation plot in **Fig 4.10**.

The EDZ produces some very useful gain when compared with a 0.5λ dipole. The typical gain is of the order of 2.5 to 3.0dBd, as shown in **Fig 4.11**. The EDZ derives its gain from the main lobe being compressed, making the EDZ a bidirectional gain antenna. The EDZ azimuth plot shown in Fig 4.9 has a half-power horizontal beamwidth of 34.8°. The elevation beamwidth (Fig 4.10) is 28.7°. These beamwidths will change depending on the height of the antenna above ground. This antenna was analysed (using *EZNEC* version 3) at a height of 30ft.

The impedance of the EDZ will also vary depending on the height above ground, the ground conductivity and other proximity factors. Typical values at a height of a half wavelength above average ground are 150–j850Ω: i.e. the feedpoint is quite reactive. However, a balanced feedline of the appropriate length and impedance can cancel the reactance and move the resistance value closer to 50Ω.

To realise the full benefits of the EDZ, the antenna needs to be installed at a minimum height of 0.5λ: lower heights will result in a distorted pattern. It also needs to be installed as a flat top and not as an inverted-V. Installation as an inverted-V also distorts the pattern and results in reduced gain in the main lobe.

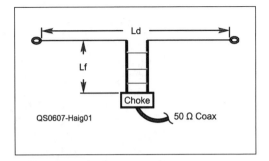

Fig 4.8: Basic layout of the extended double Zepp (diagrams reprinted with permission of the American Radio Relay League).

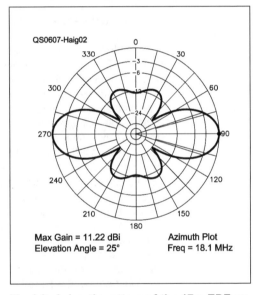

Max Gain = 11.22 dBi
Elevation Angle = 25°

Azimuth Plot
Freq = 18.1 MHz

Fig 4.9: Azimuth pattern of the 17m EDZ antenna shown in Table 4.2.

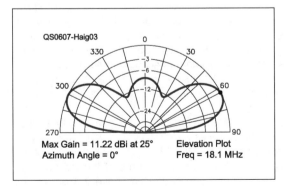

Max Gain = 11.22 dBi at 25°
Azimuth Angle = 0°

Elevation Plot
Freq = 18.1 MHz

Fig 4.10: Elevation pattern of the 17m EDZ antenna shown in Table 4.2.

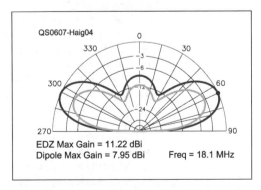

EDZ Max Gain = 11.22 dBi
Dipole Max Gain = 7.95 dBi

Freq = 18.1 MHz

Fig 4.11: Comparison of the 17m EDZ antenna shown in Table 4.2 (black) versus a half-wave dipole at the same height (grey).

Freq (MHz)	Ld (ft)	Min height (ft)	Antenna Z	Feedpoint Z	Lf (ft)	SWR
7.075	175.2	66	170.5 −j976.1	47.10 +j0.25	21.65	1.062:1
10.110	122.6	47	163.0 −j934.1	47.80 −j0.07	14.85	1.046:1
14.175	87.5	34	155.3 −j889.6	48.62 −j0.36	10.35	1.029:1
18.100	68.5	30	133.4 −j848.9	44.63 +j0.38	7.92	1.121:1
21.200	58.5	30	132.1 −j799.9	47.65 −j0.28	6.56	1.050:1
24.900	49.8	30	156.7 −j772.3	58.60 −j0.10	5.51	1.172:1
28.200	44.0	30	169.8 −j772.4	63.24 +j0.26	4.88	1.265:1

Table 4.2: EDZ antenna dimensions and other criteria for seven HF bands.

Length, matching and bandwidth

The formula for calculating the length of an EDZ is:

Length (ft) = 1240/frequency (MHz).

Table 4.2 shows some typical antenna lengths.

The EDZ can be closely matched to 50Ω by using a 0.155λ (56°) matching section of 600Ω balanced line. A 1:1 balun or choke connects to 50Ω coax of any length for the run to the station. The specified length of balanced line will cancel out the capacitive reactance of the antenna and transform the resistance value to about 50Ω. Table 4.2 lists the actual length of the matching sections (Lf) needed to match the antennas shown.

The 2:1 SWR bandwidth of the EDZ is approximately 2.2% although it will vary with height above ground. This bandwidth will cover about 150kHz of 40m, all of 30 to 12m (with separate antennas for each band) and about 600kHz of the 10m band.

Note that, as designed, the EDZ is a *single band* antenna. The same pattern can be achieved by feeding the EDZ length dipole with low-loss feedline all the way to an antenna tuner, either at the station or remotely operated in the antenna field. The antenna will load and work well on all bands at which it is a half-wave or longer, and be only slightly less efficient at the next lower band. The pattern will continue to be bidirectional for frequencies lower than the design frequency. At higher frequencies, as noted earlier, it will start to have multiple lobes, but it will still operate well into the covered areas.

Building the EDZ

The EDZ is built much like any other doublet. Choose a wire that is not prone to stretching, e.g. 7/22 gauge hard drawn copper wire. Measure the wire, allowing a little extra for the ends. Cut the doublet wire into two equal pieces and attach insulators. The wire is pushed through the hole in the insulator and wrapped back around itself. The wrap should then be soldered as unsoldered connections will lead to noise and may become intermittent. The centre insulator should be about the same width as the balanced line. End insulators can be any size that will handle the power you plan to use.

The matching section will need to be cut to the correct length, or tuned, to achieve the desired match to the coax. The tuning process will require a 1:1 balun or choke, and preferably an antenna analyser such as an MFJ-259B. The balun can be a 1:1 voltage or current type or a choke. For 40 to 10m, eight turns of twisted pair wire wound through an FT140-61 ferrite core can be used. This choke will isolate the balanced line from the coax shield and force equal currents in the balanced line conductors.

Since the velocity factor can vary on homebrewed line by a few percent, the balanced feedline should be cut about 5% longer than the calculated value. The balanced line is connected to the centre of the antenna, the choke is connected to the other end of the same line and the antenna analyser should be connected as close as possible to the choke.

Set the antenna analyser to the frequency that the antenna was designed for. Measure the resistance and reactance. If the feedline reactance is positive (inductive), shorten the balanced feedline by 1in to 2in and measure again. If the feedline reactance is negative (capacitive), you will need to lengthen the balanced feedline. Continue adjusting the length of the balanced line to eliminate all reactance at the test frequency. Once the reactance has been eliminated, the SWR should be low and close to the values shown in Table 4.2.

If you do not have access to an antenna analyser, you can use a low power transmitter and SWR indicator to measure the SWR. Lower the SWR by adjusting the length of the balanced feedline. When shortening the feedline, remove small amounts at a time to make sure you do not overshoot the correct length.

The result should be a high performance wire antenna with a clean, predictable, pattern and enough gain to seek out weak signals.

FOUR COLLINEAR ELEMENTS

With a gain of about 4.3dBd, the antenna illustrated in **Fig 4.12** is a particularly useful one for an operator who needs a bidirectional fixed beam. The dimensions in the drawing are for the 28MHz band: its total length of under 21m (70ft) is not excessive for many garden plots. It only has to be 6m (20ft) from the ground to perform well on its design frequency but naturally it benefits from being installed at a greater height because of the reduced screening effects of buildings and trees etc. The use of two quarter-wave stubs adds to the total wire length and this makes each leg about 15.2m (50ft) long. On 3.5MHz the antenna is a short dipole, with its maximum current at the dipole centre some 5m (16ft) down the feedline. Being a low dipole on this band, it is only really useful as an NVIS (high-angle) radiator for semi-local contacts.

When used on its design frequency, the currents in the half-wave elements are kept in phase by using quarter-wave shorted stubs. These are each 2.43m (8ft) long

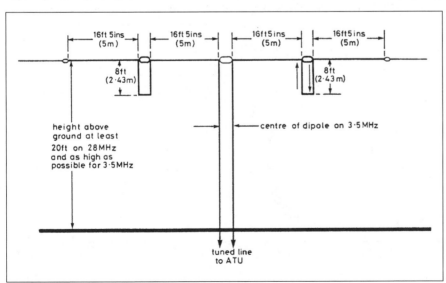

Fig 4.12: The measurements for a four-element collinear beam antenna designed for the 28MHz band which will also be a useful high-angle radiator on 3.5MHz.

and their length was calculated bearing in mind the velocity factor of the wire pairs which make up each stub. If 300Ω ribbon is used for the stubs, another velocity factor of either 0.82 for the older flat ribbon or 0.87 for the slotted variety must be kept in mind. In the latter case the stubs must each be 2.13m (7ft) long.

Despite the fact that the RF current in the stubs cancel and do not give rise to any radiation, movement in the breeze will naturally cause the stubs to move and this can alter the load conditions. To prevent undue movement, it is recommended that small weights should be taped at the bottom of each stub. For very windy locations a small cord can be taken from each stub and anchored to a suitable point.

THE HIGH-GAIN SINGLE-WIRE ('HGSW') BEAM

A 5/8-λ antenna will have a sharper pattern and higher broadside gain than a λ/2 dipole. The 'HGSW' looks similar to the four collinear elements antenna just described but in fact is three 5/8-λ antennas in line, with certain critical adjustments to allow a 50Ω feed and to allow self-feeding of the two end sections with shorted 450Ω phasing stubs. This very interesting antenna was described by Robert Wilson, AL7KK / VE7ZKK, in the July 2009 QST.

Originally designed for 20m and built and tested on that band, the HGSW can be scaled for other bands. Construction details with the dimensions for 20m are shown in **Fig 4.13** and dimensions are given later for all bands from 80m to 2m. The centre point is reactive, but this is cancelled using an inductor across the coax feedpoint. On 20m, the inductor is about 5μH and is cheap and easy to build. This simple device allows the antenna to be resonated in any desired portion of the 20m band.

The one downside is that rotation is not possible when the HGSW is installed between two trees or towers although if you want a strong signal in two directions it is tough to beat. With multiple supports, two or more HGSW antennas could be built for your favourite directions. Your maximum signal will be in a 28° wide beam in each of the two broadside directions (see **Fig 4.14**). There are some valuable small side lobes that allow contacts with strong stations in almost all directions, but the two main lobes at right angles to the wire will always be best.

The height of the antenna is important. Elevation will tune the SWR of the antenna and, if it is less than a λ/2 high, you may need to make centre section length adjustments to lower the SWR. Based on his experience, AL7KK strongly recom-

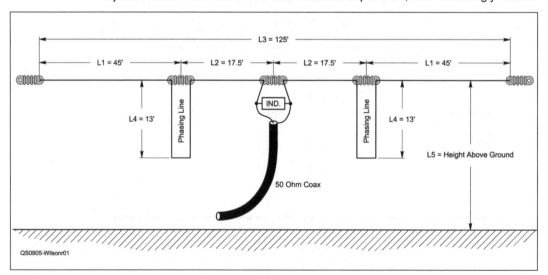

Fig 4.13: Drawing of HGSW antenna with dimensions for the 20m band (diagrams reprinted with permission of the American Radio Relay League).

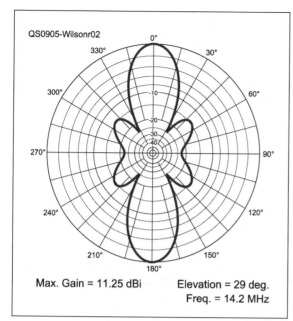

Max. Gain = 11.25 dBi   Elevation = 29 deg.
Freq. = 14.2 MHz

Fig 4.14: *EZNEC* azimuth plot of the 20m HGSW at a height of λ/2.

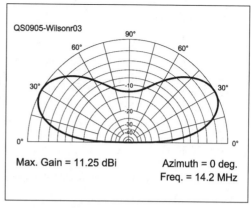

Max. Gain = 11.25 dBi   Azimuth = 0 deg.
Freq. = 14.2 MHz

Fig 4.15: *EZNEC* elevation plot of the 20m HGSW at a height of λ/2.

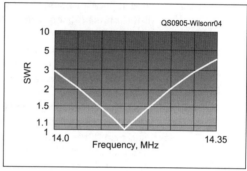

Fig 4.16: Predicted *EZNEC* model of SWR of 20m HGSW at a height of λ/2.

mends having a minimum height of λ/2.

The parts list for the 20m version is as follows: 5 ceramic insulators, 129ft of 14 gauge antenna wire (hard drawn copper or copper plated steel wire is to be preferred), 28ft of 450Ω window line, 60in of 16 gauge enamelled copper wire (for the inductor), and a 1-3/8in diameter by 2in long coil form (plastic water pipe or similar). There will be eight insulator connections each with a 6in foldover, which should be soldered for strength and conductivity. Last will be a coax connector and a pair of 6in 14 gauge wires for the feedpoint.

The antenna is straightforward to build and will require a total of eight simple insulator connections. Each will have a 6in wire foldover twisted and soldered at an insulator. First, make up two sections of wire exactly 46ft long with insulators at each end. This will give two wires with the correct 45ft lengths. These will be the two end sections of the antenna. Next, assemble the centre section of the antenna by making up two 18.5ft sections of wire and attaching them to a single centre insulator, again with a 6in overlap each. This centre point will be the feedpoint shown in the diagram. Here there will be two attachments, first a coax connector, second will be the 5μH inductor. The inductor for the 20m HGSW antenna can be made by wrapping 13 turns of 16 gauge enamelled wire around a small section of 1-3/8in diameter PVC water pipe. The two holes should be drilled 1in apart for the ends of the wire. Clean the insulation from the coil tail ends, and solder it in series between the centre conductor of the coaxial cable and one side of the centre insulator.

Now take the two unconnected ends of the centre wire and connect them to one end of the 45ft wires, again using a 6in overlap. The antenna is nearly complete except for the phasing stubs. The two phasing stubs should be cut so that their active length will be 13ft from the antenna wire connection to their shorted ends. Connect the ladder line stubs across the appropriate insulators as shown in the diagram. Strip and prepare the top ends of the ladder line stubs to wrap and solder to the

Band (metres)	80	40	30	20	17	15	12	10	6	2
L1 end (2)	168	89.4	63.2	45	35.3	30	25.6	22.4	12.7	4.37
L2 centre (2)	65	34.7	24.6	17.5	13.7	11.7	9.97	8.72	4.95	1.70
L3 total size	467	248	176	125	98	83.3	71.2	62.3	35.4	12.2
L4 stubs	48.6	25.8	18.3	13	10.2	8.66	7.4	6.47	3.68	1.26
L5 height	120	64	45	32	25	21	18	16	10	10
Inductor (µH)	25.9	11.7	7.3	4.9	3.4	2.8	2.2	1.9	0.85	0.13
Gain (dBi)	11.4	11.4	11.3	11.2	11.1	11.0	11.0	11.0	11.4	10.9
Freq (MHz)	3.8	7.15	10.1	14.2	18.12	21.3	24.93	28.5	50.2	146

Table 4.3: Lengths (in feet) of an HGSW beam for 10 amateur bands.

insulators as shown. The lower ends of the two lines should be stripped and bent over and soldered together. The resultant active line length must be 13ft. The distance from the centre insulator to the ladder line should be 17.5ft. If you have a lot of wind in your area you might want to tie a 1oz lead fishing sinker to the bottom of each of the phasing lines. Alternately a string can be attached and tied to some secure point below the antenna. AL7KK says that he has had no problem with his phasing lines except that they curl slightly, which is not ordinarily a serious difficulty.

The antenna is completed by winding five turns of coax near the feedpoint into a 6in diameter coil and securing them with tie wraps. This acts as a cheap but effective choke balun.

EZNEC modelling results indicate that with the antenna at λ/2 high (32.8ft on 20m), the gain will be about 11.2dBi with a peak of the elevation lobe at 29°. Calculated azimuth, elevation and SWR plots at λ/2 height are shown in **Figs 4.14, 4.15** and **4.16** respectively. Even more gain is available, and more importantly lower elevation angles of the main lobe, with greater heights. For example at 3/4-λ, the peak elevation drops to 20°, and to 15° at 1λ.

Table 4.3 shows the lengths necessary to build an HGSW beam for all bands from 80 to 2 metres. The dimensions were scaled from the 20m model that was built and tested, while *EZNEC* was used to calculate the gain and inductor values.

THE G5RV ANTENNA

Louis Varney, G5RV, designed his famous G5RV antenna in 1946, but it was not until 1958 that he wrote about it in 'An Effective Multi-band Aerial of Simple Construction' (*RSGB Bulletin*, July 1958). He described it in greater detail, again in the *RSGB Bulletin*, in November 1966 ('The G5RV Aerial - Some Notes on Theory and Operation').

Louis Varney, G5RV, in 1998.

Finally, he wrote a further article, 'G5RV Multiband Antenna . . . Up-to-Date', published in *Radio Communication* in July 1984.

The G5RV antenna has achieved almost iconic status during the last half century, so it is perhaps worth looking at it in some detail. In this chapter we first look at the design and how it evolved, using Louis Varney's own words and the original diagrams which accompanied his articles. Then we take a 21st century look at the design, using computer analysis, a luxury that obviously Varney did not have in 1946, or even in 1984.

Louis Varney's original design, as published in 1958, is shown in the diagram opposite. Then, he wrote, "The aerial consists essentially of a 102ft flat-top split in the centre where a Pyrex type insulator is inserted, a 34ft long open-wire stub (spacing is unimportant) and sufficient length of 72 ohm coax or twin feeder to reach the transmitter. Alternatively, open-wire feeder may be employed from the centre of the aerial right back to the transmitter output or ATU." These two methods of feeding the antenna are shown in **Fig 4.17 (a)** and **(b)** respectively. It will be noted that what is shown in Fig 4.17(b) is simply a basic doublet with a 102ft top and open-wire feeder.

Describing the antenna's performance on each band, G5RV wrote that on 20m: "...the aerial really comes into its own. On this band it functions as a three half-wavelength aerial... Since the impedance at the centre is about 100 ohms, a satisfactory match to the 72 ohm feeder is obtained via the 34ft of half-wave stub. . . . By making the height a half-wave or a full wave above ground at 14 Mc/s and then raising or lowering the aerial a bit at a time while observing the standing-wave ratio on the 72 ohm twin-lead or coax feeder by means of an SWR bridge, an excellent impedance match may be obtained on this band." The technique of matching an antenna by raising or lowering it seems to have been lost over the years!

By 1966, 300Ω 'ribbon' feeder had become more widely available, and G5RV wrote, "A word about the matching stub is in order. If this is of open wire feeder construction (preferred because of lower losses, especially on 21 and 28 Mc/s) its length should be 34ft... but if 300 ohm ribbon is used, allowance must be made for the velocity factor of this type of twinlead. Since this is approximately 0.88, the actual physical length of the

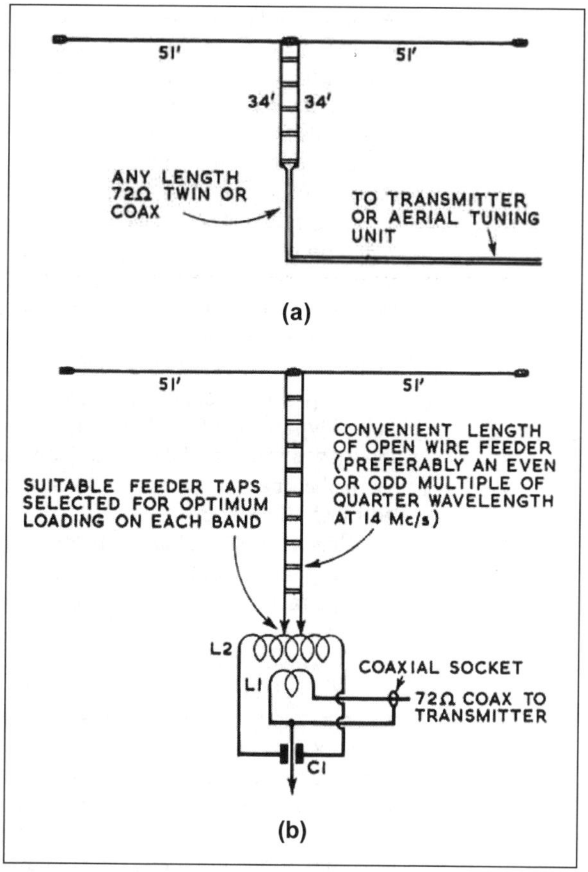

Fig 4.17: The two methods of feeding the G5RV antenna, as described by Lois Varney in his original 1958 article.

300 ohm ribbon stub should be 29ft 6in. It should be born in mind that this matching stub is intended to resonate as a half-wave impedance transformer at 14 Mc/s, which was chosen as the design centre frequency for the G5RV aerial, thus giving a very good impedance match for a 75 to 100 ohm twin-lead or coaxial cable connected to the base of the stub." Thus it is clear that, although Louis Varney described the G5RV as a multi-band antenna, he optimised it for use on 20m.

G5RV went on to say, "An alternative arrangement to that of the matching stub and twin-lead or coaxial cable feeder is to use an 83ft length of open-wire feeder measured from the centre of the flat top to the terminals of the ATU." The specific length of 83ft (modified to 84ft in G5RV's 1984 article) was chosen because it "permits parallel tuning of the ATU on all bands from 3.5 to 28 Mc/s with very low feeder losses."

G5RV's 1966 article gave current distribution diagrams for the antenna on each of the five HF bands then allocated to amateurs. He also described the ATU designed for use with the antenna.

The problem of currents flowing on the outer of the coax was recognised by G5RV, for he wrote: "Although it may be very convenient to use a length of, say, up to 100ft of coax direct from the transmitter to the base of the matching stub, it must be remembered that such an arrangement will tend to produce currents which will flow in the outer conductor of the coax, causing unwanted radiation from the coaxial feeder. This may be avoided by the use of either 75 ohm twin-lead and a suitable ATU or the open-wire feeder and ATU as already mentioned. However, the use of a wide-band balun... would be preferable if coaxial cable is to be used. Nevertheless, in practice very satisfactory operation can be achieved by the simple use of coax direct from the transmitter to the base of the matching stub even though the VSWR may reach 10 to 1 or more on 3.5 Mc/s. This figure may be reduced to about 5 to 1 on 3.5 Mc/s by 'pruning' the coax. On the higher frequency bands the VSWR on the coax lies between 5 to 1 and 1.5 to 1, the latter figure applying to 14 Mc/s where, as explained above, the matching is very good."

This suggestion of using a balun was reversed in Louis Varney's 1984 article, in which he wrote: "In the original article describing the G5RV antenna, published in the, then, *RSGB Bulletin* November 1966 [Varney himself appears to have forgotten about the earlier 1958 article - *Ed*], it was suggested that if a coaxial cable feeder was used, a balun might be employed to provide the necessary unbalanced-to-balanced transformation at the base of the matching section. This was because the antenna and its matching section constitute a *balanced* system, whereas a coaxial cable is an *unbalanced* type of feeder. However, later experiments and a better understanding of the theory of operation of the balun indicated that such a device was unsuitable because of the highly reactive load it would 'see' at the base of the matching or 'make-up' section on most HF bands.

"It is now known that if a balun is connected to a reactivbe load presenting a VSWR of more than about 2:1, its internal losses increase, resulting in heating of the windings and saturation of the core (if used). In extreme cases, with relatively high power operation, the heat generated due to the power dissipated in the device can cause it to burn out. However, the main reason for not employing a blaun in the case of the G5RV antenna is that, unlike an astu [ATU] which employs a *tuned circuit*, the balun cannot compensate for the reactive load condition presented to it by the antenna on most of the HF bands, whereas a suitable type of astu can do this most effectively and efficiently." (Louis Varney used the term 'ATU' in 1958 and 1966, but in the August 1983 *Radio Communication* he had had an article published in which he argued the case that the device ought more properly be called an 'Antenna System Tuning Unit', or 'astu'. More accurate or not, the name did not catch on.)

Instead, he recommended the use of an 'HF choke', a device which these days is often referred to as a common-mode choke balun: "Under certain conditions, either due to the inherent 'unbalanced-to-balanced' effect caused by the direct connection of a coaxial feeder to the base of the (balanced) matching section, or to pick-up of energy

3.5MHz	Flat top plus about 17ft (5.18m) of the matching section forms a $\lambda/2$ dipole partially folded up at the centre. Reactive load.
7MHz	Flat top plus 16ft (4.87m) of the matching section functiuons as a partially folded-up collinear array with two half-waves in phase. Reactive load.
10MHz	Collinear array with two half-waves in phase. Reactive load.
14MHz	$3\lambda/2$ centre-fed long wire. Matching section functions as a 1:1 impedance transformer. Resistive load, approx 90Ω.
18MHz	Two full-wave antennas, slightly folded up at the centre, fed in phase. High impedance load, slightly reactive.
21MHz	$5\lambda/2$ long wire. High impedance load, virtually non-reactive.
24MHz	$5\lambda/2$ long wire with low resistive load of approx 90 - 100Ω.
28MHz	Two x $3\lambda/2$ long wires fed in phase. High impedance load, slightly reactive.

Table 4.4: G5RV antenna theory of operation on each of the HF bands (Source: 'G5RV Multiband Antenna... Up-to-Date', by G5RV, July 1984.)

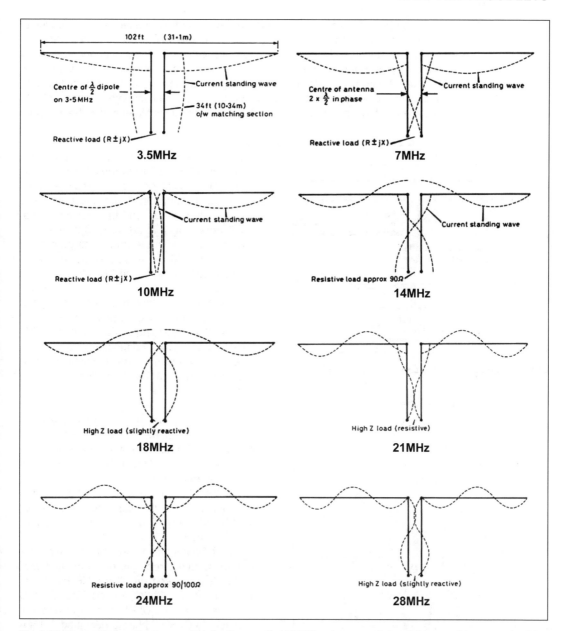

Fig 4.18: Current standing-wave distribution on the G5RV antenna and matching section on each of the HF bands. (Source: 'G5RV Multiband Antenna... Up-to-Date', by G5RV, July 1984.)

radiated by the antenna, a current may flow on the *outside* of the coaxial *outer conductor*. This is an undesirable condition and may increase chances of TVI to nearby TV receivers. This effect may be considerably reduced, or eliminated, by winding the coaxial feeder into a coil of 8 to 10 turns about 6in in diameter immediately below the point of connection of the coaxial cable to the base of the matching section."

By 1984, radio amateurs had been allocated additional bands at 10.1, 18.0 and 24.8MHz, and in his article 'G5RV Multiband Antenna . . . Up-to-Date', Louis Varney described the theory of operation on each of the HF bands, including the three new ones (**Table 4.4**). The current distribution on each band is shown in **Fig 4.18**.

For use in restricted spaces, Louis Varney wrote that, "because the most useful radiation from a horizontal or inverted-V resonant antenna takes place from the centre two-thirds of its total length, up to one-sixth of this total length at each end of the antenna may be dropped vertically, semi-vertically, or bent at some convenient angle to the main body of the antenna without significant loss of effective radiation efficiency." This would imply that the full-size G5RV could be fitted into a space just 68ft (20.72m) long, if 17ft of wire were to be dropped vertically at either end of the antenna.

HALF-SIZE G5RV

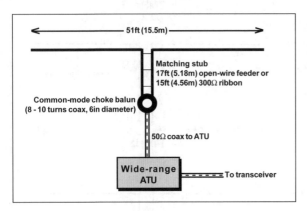

Fig 4.19: The Half-Size G5RV.

The Half-Size G5RV is shown in **Fig 4.19**. Writing in 1966, Louis Varney, G5RV, stated that, "It is quite possible to scale all wire dimensions (including that of the stub) down to exactly half-size and the resulting aerial will work from 7 to 28 Mc/s. Optimum performance and impedance matching will occur on 28 Mc/s, where the operating conditions will be as for the full-size version at 14 Mc/s."

In 1984 he added that by strapping the station end of the feeder (either balanced or coaxial) and feeding it via a suitable ATU using a good earth connection or a counterpoise wire, the half-size version may also be used on the 3.5 and 1.8MHz bands.

THE G5RV ANALYSED

Writing in the August 2010 *QST*, Joel Hallas, W1ZR, commented on three questions often asked about the G5RV antenna:

♦ What is the function of the usual 34ft section of window line or twinlead between the antenna and the coax?
♦ Should there be a balun or choke at the transition from the balanced line to coax?
♦ Should the SWR on the coax be a matter of concern?

G5RV wanted an antenna that would work well in certain directions on 20m, and that could also be used on all the HF bands, at that time just 80, 40, 20, 15 and 10m. *EZNEC* computer analysis, which of course was not available to G5RV when he designed the antenna, allows us to see the radiation pattern on 20m (**Fig 4.20**).

The section of balanced line, 34ft of open wire in Varney's article, transforms whatever the antenna impedance is to a different impedance at its bottom. To say that it provides a good match on all bands may be wishful thinking. On 20m it is a half-wave long and thus repeats the antenna impedance, as it does on 10m. The half-wave window line or twinlead that he used as a transforming section resulted in an impedance at the bottom on 20m of

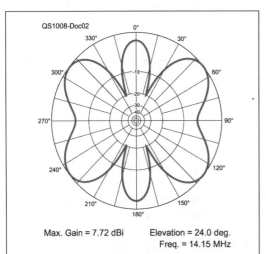

Fig 4.20: Azimuth pattern of G5RV antenna on 20m. At a typical height of 40ft, the peak take-off elevation is 24°. Note the sharp lobes perpendicular to the antenna, as well the broad lobes at other potentially useful angles. The gain at each is within a dB or two of the dual lobes of a half-wave dipole at the same height.

around 100Ω with some reactance.

Computer analysis also allows us to plot the 75Ω SWR from 3.5 to 30MHz (**Fig 4.21**). It shows that there are indeed multiple resonances; however, not many of them line up well with amateur bands.

The dimensions given by G5RV, and with a height of 40ft above ground, produce a 75Ω SWR of 6.5:1 on 3.7, 5.6:1 on 7.1, 2.4:1 on 14.2, 4.6:1 on 21.2 and 2.1:1 on 24.9MHz. Other bands are higher, typically at least 10:1.

A fundamental limitation of the design is that there are only three adjustments - the flat-top length, the height and the transforming section length. With those variables, you can probably find dimensions that will work on multiple, but not all, bands. Unlike trimming a half-wave dipole, the direction to go with each change is not obvious. W1ZR says he has never found a set of dimensions that resulted in acceptable SWR on all, or even most, bands.

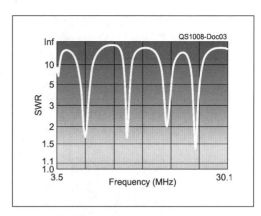

Fig 4.21: 75Ω SWR plot of Varney's original G5RV antenna design using a 34ft section of air-dielectric open wire line as transforming section. The resonances almost line up with some amateur bands, with a 1.7:1 SWR at the top of 20m.

The question about the importance of the SWR depends on the length and loss of the coax used, as well as the tuning range of the ATU used. A high SWR on the higher bands will result in significant loss for typical coax lengths. This makes the SWR at the radio look better than it really is, since the loss reduces the power that gets to the antenna and further reduces the reflected signal. This may explain why many think it has better SWR on multiple bands than it really does.

As with any balanced load to unbalanced line transition, the need for a balun depends on the amount of current that flows on the outside of the shield. This in turn depends on the ground impedance and the electrical length of the coax. Considering its use on multiple bands, it is likely that there will be some bands that have high shield currents and thus could benefit from a balun. At least one commercial manufacturer just slips multiple ferrite beads on the coax just below the transition with good results.

THE ZS6BKW ANTENNA

In 1982 Dr Brian Austin, ZS6BKW (now G0GSF), used some early computer modelling to optimise the G5RV antenna. By then, UK amateurs had access to three additional bands at 10.1, 18 and 24.9MHz, which were not available when G5RV designed his antenna, so operation was also considered on these bands. In 2007 G0GSF re-computed his design and came up with new dimensions for an antenna that presents a better than 2:1 SWR without the use of an ATU in the 40, 20, 17, 12 and 10m bands. It can also be used *with* an ATU on 80, 30 and 15m.

He wrote: "The configuration of the ZS6BKW is shown in **Fig 4.22**. The dipole radiator is L1, the series section impedance matching transformer (to give its formal name), with characteristic impedance of Z2, is L2 spaced twin-wire. The lower end of L2 presents an impedance, Z3, to the coaxial cable, Z4 (50Ω as is standard practice in all modern radio systems). A computer-based pre-

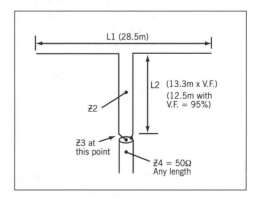

Fig 4.22: The ZS6BKW antenna as computed in 2007 by G0GSF (ex-ZS6BKW).

| Freq (MHz) | With RG213 | | With RG58 | | Matched half-wave dipole | | |
	L (dB)	η (%)	L (dB)	η (%)	RG213	RG58	VSWR
3.53	-2.1	62	-2.5	56	-0.26	-0.46	1.04
7.15	-0.45	90	-0.75	85	-0.37	-0.70	1.6
10.14	-6.4	23	-9.2	12	-0.46	-0.85	1.7
14.10	-0.84	82	-1.34	73	-0.50	-0.97	1.5
18.13	-0.83	83	-1.33	74	-0.58	-1.14	1.3
21.20	-7.9	16	-10.5	9	-0.61	-1.20	1.4
24.80	-1.02	79	-1.6	69	-0.68	-1.34	1.6
28.50	-0.97	80	-1.7	68	-0.71	-1.41	1.5

Table 4.5: Calculated total system loss and efficiency of ZS6BKW fed directly with 15m coax, 10m above rural ground, and loss and VSWR of half-wave matched dipoles fed with 15m coax 10m above rural ground.

diction technique indicated that optimum performance will occur if the antenna system has the following dimensions: L1 = 28.5m, L2 = 13.3m multiplied by the velocity factor of the line, while Z2 = 400Ω. None of these dimensions or values is especially critical. Changes to the lengths of L1 and L2 by a percent or so either way will not seriously affect performance, while Z2 between 300 and 400Ω will work, though the higher values in this range are preferable. Even 450Ω could be used but it must be appreciated that Z2 is a key element in the matching process and the optimum match occurs with a value rather lower than that."

Note that it is not necessary for the whole of this matching section to be vertical as shown in the diagram; indeed that can clearly not be the case if the antenna is mounted at its typical height of around 9m (30ft).

G0GSF continues: "With the dimensions shown in Fig 4.22, the ZS6BKW will produce a better than 2:1 VSWR when measured on the 50Ω cable over significant portions of five of the eight HF amateur bands without the use of any additional form of impedance matching or antenna tuning. They are the 40, 20, 17, 12 and 10m bands. It does not match with a VSWR less than 2:1 [without the use of an ATU] on the 80, 30 and 15m bands." G0GSF did not consider the 6m band but now believes it should work well.

Table 4.5 shows the calculated total antenna system loss and efficiency (η) without an ATU across the HF bands for the ZS6BKW fed with either RG213 or RG58 cable, and comparison with a series of single-band resonant half-wave matched dipoles at the same height and fed with 50Ω cable. The greater part of the losses occurs in the coax cable section. A loss of -1dB represents an efficiency of about 79%.

Numerous commercially-made versions of the G5RV exist and can be found in the advertisements in *RadCom* and other magazines. However, the work done by ZS6BKW / G0GSF suggests that, if it is a multi-band antenna that is desired, the ZS6BKW antenna may be a better bet, as an ATU is not required for operation on five bands. The G5RV is optimised specifically for 20m and provides a small amount of gain on that band, but requires the use of an ATU on other bands.

MULTIBAND DOUBLET FOR 10, 18 AND 24MHz

This antenna was designed by Vince Lear, G3TKN (now ZL1VL), and first appeared in the June 1993 issue of *RadCom*. It is simple to erect, and can be fed with coaxial cable, allowing the feeder to be routed as required rather than having to have a

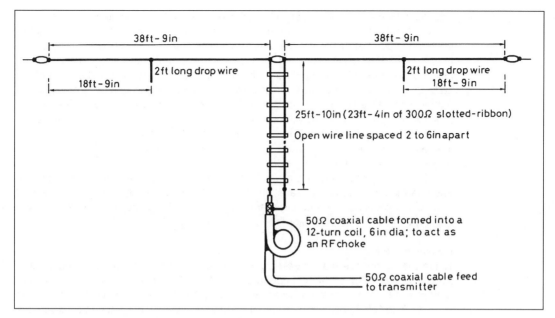

Fig 4.23: The G3TKN 10, 18 and 24MHz doublet.

special lead in for twin feeder. The multiband doublet is shown in **Fig 4.23** covers the 10, 18 and 24MHz bands. It has a low impedance coaxial feed, and should require no ATU. The antenna is simple to construct, lightweight, inexpensive, and requires little or no pruning. It should be of particular interest to those who already have antennas for the other HF bands, and require just one antenna to cover all three of the so-called 'WARC bands'.

Theory of operation

If a point a quarter-wavelength or an odd number of quarter-wavelengths from the end of a wire is taken, it is found to have a maximum current, and this results in a low impedance. By checking some odd multiples of quarter-wavelengths for each of the WARC bands using the formula, $L = 234 / f$, where L = length in feet of one quarter-wave and f = frequency in MHz, it can be seen that three quarter-wavelengths at 10.125MHz is 69ft 4in and five quarter-wavelengths at 18.1MHz is 64ft 7in and finally seven quarter wavelengths at 24.9MHz is 65ft 9in. These are all very close. In the multi-band doublet, the open wire line or 300Ω slotted ribbon stub operates with a standing wave on it in each case, and the total length of wire from one end of the antenna to the centre then down to the base of the stub is such that a point of low impedance is achieved on each of the three bands. The antenna is optimised for a frequency of 18.1MHz, where the length from one end of the antenna to the centre then down to the base of the stub is five quarter-waves. On 10.1MHz it is a little short of three quarter-waves and on 24.9 MHz it is very close to seven quarter-waves.

On the 10MHz band, each leg is 0.42λ, and each half of the antenna carries in-phase currents, thus providing slight broadside gain. In other words it operates as two half waves in-phase, or a two-element collinear. The theoretical gain of two half-waves fed in-phase is 1.9dBd. However, one could expect slightly less than this where the elements are slightly shorter, and hence where the current antinodes are closer together. SWR figures across the 10MHz band were around 1.1:1 measured at the transmitter end, and different lengths of coaxial feedline produced similar results indicating the line was operating in a flat condition. The radiation pattern at 10MHz will be similar to a two-element collinear array, maximum radiation being broadside to the wire, with a slightly narrower pattern than a dipole.

On 18MHz the antenna is three half-waves centre fed, and hence there is a low impedance point at the centre of the antenna. The stub, which is exactly half a wavelength at 18.1MHz, acts as a 1:1 impedance transformer, and simply transfers the low impedance seen at the centre of the antenna to the feedpoint at the base of the stub. It should be noted, however, that the impedance at the centre of multiple odd half-wavelength antennas increases slightly with the number of odd half-waves. In practice, no problems were encountered and SWR figures around 1.2:1 were obtained on the 18MHz band. The theoretical radiation pattern for a three half-wavelength antenna consists of four major lobes, each at 42° to the wire. The gain of each major lobe is in the region of 1dBd.

On 24MHz, each leg of the antenna is approximately one wavelength, and the antenna functions as a two wavelength centre-fed system. The radiation pattern at 24MHz will produce multiple lobes, tending towards the plane of the wire, but with slight gain in each of the major lobes.

Loading wires

When the resonance was checked on 12m, the antenna was found to resonate at 25.7MHz. This meant that the impedance at 24.9MHz would have a reactive component present, which would be capacitive, so that the impedance would be of the form (Ra -jX). The SWR was in the region of 2:1 and problems were encountered with the transceiver, which would not deliver full output at 24.9MHz.

The antenna was lengthened slightly at the ends to bring its point of resonance nearer to 24.9MHz, but this produced an unacceptable match at 18MHz, and a very slight deterioration at 10MHz. It was therefore decided to attach short loading wires a half-wavelength (at 24.9MHz) from the ends of the antenna. This meant the loading wires were at points of high impedance at 24.9MHz, but points of lower impedance at 10 and 18MHz. As a result their effect was less on these latter two bands than it was on 24MHz operation.

In practice the resonant frequency was lowered from 25.7MHz to 25.2MHz using two 620mm (2ft) loading wires. Although there was a slight lowering of resonance on the 18MHz band, it did not cause any problems, and there was certainly no noticeable difference on 10MHz. The SWR obtained at 24.9MHz was now 1.4:1 and the transceiver delivered its full output.

The loading wires provide a means of pruning the antenna for the best compromise match on 18 and 24MHz, and depending on its height above ground, and general siting, it is probably worthwhile carrying out a little adjustment of these wires. It is worth noting that when open-wire line was used for the stub, the problem did not arise on 24MHz; the bandwidth appearing greater on each band. Therefore it is only worth fitting the loading wires if matching difficulties are encountered on the 24MHz band.

Construction

A simple choke balun, consisting of a 12-turn coil of the coaxial feeder, 150mm (6in) in diameter, was made and placed at the point of connection to the base of the stub. This is the preferred type of balun for this antenna, as some reactance is present at 10 and 24MHz. Many commercial baluns are trifilar wound on a ferrite core, and while they work in a satisfactory manner into a resistive matched load, internal losses can increase if they are used where the load becomes reactive. However, a commercial W2AU type balun was tried both with the open wire line and 300Ω slotted ribbon stubs, with no noticeable drop in performance.

If the stub section is made from open-wire line, this can use 16 - 18SWG wire, spaced anywhere from 50 to 150mm (2 to 6in). Spreaders may be easily made from small diameter PVC piping or similar material.

Slotted 300Ω ribbon feeder offers an alternative for the stub, and is less obtrusive than open-wire line. The solid dielectric 300Ω ribbon is not to be recommended as it absorbs moisture and this changes its characteristics and loss very considerably.

The 300Ω slotted ribbon was connected to the centre of the antenna using a short length of polypropylene cord, threaded through one of the slots in the feeder, to take the weight of the cable. This relieved mechanical strain at the soldered joints. A dipole T-piece was used to connect the ribbon to the coaxial cable via the RF choke balun. Again a small piece of cord was threaded through the slot in the ribbon to take the weight off the points of connection to the T-piece.

Operation on other bands
The doublet has also been used on all bands from 7 to 28MHz, by extending the stub into the shack and connecting to a balanced ATU. This takes away the principal advantage of the doublet using coaxial feed, but it does offer the opportunity of all-band coverage with a balanced ATU.

G3LDO 80M ANTENNA FOR SMALL GARDENS
A half-wave dipole for 3.6MHz is 130ft (40m) long and the gardens of most modern houses do not have anything like that sort of space. But, on the lower HF bands especially, the efficiency of an antenna falls dramatically if you try to make it too small. The antenna described here is a modified version of one made by Peter Dodd, G3LDO, many years ago for a radio amateur who lived in a small two-up two-down house with nothing more than a back yard around 18ft (5.5m) square. Furthermore, it was paved, with no provision for an earth connection. The only redeeming feature was a concrete washing line pole in the far corner of the yard. A scaffold pole extension to the clothes post was made to act as a mast and the chimney pressed into service as an additional support. The objective was to get as much wire into the restricted space as possible, with the area of greatest current as high as possible.

The length of the wire element was not measured, just made to fit the space, but was about 16ft (4.9m) square. The antenna was fed in the centre and matched to the rig using an ATU in the shack. It worked but, theoretically, the performance of this antenna is very poor. With *EZNEC* it can now be seen that the feedpoint had a feed resistance of about 3Ω and a reactance greater than −*j*1000, which should have put it outside the impedance matching range of any normal ATU. No doubt matching efficiency was also poor and the feedline loss was high.

G3LDO recently used *EZNEC* in an attempt to improve the performance of this antenna and the result is as shown in **Fig 4.24**.Two loading coils with a value of 70μH

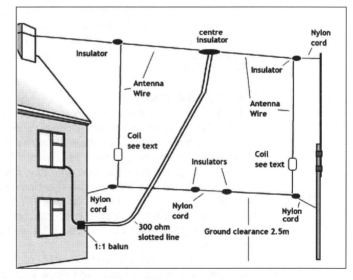

Fig 4.24: Suggested layout of a compact 80m plus other bands antenna. The RF voltages at the ends of the antenna are high during transmit so they should be high enough to avoid accidental contact. The loading coils can be provided with jumper wires if the antenna is used on the higher frequency bands.

brought the structure into near resonance with a feed impedance of R13 +j20, which is a lot more manageable as far as matching is concerned. A 70μH coil can be made by winding 75 turns of 18SWG wire on a 1.6in (40mm) diameter section of plastic waste pipe, although the value is not particularly critical because the antenna is tuned with an ATU.

The model predicted a gain of -6dBi, probably due to the current in the lower section of the open loop cancelling the radiation from the upper section, but to put this into perspective, a good quality 80m mobile antenna has a gain of around -10 to -12dBi. The gain could be improved by routing the end sections away from each other.

The *EZNEC* model also predicts that the antenna will work on other bands but, for some bands, such as 7MHz, the coil may have to be shorted out using jumper wires. The required accessibility of these coils is the reason they are placed fairly close to the ends of the elements, which are close to the ground.

This antenna does not have to be a true square or even orientated in the vertical plane; it could be made so that the square is sloping or lopsided. The most important consideration is to make it as large as your small garden or back yard will allow. The chances are that if you can make it larger than the one described the antenna will work without loading coils on 80m.

The antenna is fed with 300Ω balanced line feeder because it has a lower loss than coax with high values of SWR. The ribbon feeder is connected straight to a short length of RG213 via a 1:1 balun. The shack end of the coax feeder is connected to the coax connector on the ATU. Do not take the twin feeder straight to the balanced feeder connections of the ATU because this routes the connections via a 4:1 transformer found in most ATUs. This will worsen the impedance matching ratio. Because the antenna is electrically small, the feeder will be in close proximity to the radiating elements. This will probably cause common-mode currents on the feeder and a 1:1 current choke will be useful in minimising these.

OFF-CENTRE FED ANTENNAS

The off-centre fed antenna has been around since the 1920s. Originally designed with a single-wire feedline and named the 'Windom', after the man who wrote the classic article on this antenna, it is now more usually fed with 300 or 450Ω 'TV' type feedline or ladderline, or even coaxial cable, and is usually called an 'Off-Centre Fed Dipole' (OCFD).

THE CLASSIC WINDOM

In the April 2006 'Technical Topics' in *RadCom*, Pat Hawker, G3VA, looked back at the development and design of this classic antenna. Shown in **Fig 4.25**, it consists of a half-wavelength antenna on the lowest-frequency band to be used, with a single-wire feeder connected off-centre as shown. The antenna will operate satisfactorily on the even-harmonic frequencies, and thus a single antenna can be made to serve on the 80, 40, 20 and 10m bands. The single-wire feeder shows an impedance of approximately 600Ω to ground, and since the return circuit for the feed system is through the earth, a good ground connection is important to the effective operation of the antenna. Also, the system works best when installed over ground having high conductivity.

To quote from the 13th edition (1974) of *The ARRL Antenna Book*: the Windom was "named after the amateur who wrote a comprehensive article about it. Theoretically, the single-wire feeder can be any convenient length, since its characteristic impedance is matched by the antenna impedance at the point where the feeder is connected. However, this type of feeder is susceptible to parallel-type currents just as much as the two-conductor type and some feeder lengths will lead to 'RF in the shack' troubles, especially when the feeder goes directly to a π-network in the transmitter. Adding or subtracting one-eighth wavelength or so of line usually will help cool things off in such cases."

The 'comprehensive article' by L G Windom referred to above was 'Notes on Etheral Adornments', sub-headed 'Practical Design Data for the Single-Wire-Fed Hertz Antenna', in the September 1929 issue of *QST*. This has an editorial note "The use of the linear Hertz radiator fed by a single-wire line has been restricted in amateur work because of lack of data on its design and adjustment. This article explains how these systems may be erected with the assurance that the voltage and current distribution on both the radiator and feeder will be correct."

L G Windom wrote: "This type [of antenna] has the advantages of simplicity, ease of erection, very high efficiency and, as will appear later, can be designed on paper and erected without the usual pruning operation."

The design data resulted from a supervised experimental project at the Ohio State University, although the concept of the single-wire feeder had originated even earlier.

A system of movable trolleys was devised to allow measurement of the relative RF current at various points along the half-wave radiator. It was

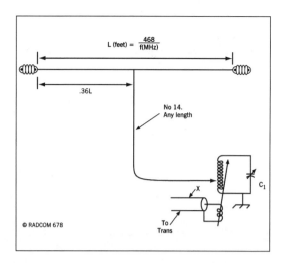

Fig 4.25: Classic version of the single-wire-fed Windom antenna, as originally shown in *The ARRL Antenna Book*. The single-wire feeder can be connected directly to the 'hot' RF output terminal of a p-network in the transmitter. Alternatively the link-coupler can be used with a separate ground terminal as shown. (This type of coupling helps reduce troubles from RF currents on the station equipment.)

soon found that the then common practice of adjusting the radiator by maximising current at the centre of the element was unsuitable when applied to an off-centre feed: **Fig 4.26(a)**. Instead, it was found necessary to use two meters closely spaced either side of the feeder tap and adjusting for equal current flowing into each section as shown in **Fig 4.26(b)**. After the radiator difficulties had been resolved, the position of the feeder was varied and the current distribution along it measured. When the correct position was located, there were no standing waves along the feeder, no matter its length, and the radiator still showed excellent current distribution. As a result of all this work, two general formulas were derived:

Fundamental wavelength = 2.07 x length of element in metres.

(An editorial footnote points out that this agrees quite closely with the usual formula of Length in feet = desired fundamental wavelength x 1.56, *or* Length in feet = 468,000 divided by desired frequency in kHz.)

The correct feeder point from the centre of the element is equal to:

Length of antenna in feet times 25 /180.

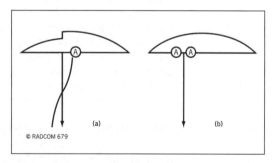

Fig 4.26: (a) Windom's 1929 article showed that the correct tapping point cannot be achieved by measuring for maximum current at the centre of the radiator, but as shown in (b) by measuring and equalising the current flowing in the element closely spaced either side of the feeder tap. This method was used to derive the design formulas given in the text.

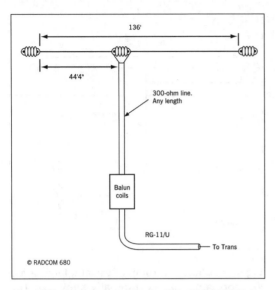

Fig 4.27: A newer version using 300Ω TV twin-line instead of a single-wire line.

Since the impedance of the feeder depends to some extent on its diameter, it is pointed out that the factor of 25 applies to 14AWG copper wire, and increases progressively to 30 for 24AWG wire. It is emphasised that the position of the tap should have no effect on the fundamental resonant frequency of the radiator. The feeder efficiency for average feeder runs is well over 95%. (Presumably this disregarded ground losses. For average or poor ground conductivity areas it would probably be an advantage to use a counterpoise wire a few feet above ground beneath the radiator fed from a non-earthed π-network ATU output.) With such an arrangement, the antenna should also work, to a reasonable degree, as a top-loaded asymmetrical-T, or as an inverted-L on bands such as 10.1, 18, 21 and 24MHz.

To check that the single-wire feeder is actually working as a transmission line rather than as part of the radiator, it was the practice in the 1930s to run a neon bulb along a section of the feeder wire to check that there were no pronounced standing-waves present. Today, it would probably be easier to use a clip-on RF current probe.

The name 'Windom' is now often used in connection with an off-centre-fed dipole using 300Ω balanced line feeder. To quote again from *The ARRL Antenna Book*: "A newer version of the off-centre fed antenna (miscalled 'Windom') uses 300Ω TV twin-line instead of a single-wire line (**Fig 4.27**). The claim has been made that the 300Ω line is matched by the antenna impedance at the connection point both on the antenna's fundamental frequency and on harmonics, but there is little theoretical justification for this. The system is particularly susceptible to parallel-line currents because of the unsymmetrical feeder connection and, probably in many cases, the line acts more like a single-wire feeder than a parallel conductor one. The parallel currents on the line can be choked off by using balun coils, as shown in the diagram. The same balun can transform the impedance to 75Ω, in cases where the line actually shows a resistive input impedance of 300Ω.

"With either of the off-centre-fed systems, the feeder should be brought away from the antenna at right-angles for at least a quarter-wavelength before any bends are made. Any necessary bends should be made gradually." (As G3VA commented: "This implies ideally a height of at least 66ft for 3.5MHz, usually impractical, but can often be implemented for 7MHz and above.")

OFF-CENTRE FED DIPOLE (OCFD)

This newer version of the 'Windom', using 300Ω TV twin feedline or similar, is now more usually called the Off-Centre Fed Dipole, or 'OCFD'. It has been discussed by Peter Dodd, G3LDO, in the *RadCom* 'Antennas' column several times.

In the June 2006 'Antennas' feature, G3LDO quoted from a letter written by John Bolton, G3FBN, who said: "I have been using a version of the OCFD since around 1985. It is known as the [Fritzel] FD4 and was invented by DJ2KY in the 1970s."

The OCFD is a multiband antenna, half a wavelength long on the lowest frequency, fed one-sixth of a wavelength from the end as shown in **Fig 4.28**. The original article by DJ2KY gave a description of how the antenna works. The impedance of the feed-point of a λ/2 wire is low in the centre (high current) and high at the ends (near

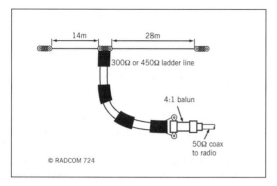

Fig 4.28: The basic OCFD antenna.

zero current). Generally, the impedance at the centre is around 60Ω and rises to 5000Ω at the ends. For a single band antenna, this would enable you to select a feed-point that would match any impedance of feeder that you might choose to use, and is shown in a graph (**Fig 4.29**).

However, the situation is different if you want to feed a multi-band antenna. **Fig 4.30** (based on a diagram in DJ2KY's article) shows the current distribution on a half-wavelength of wire on 80m superimposed on the current distribution on other higher frequency bands. The impedance is re-

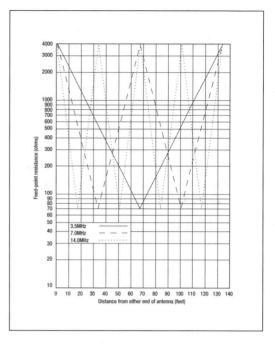

Fig 4.29: Impedance plot of an OCFD for 3.5, 7 and 14MHz as a function of the feedpoint distance from either end of the antenna (originally published in ARRL's 'QST', October 1996).

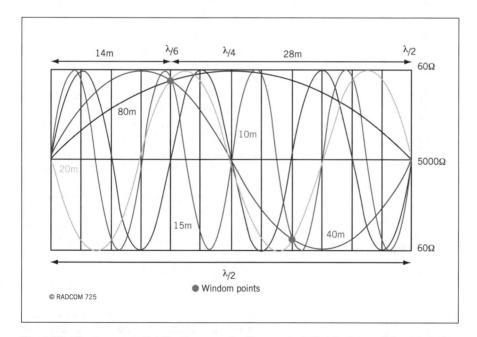

Fig 4.30: The current distribution on a half-wave length of wire on 80m superimposed on the current distribution on other higher bands. It can be seen that the current amplitudes on some of the bands coincide at λ/6 from the end, a point that DJ2KJY described as a 'Windom point'.

| MHz | Impedance | |
	R	±*j*
3.6	102	+54
7.0	134	−37
10.1	2614	−225
14.0	113	−98
18.1	217	+126
21.2	842	−419

Table 4.6: Calculated impedances of the OCFD using *EZNEC4*.

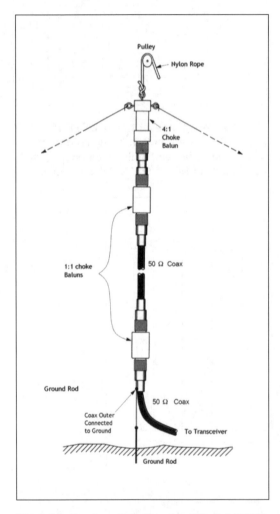

Fig 4.31: Feed system for a multiband OCFD, showing the method of reducing or eliminating common-mode currents (from *The ARRL Antenna Compendium, Volume 3*).

lated to the current amplitude - the greater the current, the lower the impedance. It can be seen that the current amplitudes on some of the bands coincide at one-sixth of a wavelength from the end, a point that DJ2KY described as a 'Windom point'.

The current distributions shown in Fig 4.30 are idealistic, showing the current distributions in free space. In practice, these currents can have slightly different amplitudes and phases due to the proximity of the ground. Furthermore, amplitudes of the current variations along the antenna element may not be constant on the higher frequencies when the antenna is fed off-centre. Nevertheless, the impedances found at the λ/6 point are fairly close together on some bands and the free-space impedances of a half-wavelength of wire on 3.6MHz has been calculated using *EZNEC4* shown in **Table 4.6**.

When the antenna is modelled close to the ground, the impedances shown in the table do change but, with the exception of 10 and 21MHz, are still within the range 100 to 200Ω.

Most OCFD builders are in general agreement regarding the position of the antenna feed-point; most of the differences relate to the feed arrangements. The FD4 antenna was 42m (138ft) long and fed at the 1/3 point. DJ2KY's article appears to have assumed that the feed-point impedance was around 360Ω and used a 6:1 transformer balun arrangement to match it to the 60Ω coax feed-line common in Germany at that time.

G3FBN reported that his version of the OCFD varied only slightly from the original FD4 design. "The overall length is 139ft (42.37m), the short leg is 46ft 4in (14.1m), the long leg is 92ft 8in (28.25m). I am feeding my version with 75Ω TV coaxial cable, via a home-brew 4:1 balun at the feedpoint. The balun comprises eight turns of 70Ω twin feeder tightly wrapped and taped to a length of 9mm ferrite rod, and all this is enclosed in a plastic 'T' electrical conduit on which is mounted a PL259 socket and suitable terminals for connecting the aerial wires. I am currently using a TS-2000 and a TS-570D, both fitted with auto ATUs. I seldom need to use the main ATU, as the SWR is within the range acceptable to both rigs. The bands covered are 3.5, 7, 14, 18, 24 and 28MHz, but the SWR is too high on 10 and 21MHz and I have alternative antennas for those bands."

Bearing in mind the asymmetrical nature of the OCFD's feed, currents on the outside of the coax are inevitable. Some method of controlling them is necessary.

Some OCFD builders go to a lot of trouble to eliminate common-mode currents from the feedline. The arrangement shown in **Fig 4.31** is a multiband OCFD, which uses a 4:1 transformer plus *two* additional current chokes on the coax. Additionally the coax braid is connected to earth. All these precautions mini-

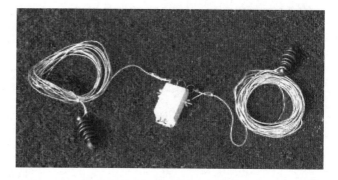

A commercially-made OCFD antenna: M0CVO's HW-40HP.

mise radiation from the feeder on transmit, particularly important if one is using high power. It also reduces interference pick-up on receive.

THE G3LDO OCFD

It would appear that, unlike the simple half-wave dipole, the configuration of the OCFD varies from constructor to constructor. Peter Dodd, G3LDO, described the version of the OCFD that he made. He constructed an OCFD using a nominal 138ft (42m) top. Because his mast is about two-thirds of the way down the garden it

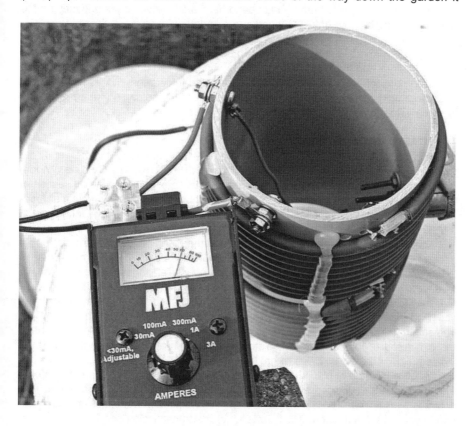

Current measurements on the twin feeder conductors (telephone line) to the G3LDO OCFD. A coax balun is used to match the twin feeder to the coax feeder.

MHz	I, L1(mA)	I, L2(mA)
3.6	320	280
7.0	90	220
10.1	450	500
14.2	330	280
18.1	430	480
21.2	90	120

Table 4.7: Measured currents on the G3LDO OCFD twin feeder.

finished up being a cross between an inverted-L and an inverted-V, with the apex about 48ft (14.6m) high. The far end of the long section is 28ft (8.5m) high while the end of the short section is 4m high. This placed the feedpoint about 40ft (12m) high.

He originally fed the antenna with 450Ω ladder line, with a balun at ground level, but found that SWR measurements were "all over the place" unless he earthed the outer braid of the coax feed to the shack at the point where it connects to the balun.

The 450Ω ladder line was then replaced with twin line telephone drop wire (this is the external wire used by BT to connect house telephones to the nearest telegraph pole). The conductors of this material are made from 1mm diameter hard drawn copper wire spaced at 3.3mm (centre to centre). The impedance is believed to be about 120Ω. The telephone wire feeder improved the SWR, although it is unclear whether this was due to losses or a better overall match. The relative conductor currents did not differ as much as expected and the measured values (see photo) are given in **Table 4.7**.

G3LDO advocates using a doublet fed with balanced feeder, which overcomes the losses caused by using coax. However, twin feeder can have its problems when routing a long length from the shack to the feedpoint. An antenna whose feed impedance does not vary wildly from band to band has certain advantages and may be fed with coax using the internal ATU found in many rigs.

Peter Dodd says, "I would encourage you to experiment with this antenna. Altering the overall length is quite easy. Moving the feedpoint can be achieved by making one end longer and the other shorter. These variables can be made easier to adjust by making the top section longer than required and folding the excess length at the end insulators back along the elements. The excess lengths can be temporarily held in place with clothes pegs while measurements are made."

THE 'CAROLINA WINDOM'

A further development of the OCFD is the Carolina Windom, manufactured and sold by Radio Works (www.radioworks.com) of Portsmouth, VA, USA. The Carolina Windom is fed approximately 1/3 from the end using RG213 coax and the vertical section of the feedline is *encouraged* to radiate due to the position of the asymmetrical feedpoint. By placing a current choke some distance from the feedpoint, the length of the radiating section of the feeder can be preset.

According to the Radio Works website, "[in] the Carolina Windom the current in each of the wire radiator sections is out of balance. Coaxial cable (which is not a balanced line) will radiate when the voltage and phase relationships are not properly balanced. The 'Dedicated Matching Unit' used to match the transmission line (coax feedline) to the antenna is a special design that enhances transmission line radiation. Part of the coaxial feedline serves not only as the transmission line (or feedline) but, simultaneously, serves as a vertical radiator. The wire portion of the antenna is the counterpoise for the vertical radiator. The result is an inverted-vertical antenna located high in the air and free of ground losses...

"A 'Line Isolator' is placed in series with the transmission line at a critical point. The Line Isolator provides a large inductive reactance at the insertion point (the action is similar to an RF choke). This effectively eliminates transmission line radiation beyond the point where it is inserted into the transmission line."

5 Verticals

AFTER THE DIPOLE, the vertical antenna in its various guises is probably the second most widely-used HF antenna today. Like the dipole, the basic quarter-wave vertical is simple to make and can almost be guaranteed to work with minimal 'pruning' required, provided it is made well and certain guidelines are followed. However, while a horizontal dipole is often easy to mount 'in the clear', a vertical, ground mounted in a typical garden for example, is liable to be screened by nearby objects such as buildings and trees. As a result its performance in typical urban or suburban locations can sometimes be disappointing. Furthermore, a quarter-wave vertical needs a ground plane, usually in the form of radial wires, to work properly, and a less than adequate ground connection can also lead to disappointing results. Nevertheless, a simple quarter-wave vertical wire *can* work well, and in certain circumstances *extremely* well, as we shall discuss later in this chapter.

There is a tendency to think that because a vertical wire takes up virtually no space at all, it is an ideal antenna for those with very limited space. Unfortunately, this is usually not the case. Because quarter-wave verticals require radial earth wires, a quarter-wave vertical antenna system can take up at least as much space as a horizontal dipole for the same frequency band. In the ideal case, quarter-wave long radials will extend in all directions and the vertical radiator would therefore be in the centre of a square a half-wavelength long by a half-wavelength wide. Nevertheless, it *is* possible to make certain compromises without affecting the performance too greatly and, provided you are prepared to put in the ground work (literally), verticals can be very effective antennas, even for those with limited space for antennas.

THE QUARTER-WAVE VERTICAL

The most basic vertical antenna is the quarter-wave. In this configuration one connection from the feeder is taken to the quarter-wave vertical radiating element, and the other is taken to ground. In this way the ground provides the 'image', or other half of the antenna, as shown in **Fig 5.1(a)**. As such the ground connection is an integral part of the antenna system as a whole, and upon its effectiveness rests the efficiency of the whole antenna. In fact this is true for any antenna of this nature that uses the ground for one of its connections.

In view of the fact that one of the connections from the feeder is taken to ground, this type of antenna is an unbalanced antenna. Accordingly it can be fed directly using unbalanced feeder, such as coax, without the need for a balun.

The impedance at the point where a resonant quarter-wavelength vertical conductor meets the ground is about 36Ω - half of the feed impedance at the centre of a resonant half-wave dipole. The current along the quarter-wave vertical antenna is at its maximum at its base and therefore the greatest radiation will take place at this point - see **Fig 5.1(b)**. The radiation will be vertically polarised and in the example illustrated will have equal field-strength levels in all directions.

Much of its radiation will be at low angles to the horizon when above a good ground, and this makes the vertical antenna very attractive for both short-distance (ground wave) and long-distance communications on the lower-frequency bands.

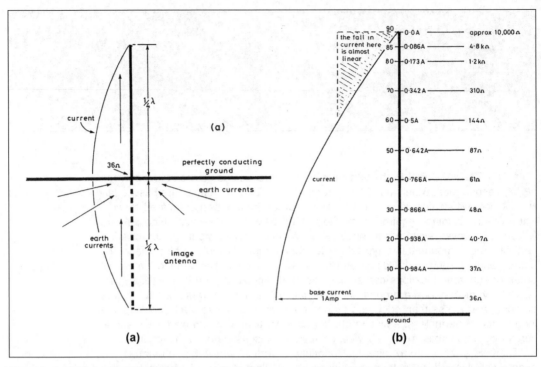

Fig 5.1: (a) The basic quarter-wave vertical antenna positioned over perfect ground, showing its earth image. Most of the earth return currents flow through the ground in the vicinity of the antenna. (b) A representation of a quarter-wave vertical antenna over perfect ground which is energised by a signal with a base current of 1A. The RF current at 10° points along its length is shown and also the impedance at these points. There is a rapid fall in current towards the top of the antenna and the impedance therefore rises greatly there. It is interesting to note that the fall in current over the final 30° of this antenna is almost linear.

The polarisation of an antenna when used for long-distance work does not matter, for the effects of refraction in the ionosphere etc will inevitably induce changes in polarisation.

In order to be able to gain the most from a vertical antenna, the ground system that is used with it must be efficient. One solution is a mat of buried wire extending to at least a quarter-wavelength and possibly a half-wavelength from the base of the antenna but for most practical situations this may not be possible. The antenna will still work with several buried radial (the more the better). Ground systems were discussed in Chapter 1 and there is more on wire radial systems later in this chapter.

As an alternative to the ground-mounted vertical it is possible to elevate the antenna and use a ground plane system, in which case the ground plane wires should be resonant, a quarter-wave long. Raising the antenna in height allows it to take advantage of the 'height gain' available.

Fig 5.1(a) represents a simplified and 'ideal' quarter-wave vertical antenna. The ground is shown to be a perfect conducting medium, a condition which can only be realised when it is replaced by a sheet of metal which has dimensions that are large relative to the length of the antenna or by a large body of salt water. The ground, if it is a perfect conductor, will behave like an electrostatic shield and provide an 'image' antenna a quarter-wave below the radiator. This image completes the missing half of a half-wave antenna, and earth return currents will be induced in the ground.

SHORTENED VERTICALS

It is seldom possible or convenient to erect a full-sized quarter-wave vertical for the lower-frequency bands, although such antennas are often used on the higher frequencies. For the lower frequency bands it is often necessary to look at ways of physically reducing their length. In **Fig 5.2(a)** the full quarter-wave is in the vertical plane and is shown to be bottom fed (impedance 36Ω). **Figs 5.2(b), (c)** and **(d)** show reducing lengths of the vertical antenna sections and corresponding increases in the lengths of the horizontal components. The total height of the antenna is therefore lowered and in (d), where only 25% of the quarter-wave is vertical, the antenna is only 0.06-wavelength above ground.

The three 'bent' quarter-wave antennas shown in (b), (c) and (d) are called 'inverted-L' antennas, and they are very popular arrangements when mast height is limited. As the vertical part of an inverted-L is reduced in length, the proportion of the radiated power at low angles and in the vertical plane also diminishes. The horizontal top section will then contribute more of the total radiation, this radiation being horizontally polarised and at high angles to the horizon. This high-angle radiation is a result of the antenna being close to the ground.

An inverted-L similar to that shown at (c), where the vertical and horizontal portions are equal in length, should give useful vertically-polarised radiation at low angles for both DX work and also local working within the ground wave range. The high-angle radiation from its top horizontal half will be effective for short range communications.

In **Fig 5.2(e)** the top half of the quarter-wave is dropped down towards the ground.

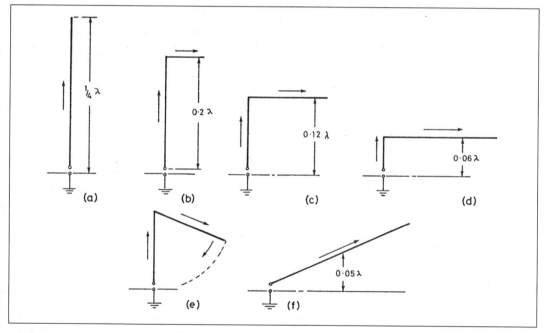

Fig 5.2: The vertical quarter-wave can have a proportion of its length bent horizontally as shown in (b), (c) and (d). When this is done the antenna is called an 'inverted-L'. As the proportion of the vertical section falls the vertically polarised radiation at low angles also falls, the horizontal top giving horizontally polarised high-angle radiation. The example shown at (d) will have most of its radiation at very high angles and will only be suitable for short to medium distance working. It will also have a much reduced ground wave. Bending the top of the inverted-L down (e) will mean that the antenna currents in the two sections will then tend to be out of phase and begin to cancel. At (f) the sloping wire will behave almost like a length of unterminated open-wire feeder.

SUCCESSFUL WIRE ANTENNAS

This will reduce both the radiation from the vertical section and also from the sloping part of the antenna, as the RF currents in the two sections will be partly in opposition. In **Fig 5.2(f)** the sloping wire, even half-way along its length, is only 0.05-wavelength above ground. This antenna will tend to behave as a lossy transmission line, having the ground as a conductor, and any radiation will be at high angles. There will also be very little ground wave, so such an arrangement will be poor both for local working or for DX.

Another feature of inverted-L antennas is that they tend to radiate most strongly in the direction away from the 'elbow', although the 'front-to-back' ratio is only a few decibels.

All the antennas shown in Fig 5.2 are quarter-wave types and they will have a base feed impedance of around 36Ω at resonance. As a result it is quite acceptable to feed the antenna with 50Ω coax as the match will be sufficiently close. Even if the earth had zero resistance so that the actual feed impedance seen in practice was 36Ω this would only result in an SWR of 1.4:1. However, with even a small earth resistance the actual feed impedance seen will be closer than this to 50Ω, thus providing a good match to 50Ω coaxial cable.

There is much more about inverted-L antennas later in this chapter.

An alternative way of reducing the physical length of quarter-wave vertical antennas is by *loading*. There are two commonly used types of loading: *base loading* and *top loading*. (Centre loading is an intermediate form but can be difficult to arrange, an important exception being in the design of very short antennas for mobile operating.) The arrangement shown in **Fig 5.3(a)** is a typical example of base loading. The inductance is at the bottom end of the antenna and it makes up the length deficiency of the radiator.

Unfortunately base loading is the least efficient method and it lowers the radiation resistance of the antenna. The maximum radiation from a quarter-wave antenna is at its high-current point, and when base loading is used this will be along the

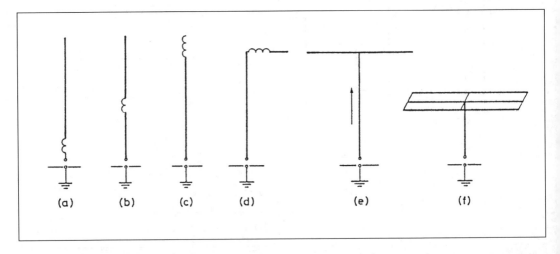

Fig 5.3: Short (under a quarter-wavelength) antennas can be brought to electrical resonance by either (a) base loading, (b) centre loading, or (c) top loading using some inductance in series. By having the loading inductance a little way down from the top of the antenna, as shown at (d) there is a reduced likelihood of corona discharges and the inductance can also be smaller. The 'T' antenna at (e) is an example of top loading, and the fact that the currents in each leg of the top are anti-phase will mean that there will be little radiation from the top. An increased amount of top-loading capacitance as shown in (f) will allow quarter-wave resonance to be obtained with a shorter vertical section.

loading coil. Furthermore any inductor used for loading will have a certain resistance and this will introduce losses as heat is dissipated. This is particularly important in the high current end of the antenna, i.e. at the base, and therefore thick wire must be used. It is all the more important because an inductor for base loading will generally be made with a length of wire which is about twice the 'missing' length of the antenna.

Fig 5.3(b) shows the centre-loading coil arrangement and **Fig 5.3(c)** an inductor top loads the antenna. This method is seldom used as shown because the inductance must be quite large, and the very high RF voltages generated at its top end may induce corona discharges unless special precautions are taken to stop this.

Fig 5.3(d) shows a combination of both inductive top loading and some additional capacitance. Extra capacitance at the top of an antenna will allow the use of a much smaller top-loading coil. In **Fig 5.3(e)** the top-loading arrangement uses just additional capacitance and does not have an inductor. This type of antenna is called a 'T' and it is often made from a centre-fed antenna such as a doublet which has had both of its feeder wires strapped (joined) together at the bottom.

By employing more top capacitance the vertical section of the antenna may be further reduced in length, as seen in **Fig 5.3(f)**. Here a multi-wire, top-loading capacitance is shown. Similar arrangements used with either 'T' or inverted-L antennas have long associations with ship-borne radio installations where there are obvious antenna length restrictions for LF work. The RF currents in the two horizontal wires at the top of a 'T' antenna are in anti-phase, and therefore there will not be much radiation from them in the horizontal plane. Any radiation there is will tend to be at right angles to the line of the wires making up the top. For a more complete suppression of the horizontal component, another pair of wires should be run out at the junction of the 'T' but at right angles to the other two top wires. This can be arranged by drooping slightly the top-loading wires with little loss in the efficiency of the vertical section.

EFFICIENCY, η

Antenna efficiency is a particularly important issue with grounded antennas. As the earth system forms part of the antenna system as a whole its performance has a major effect on the overall performance. A high earth resistance will dissipate power that would otherwise be radiated. Accordingly it is necessary to have a view of the overall antenna efficiency.

The power supplied to a quarter-wave antenna is dissipated in three main ways. The first is the radiation resistance, where power is converted into electromagnetic energy and radiated. However, it is also dissipated in the ground resistance, and the resistance of the antenna radiating element including any inductors placed within it. Of the losses the ground resistance is likely to be the greatest, although the conductor resistance should not be neglected.

It is possible to calculate the antenna efficiency. It is equal to the power radiated divided by the power supplied, and can be defined as the ratio of the radiation resistance to the total antenna system resistance:

$$\text{Efficiency } (\eta) = \frac{\text{Radiation resistance x 100\%}}{(\text{Radiation resistance + Loss resistances})}$$

It can be seen that the antenna efficiency can only be 100% when the ground resistance and resistive antenna resistances are zero. This is obviously impossible, but figures may begin to *approach* 100% in the case of an antenna made from thick low resistance conductor wire or tube situated over an almost perfect conducting plane such as sea water.

Unfortunately as a vertical is loaded to shorten it, so the value of its radiation

Height as a proportion of a wavelength (°)	Base loaded (ohms)	Top loaded (ohms)
90	36.00	36.00
85	30.20	35.70
80	25.30	34.90
75	21.10	33.50
70	17.65	31.78
65	14.61	29.57
60	12.00	27.00
55	9.75	24.15
50	7.82	21.12
45	6.17	18.00
40	4.76	14.87
35	3.57	11.84
30	2.58	9.00
25	1.76	6.42
20	1.11	4.21
15	0.62	2.41
10	0.27	1.08
5	0.06	0.27

Table 5.1: Radiation resistance of short vertical antennas (according to W J Byron, W7DHD).

resistance falls and the other resistance losses become more significant.

In defining the length of the antenna relative to a wavelength the number of degrees is often used. Thus a full wavelength is 360° and a quarter-wavelength is 90°. For top-loaded verticals, the efficiency only drops off seriously when the antenna's vertical length is below 35° (0.1λ), and fortunately on the 1.8MHz band this length can be achieved when using a 15m (50ft) support mast. When using base loading the situation is a little worse, where the efficiency of a 35° vertical falls to only 24%, and the very short 10° (about 5m or 15ft for 1.8MHz) antenna becomes only 2.4% efficient.

The radiation resistance of short vertical antennas is given in **Table 5.1**. These figures indicate the importance of ensuring that the losses in the radiating antenna conductor, with its loading coil (if any), are reduced to the minimum and it is for this reason that large loading coils with thick wire are often seen on vertical antennas. The table also makes clear the importance of investing in as good an earth system as possible.

GROUND RADIALS

Most DXers on the low bands (160, 80 and 40m) use vertical antennas. If the antenna or antennas are elevated above ground, they should be fitted with elevated, resonant (quarter-wave long) radials. Generally, two, three or four elevated radials are used, but even just one radial will work, in which case the antenna resembles an inverted-V dipole turned on its side, with one leg vertical and the other (the single radial) either horizontal or sloping down slightly from the feedpoint towards the ground.

But what if the vertical antenna is not elevated above ground, but instead if the antenna is mounted *on* the ground, with the feedpoint just above ground level?

For a ground-mounted vertical mounted over average soil, you will need at least 16 radials, 30ft (9m) long for frequencies of 3.5MHz and above. That is 480ft (144m) of wire. The radials should be laid on (or just under) the soil.

More and longer is better, especially for 80m operation (and even more so for 160m). John Stanley, K4ERO, noted in a 1976 *QST* article, 'Optimum Ground Systems for Vertical Antennas', that if you have the luxury of laying down 120 radials, 33m (108ft) long, the same 80m antenna will have 3dB extra gain compared with the 16 radial model described above. The downside is that it will take around 13,000ft (4000m) of wire – yes, two and a half miles!

Small diameter wire can be used for these radials because there are so many of them to share the return currents. They are also in parallel with the ground currents in the earth.

Ground radials need not be resonant. This is a misconception based on that necessity for elevated radials or ground-plane type elements. Ground radials are different from the elevated ground-plane radials in this regard since the former supplement ground currents and do not try to replace them entirely. Elevated ground-plane radials, especially if few in number, need to be a bit longer than λ/4 at the

An example of a very extensive ground radial system. In this case the tower itself, insulated from ground, is the vertical radiator, but the same requirement for an efficient ground system applies to a wire vertical, whether it be suspended from a tree branch or taped to a fibreglass fishing rod. (Note that the wires continue for a considerable distance a few inches under the gravel and then the lawn!) This is the base of one element of an 80m 4-square vertical array at K3LR's contest station. Such an extensive radial system may be beyond the means of most, but the photograph nicely illustrates the advice to be followed: 'the more the better'! (Photo reprinted with permission of the American Radio Relay League.)

operating frequency. What you should avoid with ground radials is to put the feedpoint a short distance in the air, then run the radials down and along the ground.

Ground radials do not actually need to be much longer than the antenna is tall. A shortened antenna with loading coils will have a more compact near field where the majority of the antenna field is. The ground needs only reach out as far as the near field extends. Field intensity drops off with the square of the distance from the base of the antenna.

Keen low-band DXers invest a lot of time and effort in building a good ground radial system, particularly with a multi-element vertical system, such as a four-square array, where a radial system is required for each vertical element.

VERTICALS BY THE SEA

We have seen how important the ground connection is when using a vertical antenna system. If you are inland, this means you need to lay down as large a radial system as is feasible in order to reduce losses as far as possible. But what happens if you are able to put up a vertical antenna system directly above (or in most more practical cases) directly *adjacent to* the sea? Richard Newstead, G3CWI, described the performance of verticals close to the sea in his 'Portable' column in the July 2008 *RadCom*.

The sea is a very good electrical conductor and closely approximates a perfect

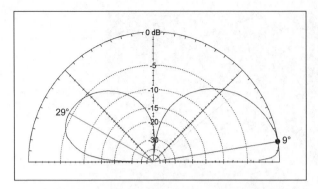

Fig 5.4: A vertical slice through the radiation pattern of a simple quarter-wave vertical mounted on a beach.

conductor for radio waves. This property can be used to good effect on the HF bands. Most HF DX signals arrive at quite low angles (between 2° and 15°). To optimise performance at these angles would require a *horizontal* antenna to be very high - typically several wavelengths above the ground. This is usually impractical and so we tend to accept relatively poor DX performance from low horizontal antennas. One way around this is to use vertically-polarised antennas, but for these to work well at low angles requires an extensive earth system with many radials. At the seashore, there is no benefit in using horizontal antennas (except for the fact that there is nothing like buildings, trees or rising ground to block the signals in the direction of the sea), but the sea provides a far better ground plane for vertical antennas than can ever be replicated with radial earth systems. This 'super ground plane' lowers the angle of radiation of the antenna in the seaward direction, vastly improving its DX performance.

Fig 5.4 is a vertical slice through the radiation pattern of a simple quarter-wave vertical mounted on a beach. The left-hand lobe is over the land and has its maximum radiation at 29° above the horizon. The right-hand lobe is towards the sea and here the maximum is at just 9°. No only that but, due to the lower losses in the seaward direction, the peak is nearly 5dB stronger overall than the landward lobe and nearly 10dB stronger at 9°. This effect diminishes rapidly as you move from the shoreline and more than a wavelength or two from the sea it tends to disappear altogether.

Just getting the antenna polarisation right is only half the story. You also need to decide what DX will come in from a seaward direction and plan your band and operating times accordingly. For example, if you were operating from the beach at Blackpool, on the north-west coast of England, you could expect enhanced propagation towards the north-west. This is the ideal direction for working into the USA on the short path and so you should plan your operating around bands that would be open when you expect to be on the beach. South coast beaches might favour contacts with South America or Africa, while the east coast could be good for Japan.

Fig 5.4 shows that, in theory at least, a simple vertical, mounted close to the sea, can actually outperform a good Yagi on a tall mast. But what about in practice?

One of your editors, Steve Telenius-Lowe, 9M6DXX, has been fortunate enough on several occasions to have had the opportunity of comparing vertical antennas sited close to the ocean with multi-element horizontal Yagis. In 2007, while on the 3B7C St Brandon (Indian Ocean) DXpedition, a number of experiments were carried out comparing verticals mounted within a few metres of the ocean with 2, 3 and 4-element monoband Yagis for different bands mounted at 40ft and also very close to the sea. The antennas under test were a vertical half-wave wire dipole on 15m, quarter-wave monopoles with a pair of elevated radials on both 17 and 30m, and a 2-element parasitic array on 20m with quarter-wave elements, elevated radials and quarter-wave spacing.

After numerous A/B comparisons were carried out, 3B7C team members came to a number of conclusions with which everyone agreed. Firstly, in terms of both transmitted and received signal strengths, there was very little or nothing to choose between even a single vertical and a 3- or 4-element monoband Yagi *in its preferred*

Imagine a full-size 4-element Yagi on 80m! But, if by the sea, a single quarter-wave vertical can outperform a 3- or 4-element Yagi in the same location. Pictured is an 80m quarter-wave vertical made of a single length of wire taped to an 18m long fibreglass 'Spiderbeam' pole. 24 x 20m-long ground radials were also used. 4W6A, Timor-Leste, September 2011.

direction. On 30m, the single quarter-wave vertical often outperformed the full-size 2-element Yagi (which admittedly was mounted less than a half-wave above ground).

More recently, on the September 2011 4W6A DXpedition to Timor-Leste (East Timor), similar tests were done. On this occasion, a Butternut HF6V-X multiband vertical (a 3/8-λ on 20m) was compared with a 2-element horizontal G3TXQ Hexbeam. On 20m, the Hexbeam generally outperformed the vertical by a small margin on relatively local signals such as Japan (approximately 5000km distant), but the vertical was a good S-point better than the Hexbeam on long path signals into Europe (in the direction of the sea path), even when the Hexbeam was beaming in that direction.

There is, however, one disadvantage to the use of verticals compared with Yagis when at a multi-transmitter environment. The directional characteristics of a Yagi help to prevent mutual interference from one station to another if the Yagis are not beaming towards each other. When verticals are used, interference from one station to another can make operating on certain combinations of bands impossible. For example, at 3B7C although it was possible to operate two stations simultaneously on 15m (one on CW or SSB using a Yagi and the other on the other mode using a vertical), and using the same arrangement on 17m, it was *not* possible to operate two stations on both 15m and 17m at the same time. This was not because of interference from *within* the band, but because of interference between the stations on different bands that were both using verticals. However, at a single-transmitter station, a vertical close to the ocean is hard to beat.

FISHING POLES FOR VERTICAL WIRE ANTENNAS

Vertical wire antennas can be suspended from a suitable tree branch but, where such a tree or branch is not available, or not in a suitable location for the antenna, another means of support must be devised. Most popular these days are the wide variety of telescopic fibreglass poles that are now available. Originally based on fishing rods and sometimes called whips, roach poles, perch poles or squid poles, they come in many different types and lengths.

The top few sections are generally far too spindly to allow them to be used as supports for horizontal HF wire antennas such as dipoles, although very light wire can be used to make an inverted-V dipole, with the coax running vertically down the mast to ground level. However, for the HF operator fishing poles are of most use for supporting vertical wires.

Telescopic fishing poles are quickly erected but rely on friction to keep them

Take care of the bung, they are hard to replace if lost...

...though a Velcro tab can be used to replace a lost bung.

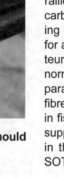

Beware of sharp edges if the pole should break.

extended. Probably the first place to look for such poles is a local fishing shop but they are also available at radio rallies and on the Internet. In fact fishermen tend to prefer carbon-fibre poles as they are very strong as well as being light, but these are often expensive (more than £100 for a 10m pole). Carbon-fibre poles *can* be used for amateur radio but because they are conductive they are *not* normally suitable for antennas such as verticals that run parallel to the pole. Better - and cheaper - are the glass-fibre poles, although these are less commonly available in fishing shops at the sorts of lengths that are useful for supporting antennas. The 7m (23ft) poles are available in the UK from SOTA Beams (www.sotabeams.co.uk/ SOTAPole.htm)

7m, 9m and 10m lengths are especially popular for masts. A typical 7m pole will weigh under 0.8kg, while a 10m pole will weigh about 1.5kg and thus they can easily be carried and are short enough to put in the boot of a car or even to carry on a bus, train or plane. Longer telescopic poles - 12m, 18m and even 26m - are also available (for example from Spiderbeam in Germany, see www.spiderbeam.com), but these are significantly more costly and heavy. These very long poles are most useful for club activities or DXpedition work.

These poles are best guyed loosely as this transfers less force in a downward direction on the pole and thus they will be less likely to collapse unexpectedly. If you are intending to operate for more than a couple of hours, it can be worth winding some insulating tape around the pole joints as this reduces the chances of them collapsing. Writing in *RadCom* in July 2009, Richard Newstead, G3CWI, said he has experimented with drilling and pinning the joints but that it was not very successful as the alignment to insert the pin was too critical.

Left and above left: G3CWI demonstrates the method of making a temporary repair should you be unlucky enough to break a pole. Slide one part of the broken section over the other. You end up with a usable, but slightly shorter, pole.

In strong winds the top of the pole will bend towards the wind. In some cases, the wind can even break the pole. To avoid this, move the base of the pole so that the whole pole leans into the wind. G3CWI has operated with poles like this in winds too strong to stand up in! If you are unlucky and the pole does break, beware of the very sharp shards of fibreglass. All is not lost, though, as a temporary repair is possible by taking the pole apart and threading the sections up from the bottom before reassembling the pole. The photos show how to make a repair of this sort.

AN EXTENDED λ/4 40M VERTICAL

This antenna design, by John Sonley, G3XZV, was published in the March 2011 *RadCom*. It uses a 12m high telescopic fibreglass mast from Spiderbeam (www.spiderbeam.com); this has the durability necessary for a permanent installation. At 12m the telescopic mast would be somewhat longer than is required for a full λ/4 at the design frequency of 7100kHz. There are benefits from making use of the extra height: it means an increased resistive component of the feedpoint load, thereby increasing the efficiency of the antenna when fed against an unquantified (but hopefully fairly low resistance) radial earth system, and it pushes the current maximum a little higher up the antenna.

G3XZV used 1.5mm enamelled copper wire as the radiating element, running it up the *inside* of the telescopic pole. The overall height of the antenna from the feedpoint matching network to the end of the radiating element was measured at 12.45m. The *dimensional ratio* (see **Fig 5.5**) of the antenna, calculated by dividing the antenna height by the radiating element diameter, was 12450mm/1.5mm = 8300. For a frequency of 7100kHz, an electrical λ/4 can be calculated (in metres) as λ/4 = 75.15 / f (MHz) = 10.58m. This is the same as 90° electri-

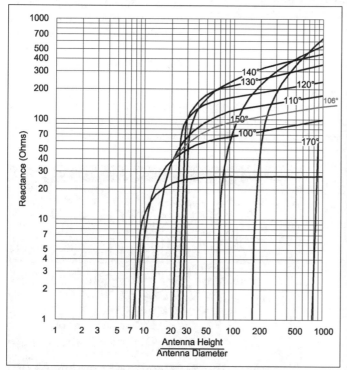

Fig 5.5: Feedpoint resistances of monopoles with different antenna height / diameter ratios, above a perfect ground (edited from *Low-Band DXing*, courtesy ARRL).

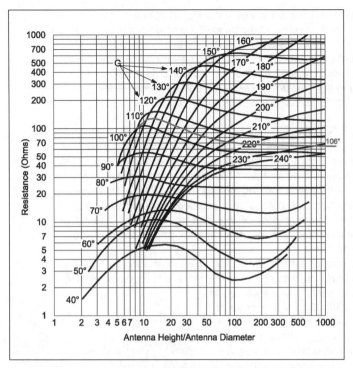

Fig 5.6: Feedpoint reactances (over perfect ground) of monopoles with different antenna height / diameter ratios (edited from *Low-Band DXing*, courtesy ARRL).

cal length (one quarter of the 360° circle that represents one complete cycle of a sine wave). For an actual length of 12.45m at 7100kHz, the radiator's electrical length is 90° x (12.45/10.58) = 106°.

Whilst the resistive and reactive components can be calculated, graphs from *Low-Band DXing*, by John Devoldere, ON4UN (**Fig 5.5** and **Fig 5.6**) provide a fairly painless way of determining the figures. The resistive component can be estimated from Fig 5.5, which has an approximate 106° electrical length line added. Although the dimensional ratio (height/diameter) of the antenna, 8300, is off the graph, it's fairly clear that the value is tending to around 70Ω for ratios above 1000. Likewise, extending the reactance graph of Fig 5.6 suggests that the reactance is about +160Ω. So the antenna impedance is likely to be around 70 + j160Ω. In order to feed this from a 50Ω source we need a matching network of some kind.

The matching network

With the resistive component of the load greater in value than that of the RG213-U coax, the matching network is as shown in **Fig 5.7**. To calculate the values of L1 and C1, the freely available DOS programs of G4FGQ (www.zerobeat.net/G4FGQ) proved invaluable and very easy to use. The program *LTUNER*, when provided with all the design parameters so far discussed, defined that L1

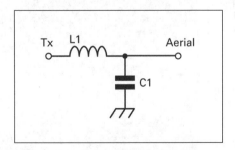

Fig 5.7: Matching network for the extended 40m vertical.

Matching unit of the extended 40m vertical.

= 3.0µH and C1 = 260pF. Program *SOLNOID3* took the guesswork out of designing L1 and came up with a coil of 11 turns using 1.5mm enamelled copper wire, 50mm in diameter and 75mm long. As the photo shows, theory and practice did not *quite* come together and the coil needed squeezing somewhat to achieve best match to the coax.

Physical construction

A visit to the local supermarket provided the ideal weatherproof housing for the network - a 13 x 20cm, 2-litre polythene food box with a clip-on lid. An aluminium base plate was selected that just comfortably fitted inside the base of the polythene box. This was used to mount C1, a 350pF wide-spaced variable capacitor, with L1 supported on small stand-off ceramic insulators. A small cutout in the base of the box allows access to the ceramic connecting block that joins the coax feeder to the network. Although the coax connection is largely protected by the box, to reduce

further the probability of rain water penetrating the coax, the braid connection was heated using a soldering iron and a candle pressed on to the hot braid; molten candle wax flowed freely by capillary action well into the structure of the braid. Following final tuning, the holes for the spindle of C1 and the antenna element were sealed with Blu-Tack. The cut-out at the bottom of the box was left unsealed to provide ventilation and prevent condensation. When electrically complete, the poly box was screwed through its base on to the wooden support post.

At 3.3kg, the support structure is simple as the telescopic fibreglass pole is lightweight. The support base is formed from a 7.5cm square wooden fence post about 1.5m long. Two 61cm lengths of suitably-drilled 2.5cm angle iron were screwed to the fence post to provide an attachment point and pivot for the fibreglass pole. A bag of fast-setting fence post premix concrete was used to cap off the hole.

In order to strengthen the base of the fibreglass pole, a 50cm length of 50mm outside diameter, 5mm wall thickness stainless steel tube was placed inside the bottom of the pole.

Close to the support post, the telescopic pole was fully extended, horizontally. The telescopic sections of the pole were temporarily secured with PVC tape and the base section was lightly secured to the angle iron supports. A 15m length of 1.5mm enamelled copper wire was fed into the far, narrow end of the telescopic mast and passed right through the pole to emerge near the tuning network. When all the wire was inserted, the end of the copper wire was looped to hook over the far end section of the fibreglass pole and then firmly secured with self amalgamating tape in a manner which also sealed the top end of the pole against water ingress.

Although the 12m pole would appear to be self-supporting even in fairly windy conditions, it was guyed with three lengths of 3mm dark green polypropylene cord about half-way up the pole.

Mechanical arrangement of the support pole, angle iron and fibreglass pole.

Earth system

A ring of copper braid was positioned around the support structure of the antenna. Lengths of 1.5mm enamelled copper wire were laid out on top of the lawn in straight lines as far as they would reach. The hard job was slitting the turf with a spade and pushing the copper wire 2 to 3cm below turf level. After a full day of 'slitting', about 40 to 50 lengths of wire, of varying lengths, were buried. The central ends were soldered to the copper braid ring, which was buried just below ground level. A single soldered braid connection was fed directly from this to the LC network box.

Tuning

The fibreglass pole is light and it was a simple one-man task to elevate it. Once the pole was upright the antenna wire was cut to a convenient length to connect within the network box. A 70cm length of thin clear plastic tube was pushed over the antenna wire within the pole, to provide better insulation between the wire antenna and the stainless steel strengthening insert. Finally, the wire end was fed through a small hole drilled in the top of the box. A choc-block terminal provides the connection between the tuner and the radiating element.

A length of RG213-U 50Ω coax feeder was run from the shack to the antenna. A couple of metres from the antenna base the cable was cut and PL259 plugs installed, coupled by a standard joiner. This meant that an MFJ-259 antenna analyser could conveniently be connected to the antenna to aid set-up. It also meant that there is an easy way to replace the last few metres of coax in case of damage by water ingress or wildlife. The whole tuning exercise took only minutes to complete and required just a slight compression of the coil and turning of the capacitor to achieve a perfect 1:1 match at the design frequency, 7100kHz; at the band edges the SWR is 1.3:1.

You can tell when an antenna is working well: the first call usually gets through! This was G3XZV's experience with this vertical when calling at 300W PEP. Transatlantic calls usually get 58 - 59+ reports, with VK getting 58. Activity was on SSB between 9.00pm and 10.30pm local time.

An 80m version?

Spiderbeam now supplies a 26m version of the fibreglass telescopic pole used in this article. This would form an excellent support for an extended quarter-wave vertical for 80m. At 26m the pole (together with some interconnecting cable within the tuner) would have an electrical length of approximately 120° at 3795kHz. From the graphs it can be determined that a 1.1mm copper wire within the pole would present a feedpoint load of around 120 + j250Ω. Using *LTUNER*, L1 = 7.2µH, C1 = 360pF. *SOLNOID3* informs us that a suitable air-cored coil would be 13 turns of 1.1mm enamelled copper wire, coil length = 75mm, coil diameter = 65mm.

A SUSPENDED λ/4 40M WIRE VERTICAL MONOPOLE

So far we have looked at the use of fibreglass fishing rods to support vertical wire antennas. This antenna is instead suspended from a tree branch. The antenna described here by Bob Glorioso, W1IS (in the August 2011 *QST*) is also a bit unconventional as it has only two radials. Why? Well, you really only *need* two radials on any *elevated* vertical to provide a balanced counterpoise. The antenna, with dimensions for 40m, is shown in **Fig 5.8**. The catch - the radials have to be in line, 180° apart, to obtain omnidirectional coverage, even if they have to be woven through trees. To show that you only need two radials the *EZNEC* azimuth pattern is given in **Fig 5.9**, even though it is just a boring circle. The elevation plot (**Fig 5.10**) shows that the take-off angle is a respectable 21°, good for DX even though the gain is not high compared with a horizontal antenna - a 40m horizontal dipole would have to be 90ft above typical ground to achieve the same radiation angle.

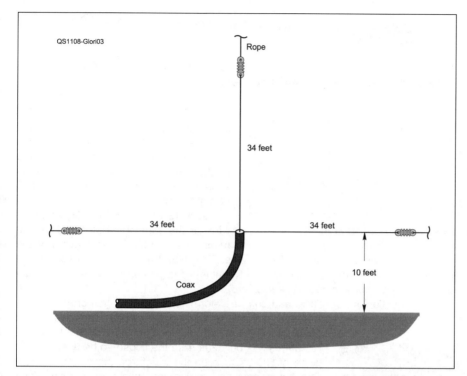

Fig 5.8: Dimensions of the 40m elevated vertical (illustrations reprinted with permission of the American Radio Relay League).

The antenna described here hangs from the limb of a pine tree about 45ft high, which leaves room for the 34ft vertical radiator and 10ft of space from the base of the antenna to the ground - plenty of room under the antenna to mow the lawn. Note that the proximity of the tree to the antenna can influence the tuning so it is best to start with longer wires and prune them to get the SWR lowest in the part of the band that you use. W1IS spends most of his time on the lower end of the CW portion with a few

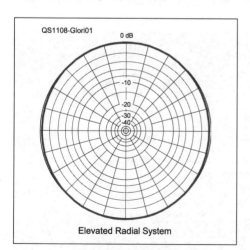

Fig 5.9: 7.1MHz azimuth plot at 21°. Note that it is omnidirectional in spite of only having two radials.

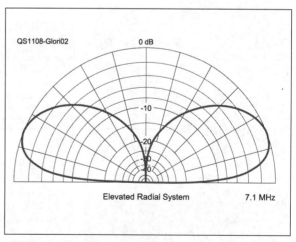

Fig 5.10: Elevation plot of the 40m elevated vertical monopole. Note the peak at 21° with a maximum gain of -0.26dBi.

Insulator at the end of one of the radials. Note the extra length of wire wrapped back on itself and used for adjusting resonance.

Frequency (MHz)	SWR
7.0	1.00:1
7.1	1.05:1
7.2	1.35:1
7.3	1.75:1

Table 5.2: Measured SWR across 40m band.

trips up to as high as 7.2MHz. **Table 5.2** shows that the SWR is less than 1.35:1 over that part of the band and only rises to 1.75:1 at 7300kHz. Nevertheless, you might want to cut the antenna a little shorter if you mainly operate in the SSB part of the band.

W1IS used 12AWG silky stranded wire for the vertical radiator and recommends using 14AWG or larger. For the two elevated radials he used 14AWG wire. The mount for the coax, radiator and radials was made from a scrap piece of double-sided printed circuit board and an acrylic insulator as strain relief (see photo).

Construction is not critical and can be determined from the photographs. W1IS used a light cord tied to a screw in a tree to hold up the radials. The load on the radials is very light as trees don't move much at that height. His antenna is only 20ft from the house so he used a short piece of RG-8X to keep the weight on the antenna down. The thinner coax and cord for the radials keeps the antenna visibility down as it is on the street side of the house.

Tune the antenna by lengthening or shortening the radials and the radiator a few inches at a time. An antenna analyser is very helpful for this process. All three elements should be the same length when you are finished.

This is a terrific DX antenna but is marginal for contacts shorter than a few thousand miles. Compared with a 130ft doublet fed with ladder line about 50ft high DX stations are regularly an S-unit or more stronger on the vertical while

The vertical monopole suspended from a pine tree at 45ft.

Base connection point for radiator, radials and coax.

most domestic stations see the same advantage on the doublet. Independent of the orientation of the doublet, the take-off angle is about 40°, nearly twice that of the vertical, which is why the vertical beats it for DX in all directions.

G3KHZ DXPEDITION VERTICALS

We have already seen how effective vertical antennas can be when located very close to the sea. The antennas described here were specifically designed for use on a DXpedition where the antennas would be mounted within a few metres of the ocean. Derek Cox, G3KHZ, used *EZNEC* to model a series of seven vertical wire antennas for the 10 - 40m bands before building them. The resulting antennas have been used successfully at ocean-front locations on several DXpeditions to Papua New Guinea (P29) as well as on the Southern Line Islands of Kiribati (T32).

The antennas were designed to fit on to

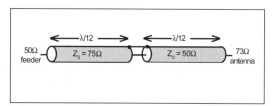

Band	Length of half element	Feedpoint height above ground	Feedpoint impedance
10m	2.59m	4.00m	73Ω
12m	2.94m	4.46m	73Ω
15m	3.40m	5.87m	73Ω
17m	3.94m	6.40m	73Ω

Table 5.3: G3KHZ vertical dipoles for 10 - 17m.

Fig 5.11: Impedance matching transformers for G3KHZ 10, 12, 15 and 17m vertical dipole antennas. The velocity factor of the cables must be taken into account, e.g. for a design frequency of 18.1MHz, λ = 300/18.1 = 16.57m, so λ/12 = 1.38m. If the velocity factor is 0.66, the length of the cable is 1.38m x 0.66 = 0.91m. The two lengths of cable are joined using BNC or PL259 / SO239 plugs and sockets and coiled up to form a choke balun.

A series of G3KHZ vertical wire antennas lined up along the seashore at Flint Island, T32VI, in April 2010.

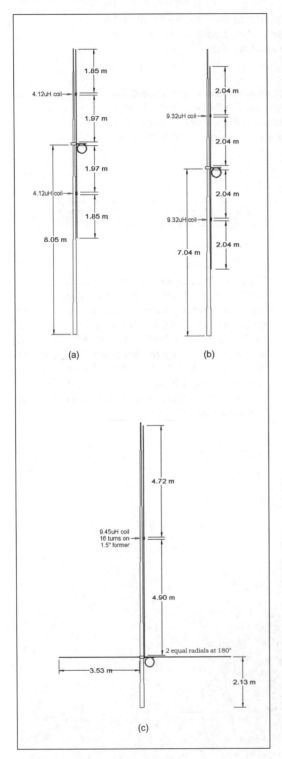

(a) (b) (c)

Fig 5.12: Constructional details for G3KHZ DXpedition wire verticals for (a) 20m, (b) 30m, and (c) 40m.

Band	Antenna type	Gain @ elevation
10m	Vertical dipole	5.73dBi @ 7°
12m	Vertical dipole	6.50dBi @ 7°
15m	Vertical dipole	6.68dBi @ 6°
17m	Vertical dipole	6.69dBi @ 6°
20m	Loaded dipole	6.66dBi @ 6°
30m	Loaded dipole	5.73dBi @ 7°
40m	Loaded ground plane	4.70dBi @ 9°

Table 5.4: Maximum gain (in the direction of the sea) and elevation angle of maximum gain of G3KHZ designed wire vertical antennas.

'Spiderbeam' 12m long fibreglass poles. As a result, full-length vertical half-wave dipoles were used on 10, 12, 15 and 17m, loaded vertical dipoles on 20 and 30m, and a loaded quarter-wave ground plane on 40m (no antennas were designed or made for 80 or 160m).

In the case on the four full-size dipoles (10, 12, 15 and 17m), G3KHZ used *EZNEC* to calculate the length of the antenna and the height of the feedpoint that gave maximum gain over the sea together with a 73Ω feed impedance. The dimensions and optimum height of the feedpoint are given in **Table 5.3**. Impedance transformers, made up of λ/12 lengths of 75Ω and 50Ω coax, are used to provide a good match to 50Ω feeder

Derek Cox, G3KHZ, and Mike McGirr, K9AJ, making final adjustments to one of the vertical wire antennas used on Starbuck Island, T32SI, in April 2010.

(see **Fig 5.11**). The impedance transformers are coiled up and double as coaxial common-mode choke baluns.

On the three lower frequency bands, the 12m poles are not long enough for full size dipoles, so the 20m and 30m antennas are loaded dipoles and the 40m antenna is a loaded ground plane. See **Fig 5.12** for constructional details. These three antennas all have a 50Ω feed impedance so impedance matching transformers are not required on these bands, although it is still important to have a 1:1 balun at the feedpoint (this is especially the case for the 40m ground plane).

Using the dimensions given in **Table 5.3** and in **Fig 5.12**, *EZNEC* calculates the gain (in the direction of the sea) for each antenna to be as shown in **Table 5.4**. A typical *EZNEC* plot (in this case for the 17m antenna) is shown in **Fig 5.13**.

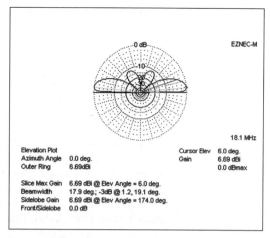

Fig 5.13: *EZNEC* plot of G3KHZ 17m vertical wire dipole (located adjacent to the sea).

INVERTED-L ANTENNAS

The inverted-L antenna can be thought of as being the 'poor-man's vertical'. It is used when it is not possible to put up a full-length quarter-wave vertical, either because there is no support available that is high enough to suspend a wire from, or because the height required is too great for a self-supporting vertical. Since it is relatively easy to make or support full-size quarter-wave verticals for all the bands from 7MHz upwards, inverted-Ls are usually only used on the two lower-frequency bands, i.e. 3.5 and 1.8MHz.

The inverted-L is simply a quarter-wave vertical with the top section bent over horizontally, as shown in **Fig 5.14**. Like the quarter-wave vertical, the inverted-L requires a good ground system of radials to work properly. The vertical section should be as long (high) as possible. The horizontal section introduces some horizontal polarisation so, for long-distance working, the inverted-L is not as effective as a full-size quarter-wave vertical, but for those without the wherewithal to erect a full-size antenna for the low bands it can come a close second.

It is possible to make inverted-L antennas *longer* than a quarter-wave by in-

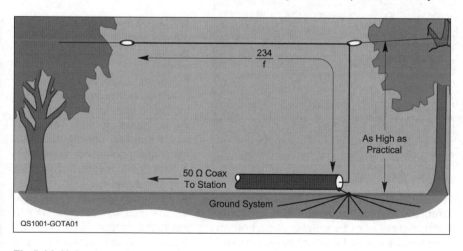

Fig 5.14: Using trees to support a quarter-wave wire inverted-L antenna (reprinted with permission of the American Radio Relay League).

creasing the length of the horizontal leg (it is assumed that the length of the vertical section is already as great as circumstances will allow). The recommended length of an extended inverted-L is 3/8-λ, or approximately 30m (98ft) for 3.8MHz. An ATU should be used at the feedpoint and then 50Ω coaxial cable can be used to the transceiver. One reason for extending the length of an inverted-L is to raise the maximum current point – which does most of the radiating – from the base of the antenna up into the air.

Experiments with inverted-L antennas

On several occasions Steve Telenius-Lowe, 9M6DXX, had the opportunity, along with John Plenderleith, 9M6XRO, to spend some time experimenting with inverted-L antennas on both 160 and 80m. They were lucky enough to find a location right by the sea where it was not only possible to put up antennas on the beach, but also to have access to the top storey of an hotel building. This made putting up a 65ft semi-vertical wire relatively easy. While this set of circumstances is unlikely at home stations, there must be numerous holiday locations by the sea where it is simple to erect a quarter-wave wire vertical or inverted-L for 80m. If you have access to a fairly high support, the horizontal space required for such antennas can be quite small and they provide low-visual impact, yet highly effective, DX antennas.

The antennas used were a 60m (200ft) long inverted-L (3/8-λ on 160m and 3/4-λ on 80m), a 39m (128ft) long inverted-L (λ/4 on 160m and λ/2 on 80m), and a λ/4 vertical wire fed against several random-length radials on 80m. The following is a summary of the findings, some of which may seem obvious, but others less so:

♦ The λ/2 inverted-L did not radiate well, even after it had been persuaded to load up using a wide-range ATU;
♦ Against expectations, the λ/4 inverted-L worked better for DX than the 3/8-λ one, possibly because the horizontal section, being that much shorter, contributed less horizontally-polarised radiation;
♦ The 3/4-λ inverted-L worked surprisingly well;
♦ If you can operate by the sea, get the feedpoint as close as you can to the water;
♦ Use as many radials as possible, making them shorter if necessary to increase the number;

160m wire λ/4 inverted-L, made up of 39ft (12m) vertical section taped to a fibreglass 'fishing' pole, and 89ft horizontal wire, tied off with lightweight cord to a distant tree branch. Several random-length radials were laid directly on the sand. The antenna worked very well, primarily due to the proximity of the ocean.

♦ It doesn't matter if the vertical section is not fully vertical; for a given support height it *may* be advantageous to have a longer 'semi-vertical' section by sloping it slightly away from the truly vertical;

♦ Finally, and perhaps most obviously, ensure the vertical section is as high as possible.

The results could not have been more different between the two inverted-Ls and are perhaps counter-intuitive, with the shorter antenna working better on 160m than 80m and the longer one working better on 80m than 160m.

FISHING FOR DX: G0GBI FISHING ROD INVERTED-L

This antenna idea was described by Glenn Loake, G0GBI, in the July 2010 *RadCom*. It builds on the popular use of a fishing rod as a support for a wire vertical or inverted-L by utilising fishing reel and line as well, as shown in **Fig 5.15**. The basic principle is to use a fishing rod and reel to loft a weighted, non-conductive leader line to the top of a tree. The weight should cause the line to hook over a branch and head for ground level. The other end of the line is permanently attached to a 132ft (40.2m) length of

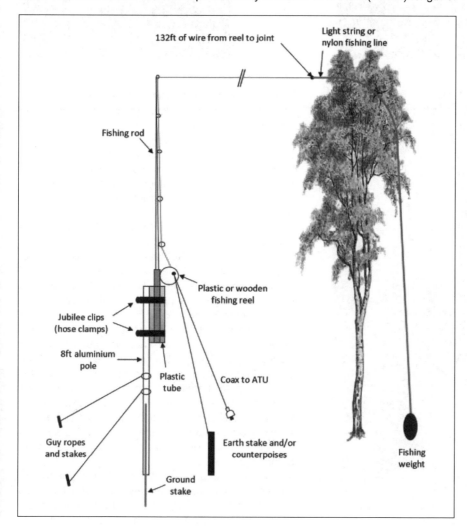

Fig 5.15: General arrangement of the fishing rod antenna system.

Left: The rod support: note how the tube protrudes an inch or so above the support pole.

Below: Attaching the feed (the antenna was not deployed at this point, which is why the antenna wire is not visible).

The completed fishing rod inverted-L, showing the support pole, sleeve, reel and rod.

wire that acts as the antenna element. A stand for the fishing rod plus a couple of guys and some wiring completes the set-up.

The parts are quite easy to obtain. When the antenna is dismantled it fits easily into a car. The only long piece is the aluminium support tube, which could be cut in half and then sleeve joined. It should take less than 10 minutes to erect once a suitable tree has been selected.

None of the parts are terribly critical, so the following is just a guide. You will need a *beach caster* type fishing rod. G0GBI used a telescopic one, but any kind about 8 - 10ft long will do (though you should avoid the conductive carbon-fibre types). You will also need a centre pin type plastic or wooden fishing reel; a commercial fly reel will be fine. Make a connection point in the side of the reel by putting a bolt through it or remove the reel winder knob and put a bolt in its place. Use a solder tag to connect one end of a 132ft piece of thin wire; any wire can be used provided it is thin enough to fit comfortably on the spool with space to spare. Next, attach about a 60ft (20m) length of light string or nylon fishing line to the other end of the wire. A solder tag at the end of the wire provides a handy attachment point. Wind the string on to the reel on top of the wire.

The rod support is constructed from a length of aluminium tube, approximately 8ft (2.5m) long and 1.5in (37mm) diameter, although the dimensions are not at all critical. Attached to the support is a piece of PVC pipe of a suitable diameter to take the bottom of

Band	Length	
	(m)	(ft in)
160m	39.5m	129'6"
80m	20.5m	67'5"
40m	10.5m	34'8"
30m	7.4m	24'4"
20m	5.3m	17'4"
17m	4.1m	13'7"
15m	3.5m	11'7"
12m	3.0m	9'10"
10m	2.7m	8'9"

Table 5.5: Suggested counterpoise lengths.

the fishing rod. The pipe is about 16in (40cm) long and does not need to be a tight fit to the rod. The plastic pipe can be attached to the support rod using two jubilee clips (hose clamps), as shown in the photo. A piece of steel reinforcing bar about 4 - 5ft long is used as a ground stake.

The final parts to make are the feed and counterpoise. The prototype used a 10ft (3m) length of RG58 coax with a PL259 plug on one end. The other end had an alligator clip on the centre conductor to connect to the end of the antenna wire. The counterpoise length in metres is calculated as 75/frequency (MHz), which allows a bit of extra length for trimming. **Table 5.5** gives suggested values for the mid-point of the HF bands, though you may well find that trimming these by 5% or so will be better. A single counterpoise wire per band was used, although more would probably be better.

To deploy the antenna you need to know how to beach cast a fishing rod. If you don't, please find someone to teach you otherwise you could injure yourself or others. Select a suitable tree and make sure that there are no people or animals nearby that could be hurt when you cast the leader. Trees beside footpaths are particularly prone to people walking near them, and folk tend to get upset if you hit them with flying lead. Respect the wildlife that may be in the tree - after all it's their home!

Thread the leader through the rod loops (just like a fishing line) and attach the weight to the end of the leader. Let a good bit of slack off the reel, ensuring it doesn't tangle. Don't try to cast straight off the reel or a 'bird's nest' (tangle) will result. Beach cast towards the top of the tree. With luck the weight will carry the leader over a high branch and fall to the ground. Pull the leader over the branch so that the end of the antenna wire is several feet from the leaf canopy. Tie off the leader at the base of the tree. Go back to the rod and pay out the antenna wire as you walk away from the tree. When the wire is fully extended, set up the ground stake, slip the rod support over it and then put the rod in the top of the support. If the antenna wire is a bit saggy then you can go back to the tree and tighten it by pulling on the leader.

Depending on the stoutness of the ground stake and the weight of the antenna wire, you may find it necessary to use some guys to keep the rod support upright. Finally, connect the feed to the bolt on the reel and arrange your counterpoise.

Another method of feeding the antenna is to put an automatic ATU on the ground at the base of the antenna with a wire connected to the driven element. The ATU earth can then be connected to the counterpoise or even just to an earth stake. G0GBI says that if it is windy the SWR will vary alarmingly as the tree sways about, but in practice he has not had any real problems. He uses a small LDG auto tuner.

REMOTELY TUNED INVERTED-L

If an automatic ATU is available, a practical remotely tuned multiband inverted-L is a possibility. See **Fig 5.16**. As with any inverted-L, the vertical section should be as long as possible. A good overall length to aim for would be about 86ft, although this is not critical since the antenna system is brought to resonance with the ATU. For multiband use, a length of around 65ft should be avoided as this would be close to a half-wave on 40m and thus would present a high impedance to the ATU and might therefore be difficult to match.

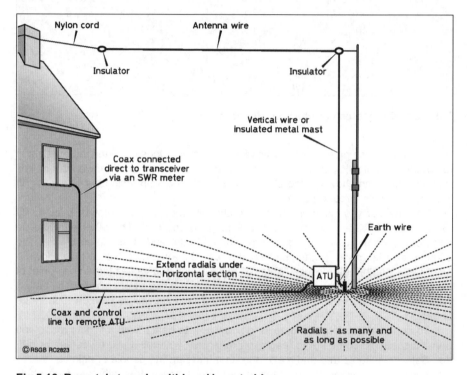

Fig 5.16: Remotely tuned multi-band inverted-L.

160M INVERTED-L PERFORMANCE

Amateurs who wish to operate on the 160m band, but only have a limited space for antennas, often use an inverted-L. It is arguably the best 'compromise' antenna for 160m if you are short of space. But just *how* well does it work? In the May 2008 *QST*, Al Christman, K3LC, described computer simulations of several different configurations of 160m inverted-L antennas. The height of the vertical section of the radiator and the length of the radials are varied in 20ft intervals from 30 to 90ft. The complete *QST* article includes calculated data for input resistance, peak forward gain, SWR bandwidth, efficiency, front-to-back ratio and front-to-side ratio for each case. Here, we present an edited summary of this study.

For those who do not have access to a support high enough to hold up a full-size 160m monopole the choice is straightforward - either use a shortened monopole with base, centre or distributed loading, or use a full-size λ/4 antenna with the vertical portion going to the top of an available support and the rest extended horizontally to a second support, as shown in **Fig 5.17**. While either technique can be used, the second provides for efficiency and bandwidth approaching that of a full-size monopole. The loaded antenna has lower radiation resistance, resulting in more of the transmit power being lost in the resistance of an imperfect ground, and generally has nar-

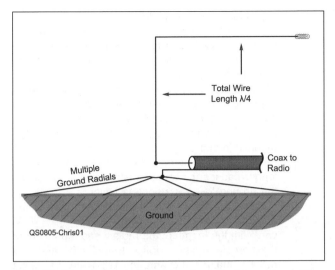

Fig 5.17: The configuration of an inverted-L antenna (diagrams reprinted with permission of the American Radio Relay League).

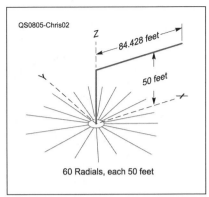

Fig 5.18: This inverted-L antenna uses a ground screen composed of 60 buried radials, each of which is 50ft long. The height of the vertical section of the radiator is 50ft, and the horizontal portion has a length of 84.428ft, which resonates the antenna at 1830kHz.

rower bandwidth (unless the losses are *so* high that it starts acting like a dummy load). The only downside of the inverted-L is that it requires a second support and has some directivity - but perhaps that can be used to advantage.

All of the antennas described here were modeled using *EZNEC/4* with a double precision calculating engine. Unlike other *EZNEC* versions, this version of the software is capable of simulating vertical antennas with radials buried in real ground. The soil was assumed to be 'average' (conductivity of 0.005 siemens per metre, dielectric constant of 13). The radiator (both vertical and horizontal portions) is made from 12 gauge copper wire and the radials modelled with 16 gauge copper wire. The number of radials was fixed at 60 because it is well known that it is important for a vertical antenna to have a good ground system. Tapered segment lengths were used for all wires, in accordance with the most conservative NEC modelling guidelines. The inner segment of each radial is about 1ft long, and slopes downwards from the base of the vertical element (at exactly H = 0) to its ultimate burial depth of 3in; the remaining length of the radial is completely horizontal.

The height of the vertical section of the inverted-L radiator was initially set at 30ft, using 60 buried radials that were also 30ft long. The length of the horizontal portion of the wire was then adjusted in order to resonate the antenna at a frequency of 1830kHz, after which all of the important performance data was collected. Next the length of the vertical section was progressively increased to 50, 70 and finally 90ft, with the tuning and measurement process being repeated each time. This entire sequence was then carried out again, as the length of the buried radials was increased in succession from 30 to 50 to 70 to 90ft.

Fig 5.18 shows what the antenna looks like when the height of the vertical section is 50ft, and the 60 buried radials are also 50ft long. In this case, the horizontal portion of the inverted-L had to be cut to a length of 84.428ft to achieve resonance (input reactance close to zero) at 1830kHz.

Modelling results
The resulting elevation-plane radiation pattern, in the plane containing the inverted-L, is given in **Fig 5.19**. Notice that maximum gain is actually directed *opposite* to that of the horizontal section of the radiating element; if you want to beam the strongest

SUCCESSFUL WIRE ANTENNAS

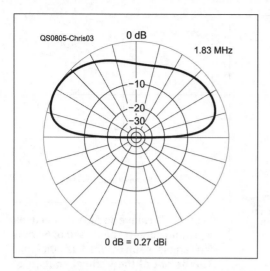

Fig 5.19: This is the elevation-plane radiation pattern of the antenna shown in Fig 5.18, in the plane containing the inverted-L wire. The front of the main lobe is directed towards the left, opposite to the position of the horizontal section of the radiator element. The peak gain is 0.27dBi at 30.1° take-off angle, and the front-to-back ratio is 1.42dB.

signal to the north-east, the horizontal portion of the L must extend towards the south-west. However, the front-to-back and front-to-side ratios are modest for all of the designs studied here, and are always less than 3dB.

Table 5.6 displays the input resistance at resonance for the various inverted-L configurations. We can see that, if the length of the radials is held constant, making the antenna taller will increase the magnitude of the input resistance. In contrast, if the height of the radiator is fixed, making the radials longer causes the input resistance to fall because the ground loss resistance is lower.

Table 5.7 shows how the maximum gain of the antenna and its corresponding take-off angle (TOA) vary with the length of the radials and the height of the vertical section. Notice that, for 30 and 50ft radials, making the antenna taller always yields more gain, at least for the range of heights discussed here. However, with 70 and 90ft radials, an element with a height of 70ft is actually a bit better than one that is 90ft tall.

When it comes to elevation angles, increasing the height of the antenna always produces a lower TOA, for radials of any particular length. For example, an element height of 30ft generates maximum gain at an elevation angle of 38.4° (on average) versus a typical TOA of 30.5° for a height of 50ft. Increasing the antenna height to 70ft drops the TOA to about 27.1°, while a height of 90ft results in a peak elevation angle of 25°.

The bandwidth capability of each antenna is listed in **Table 5.8**. These values were determined by calculating the standing wave ratio as a function of frequency, with the input resistance at resonance used as the reference impedance. If the radial length is fixed, making the antenna taller always increases the SWR bandwidth. On the other hand, for a given radiator height, making the radials longer always reduces the bandwidth.

Height (feet)	30	50	70	90
Radial Length (feet)	Input Resistance (Ω)			
30	19.15	25.43	33.52	40.99
50	14.72	21.35	29.43	36.81
70	12.29	19.16	27.17	34.43
90	11.02	17.97	25.86	32.99

Table 5.6: Input resistance for inverted-L antennas at resonance, as a function of radial length and antenna height. In each case, the ground screen is composed of 60 radials in 'average' soil (see text). The horizontal portion of the wire radiator is trimmed to resonate the antenna at 1830kHz.

Height (ft)	30	50	70	90
Radial Length (ft)	Gain (dBi) and Take-off Angle (Degrees)			
30	−1.77 @ 38.4	−0.41 @ 30.6	−0.01 @ 27.2	+0.11 @ 25.0
50	−0.82 @ 39.3	+0.27 @ 30.1	+0.51 @ 27.2	+0.55 @ 24.7
70	−0.21 @ 37.9	+0.66 @ 30.1	+0.82 @ 26.5	+0.81 @ 25.2
90	+0.16 @ 38.0	+0.89 @ 31.3	+1.01 @ 27.4	+0.99 @ 24.9

Table 5.7: Peak forward gain and corresponding take-off angle for inverted-L antennas, as a function of radial length and antenna height. In each case, maximum gain occurs in the plane containing the radiating element, and is oriented opposite to the direction of the horizontal portion of the L.

Efficiency and other data

EZNEC has the ability to estimate the average gain of an antenna and compare this with a theoretical lossless antenna operating in a lossless environment. Its average gain (over all angles of elevation and azimuth) is exactly 1, or 0dB, and its efficiency is therefore 100%, while an antenna whose average gain is -3dB must have an efficiency of 50%. **Table 5.9** provides a compilation of the efficiencies of our inverted-L antennas, based on the computer-predicted values for their average gain.

If the antenna height is held constant, we can see that making the radials longer always increases the efficiency. This intuitively makes sense because we expect a larger ground screen to reduce losses in the system. If the length of the radials is fixed at either 30 or 50ft, making the antenna taller always improves the efficiency. The story changes, though, if longer radials are installed. For 70ft radials, maximum efficiency is achieved when the height is 70ft (a height of 90ft works almost as well, followed by a height of 50ft). If the length of the radials is 90ft, a 70ft vertical again performs best, but now the 50ft tall element takes second place, with the 90ft vertical in third position. Notice that the inverted-L with the highest efficiency of all those tested (39.4%) uses 90ft radials in combination with a 70ft vertical section. In contrast, the worst antenna (which uses 30ft long radials and a 30ft tall vertical element) is roughly half as efficient (19.8%).

Fig 5.19 showed that the inverted-L did not have a significant amount of directionality in the azimuthal plane and this was true for all the antennas analysed.

Height (ft)	30	50	70	90
Radial Length (ft)	2:1 SWR Bandwidth (kHz)			
30	57	74	97	119
50	44	62	86	106
70	36	55	78	99
90	32	52	74	94

Table 5.8: 2:1 SWR bandwidth for inverted-L antennas, as a function of radial length and antenna height. In each case, the reference impedance for the SWR is the input resistance value given in Table 5.6.

Height (ft)	30	50	70	90
Radial Length (ft)	Efficiency (%)			
30	19.8	28.2	30.8	31.6
50	25.2	33.3	34.9	35.0
70	29.5	36.7	37.6	37.2
90	32.7	39.1	39.4	38.8

Table 5.9: Efficiency of the various inverted-L antennas, as a function of radial length and antenna height. In each case, the efficiency is calculated from the average gain of the antenna, as given by *EZNEC*. (Note that the efficiency of a full-size λ/4 vertical, calculated by this method, is only 40.6% - see text.)

For purposes of comparison, a full-size λ/4 vertical was also modelled, using 60 λ/4 (134.368ft) radials buried in average soil. A height of 130.826ft was required to obtain resonance at 1830kHz. The resulting input resistance was 38.25Ω. The gain was 1.15dBi at 21.8° take-off angle, the 2:1 SWR bandwidth 109kHz and the efficiency 40.6%. It is interesting to see that the performance of this antenna is not significantly better than that of the best inverted-L designs in our study, although it is much taller and has a much larger ground system.

Computer models are imperfect representations of the real world, and cannot possibly include all of the features that are actually present, such as buildings, vegetation, other conductive objects, irregularities in the terrain, non-uniformity of the ground constants and other local parameters. However, it is hoped that the information in this study will be helpful to those who are considering the use of an inverted-L on topband.

G3PJT 160M T-VERTICAL

The simple vertical T antenna shown in **Fig 5.20** is often recommended for 160m use because of its low angle of radiation. One of its principal advantages is that its dimensions are more realistic than those of a full-size 160m vertical. However, most of the recommendations on making a vertical T are somewhat casual, usually couched in terms like "for 160m use your doublet with the feeders strapped together, fed against ground via your ATU". Such a nonchalant approach is unlikely to lead to the best results. An article by Bob Whelan, G3PJT, in the July 2009 *RadCom* suggests a better way.

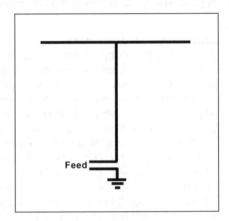

Feed

Fig 5.20: Basic T antenna.

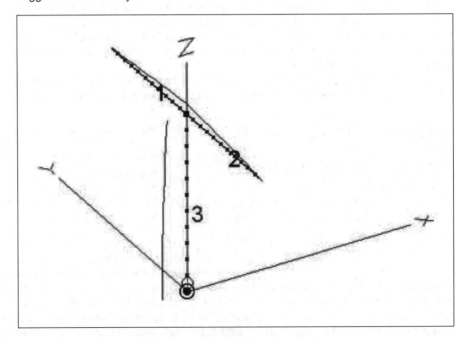

Fig 5.21: Modelling the T antenna in *EZNEC*.

A T antenna erected at a typical height of between 10 and 20m and having a span of 30 to 40m will have a feed impedance R ± *j* X of between 4 - *j* 190Ω and 23 + *j* 150Ω. These impedances not only mean that some sort of antenna tuning unit will be required to match to 50Ω coax but also that losses due to ground quality and the system as a whole need to be minimised.

To put this in a practical perspective, G3PJT's doublet was 17m high with a span of about 30m. Modelling this using *EZNEC+* (**Fig 5.21**) showed that at 1820kHz an impedance of around 11+*j* 16Ω could be expected, to which an estimate of other losses needed to be added. The *TLA* program showed that such an impedance would need a L section shunt C of 2286pF and series L of 1.8µH to the antenna, as shown in **Fig 5.22**. (*TLA* is the ARRL Transmission Line Advanced program, bundled with the *ARRL Antenna Handbook*, available from the RSGB Bookshop and ARRL.) However, when G3PJT matched the antenna with this network, he found that a shunt C of 2850pF alone gave an excellent match at 1820kHz. Such a simple arrangement is very low loss.

So much for the theoretical calculated impedance, but what was the *actual* impedance of the antenna? G3PJT used the program I_network.exe (by R J Edwards, G4FGQ (SK), available at http://zerobeat.net/G4FGQ/index.htm) to perform the inverse calculation from *TLA*. This showed that his T antenna impedance was more like 14+ *j* 22Ω, which of course includes all the losses. This indicated that his ground loss was only around 3Ω, which seemed very low, but it did raise two questions: (a) what is the range of antenna impedances that only require a shunt capacitor to match to 50Ω?, and (b) what would be the dimensions of such a T antenna?

TLA calculated that 5+ *j* 14Ω, 10+ *j* 19Ω, 20+ *j* 24Ω and 30+ *j* 24Ω would fill the

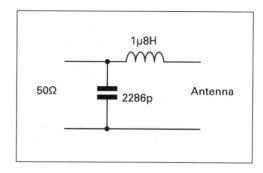

Fig 5.22: L matching section.

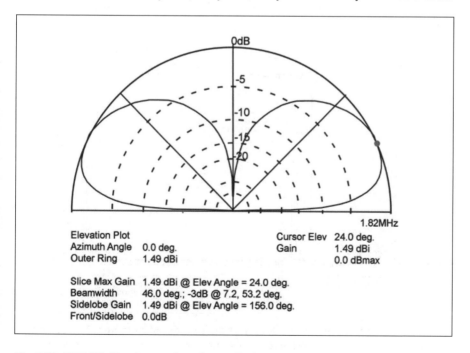

Fig 5.23: G3PJT's T antenna elevation radiation pattern.

Height (m)	Span (m)
11.0	50.0
17.5	34.0
23.0	23.4

Table 5.10: Suggested dimension for a T antenna requiring only a shunt capacitor to match to 50Ω.

bill. To use these values as the basis in *EZNEC* you need to insert a load that is representative of your earth loss. In G3PJT's case, based on the above, he estimated this at about 5Ω and so inserted a 5Ω load in *EZNEC*. Modelling his own antenna in *EZNEC* (**Fig 5.23**) showed that its performance was pretty good, with maximum gain 1.49dBi achieved at an elevation angle of 24°.

More modelling suggested the T antenna dimensions given in **Table 5.10** for an efficient and simple match. These dimensions may need to be adjusted to trim the antenna to the frequency desired. Of course, ground losses will affect these values too and should be minimised. If you want to have a very efficient and simple matching arrangement as well as an effective DX antenna on 160m these dimensions are the ones to go for.

THE FOLDED VERTICAL ANTENNA

One of the problems with an ordinary vertical antenna is the relatively low radiation resistance that can lead to low values of efficiency, especially when the earth connection is poor. This can be overcome to a degree by using a folded vertical antenna. By using a length of 300Ω ribbon as a 'half-folded dipole' or 'folded unipole', the radiation resistance of the antenna is raised to a value in the region of 80 -150Ω, depending on configuration and height. This means that even when used with an average earth system the antenna will have an efficiency of around 40%.

The version described here uses a shortened 300Ω ribbon section to which is added a length of single wire. To calculate the length of the ribbon needed, an electrical quarter-wavelength at the desired frequency must be multiplied by the velocity factor of the ribbon used (slotted ribbon has a velocity factor of 0.87). This

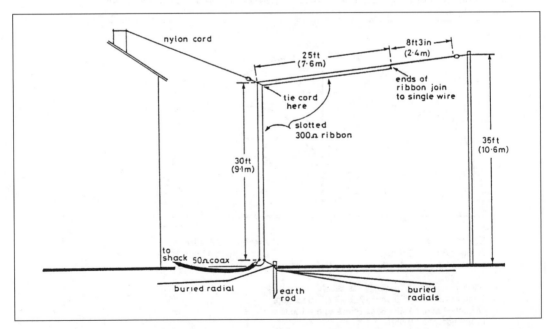

Fig 5.24: The folded vertical antenna which uses 300Ω ribbon for most of its length. The use of the 'folded dipole' principle raises the feed impedance of this antenna from around 15Ω to four times this figure. A reasonable match can be obtained with 50Ω coaxial feeder.

length is less than a quarter-wave, and it must have an additional wire connected at its end to make it up to be an electrical quarter-wavelength. This technique is very similar to that used when constructing folded half-wave dipoles from 300Ω ribbon (see Chapter 3).

The folded antenna illustrated in **Fig 5.24** is designed for 3.7MHz operation and it only needs 10.6m (35ft) high supports. The efficiency of the antenna is proportionally higher than a single wire vertical because the length of its vertical section is increased as a proportion of the total quarter-wavelength. A minimum of six buried radial wires, each being at least a quarter-wavelength long, are recommended for a suitable earth system, although with the limitations of many garden plots this may not be achievable. For a given length of wire, it is better to use many shorter radials than fewer longer ones. Versions of this antenna may be scaled up or down for use on other bands.

The step-up of feed impedance brought about by using this folded dipole technique allows the use of a 50Ω coaxial feeder. The greater distance between the vertical part of this antenna and any buildings etc, the more effective the antenna will be for low-angle long-distance communication.

THE QUARTER-WAVE SLOPER

Sloper antennas have become popular as low-band antennas that can be erected alongside an HF beam on a tower. Although sloping dipoles as described in Chapter 3 are very similar, these slopers comprise a single section and are usually classed as a form of vertical antenna. They provide a little directivity and can be erected very easily, making them an ideal antenna for many stations.

The quarter-wave sloper or 'half-sloper' antenna is really half of an inverted-V dipole. A quarter-wave antenna is normally arranged to be bottom-fed, which means that the maximum radiation is at the base of the antenna. By inverting the feedpoint of a quarter-wave as shown in **Fig 5.25(a)**, the position of the current maximum and therefore the greatest radiation can be moved to the top of the antenna.

The 'ground' against which slopers are fed is usually the metallic mass of the support tower, although for this to be as efficient as possible, a good low resistance ground at the foot of the tower remains important. The slope angle, 'L', of a half-sloper is usually 45°, and its maximum radiation is in the direction of the wire away

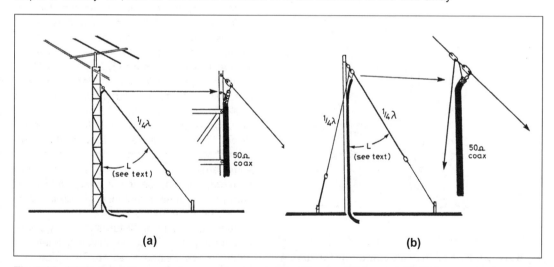

(a)   **(b)**

Fig 5.25: (a) A quarter-wave sloper antenna used with a metal tower; (b) Using a quarter-wave-length of wire which is almost vertical to replace the metal tower. The feed impedance of the sloper depends upon several variables, one being the angle 'L'.

from its feedpoint. Buried radials or earth mats etc are needed if the best results are to be realised.

The feed impedance of the sloper depends on a variety of factors. For a start, the feed impedance of a quarter-wave antenna is normally about 36Ω but a quarter-wave sloper antenna can have a feed impedance which may lie anywhere between 30 and 60Ω. The actual impedance depends upon three variables: the length of the wire, the tower or mast height, and the enclosed angle between the wire and its support. If a metal tower is used this becomes a part of the resonant system and there will be a voltage maximum somewhere between the antenna feedpoint and ground. Any other antennas, such as beams, which may be located on top of the support tower will also influence the feed impedance and the antenna's performance. Any guy wires which support the tower must be made non-resonant by breaking them into suitable lengths with insulators.

The version as shown in **Fig 5.25(b)** uses a non-metallic support mast, and it has an additional quarter-wavelength of wire which effectively forms the missing half of the dipole. This should drop vertically or almost vertically down towards the ground. If the feeder SWR is high it can often be brought down to an acceptable figure by changing the wire slope angle. It should be possible to bring the SWR down to a level of 1.5:1 or better.

It is possible to make an all-band version of the half-sloper. This cannot be achieved when using 50Ω coaxial feed, so instead an open-wire line to an ATU is suggested. The measured bandwidths of half-slopers are about 50kHz at 1.8MHz, 100kHz at 3.6MHz, 200kHz at 7 MHz and so on, becoming progressively greater as the frequency increases.

A 5/8-λ VERTICAL FOR 10M

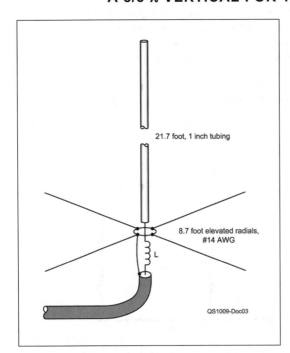

21.7 foot, 1 inch tubing

8.7 foot elevated radials, #14 AWG

L

QS1009-Doc03

Fig 5.26: Configuration of 5/8-λ antenna for 10m. A wire can be used instead of the tubing illustrated - see text (diagrams reprinted with permission of the American Radio Relay League).

A 5/8-wave vertical monopole is the longest simple monopole that will have its peak radiation at the low angles suitable for long distance communications. **Fig 5.26** shows a 5/8-λ vertical, with dimensions for the 10m band.

A λ/4 monopole over real ground will work almost as well, and can be fed directly with 50Ω coax, but the 5/8-λ has about 2dB gain at the lower angles (14°) as shown in **Fig 5.27**. As also noted in the figure, a 3/4-λ vertical has its peak radiation at relatively *high* angles (47°), so while slightly easier to feed than the 5/8-λ, it is not as useful for terrestrial communications - taller isn't *always* better.

Another advantage of the 5/8-λ antenna is that it is somewhat less dependent on the ground system at the feedpoint - important in some areas. While matching is needed, the required matching device is pretty simple; for 10m just a series inductance of about 1.2μH should do. *The ARRL Handbook* suggests a starting point of 12 or 13 turns of 12AWG wire at 8 turns per inch with an inside diameter of 3/4in - a few inches of scrap PVC pipe and some leftover house wire is much less expensive than a general-purpose ATU!

The configuration shown in Fig 5.26 was

modelled with *EZNEC* and gave an SWR of less than 2:1 from 28 to 29MHz. While four elevated radials were used in the model, a larger number of buried or on-ground radials should give similar results with the antenna base at ground level. If a vertical support is available, a wire monopole could be used, although the coil will need to be about twice as long and the bandwidth and SWR will not be as good. Alternately, two parallel wires spaced about 3in should act a lot like a single piece of tubing. Your ground and other conditions may be somewhat different than those in the *EZNEC* model, so plan to spend a bit of time adjusting the coil, but when set, it will be an effective antenna at low cost.

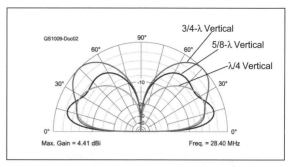

Fig 5.27: Comparison of modelled elevation patterns of λ/4 wave, 5/8-λ and 3/4-λ monopoles. In each case, the antennas were fed against a ground system of four elevated λ/4 radials 1ft above and isolated from typical ground.

THE NO-COUNTERPOISE VERTICAL
The single vertical no-counterpoise antenna (attributed to Jeff Imel, K9ESE) is an end-fed, multiband antenna that can cover a very wide frequency range. It will cover bands from 7 to 28MHz and its low angle of radiation characteristic makes for a good DX antenna. The antenna is shown in **Fig 5.28** and is made of a single length of insulated wire and the bottom section of twin feeder. The two conductors of the antenna are fed with a balanced tuner or via a balun and a standard ATU.

As this antenna is end fed, the problem of a centre feedpoint is circumvented and it can be conveniently supported from a tree or a tall building. Alternatively, a fishing pole could be used as a support. A half-size version will cover 14 to 52MHz.

THE M3KXZ ANTENNA
Pete Millis, M3KXZ, has designed and built a two-element vertical phased array based using the no-counterpoise principle, which came about as he was looking for a simple solution to the problem of making a phased multiband array for portable QRP use. The 'no-counterpoise' antenna presents an easy to match impedance across a very broad range of frequencies, with the resistive and reactive components never rising above a few hundred ohms. If twin feedline is used, line losses resulting from high SWR will remain very small, especially when the line length is short (as in a typical portable type operation).

M3KXZ decided to see how a pair of vertical 'no-counterpoise' antennas would perform when used in a phased array. He notes: "Computer modelling with *EZNEC* indicated that performance with two 25ft 'no-counterpoise' antennas would be good for the range

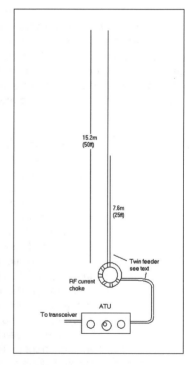

Fig 5.28: A 'no-counterpoise' multiband vertical antenna.

20m to 6m when spaced 3m apart, with an excellent bi-directional end-fire pattern when fed 180° out of phase, and an excellent broadside pattern when fed in phase on the higher frequencies, approaching omni-directional on 20m.

"Broadside directivity can be improved on the lower frequencies (20m) by increasing the distance between the elements, but this results in additional lobe formation on the higher bands. For the computer modelling, I simulated the array as two vertical 'no-counterpoise' antennas with an individual source at the base of

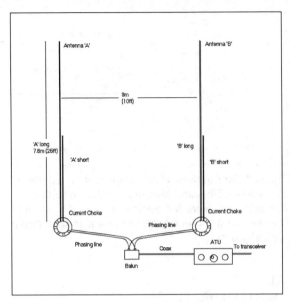

Fig 5.29: The 'no-counterpoise' antenna two-element phased array for 20m through 6m, by M3KXZ. The 1:1 baluns consist of 8 turns of the phasing line (twin core speaker wire) on an FT114-43 toroid. The long and short antenna elements are 7.6m (25ft) and 3.8m (12.5ft) respectively.

each, and fed either in phase or 180° out of phase".

The construction of the antenna is shown in **Fig 5.29**. M3KXZ built his antenna out of twin speaker wire and used the same material to make the phasing lines on the grounds that it should have lower losses than coax considering the high SWR between the balun and the two verticals. The twin feed phasing lines are decoupled from the antennas using a simple 1:1 balun at the base of each antenna. The baluns are constructed by winding eight turns of the phasing line around an FT114-43 toroid and are required because the antennas are unbalanced but the phasing lines need to be balanced. The lead phasing lines are coupled to an unbalanced tuner via a 4:1 current balun and a short length of coax. The balun on each end of the phasing lines serves to help force the phasing lines to be balanced. Both phasing lines are attached to the 4:1 balun at the tuner end. When the antennas are fed such that A long and B long (see Fig 5.29) are both connected to one terminal on the 4:1 balun and A short and B short are both connected to the other, the array is fed in phase. If the connections to one antenna are reversed, the array is fed 180° out of phase.

The late L B Cebik, W4RNL, analysed M3KXZ's antenna and the following is a brief outline of his comments. "The antenna is interesting in several respects. First, it uses a very simple structure and common materials. The second significant aspect of the antenna is its performance. A single element length covers a spread of bands, for example, 20 to 6m using a total length of 25ft. The normal limit for either a $\lambda/4$ monopole or a $\lambda/2$ dipole is about 2.5:1, which would suggest a cut-off of about 35 - 36MHz, if the original antenna is cut for 14MHz. Once a monopole exceeds about 5/8-λ or a dipole exceeds 1.25-λ the main radiation is no longer broadside to the wire. For a vertical antenna, the long lengths result in very high angle radiation, rather than the low angle radiation that we normally need. However, the M3KXZ antenna and array yield very usable patterns from 20 through to 6m. In addition, the gain of the antenna is close to the gain available from either vertical dipoles / doublets or from elevated monopoles with radials on all bands.

"One consequence of the lower double-wire or transmission-line section is that the dominant radiation currents do not follow the patterns that they would in a straight dipole / doublet, whatever the feedpoint. Hence, M3KXZ has found essentially an antenna designer's grail or silver bullet: an arrangement of wires that extends the range of desirable pattern formation beyond its normal limits while sustaining good gain for an antenna of its type and leaving quite workable feedpoint impedance values.

"The M3KXZ antenna and array constitute an ingenious arrangement of element parts that achieves low-angle vertically-polarised radiation over an extended operating bandwidth that common configurations cannot match. The 2-element version of the array offers some gain and pattern shaping for bi-directional operating. Even with improved materials designed for both RF service and durability through seasonal weather cycles, the antennas are inexpensive. Moreover, they are relatively short for

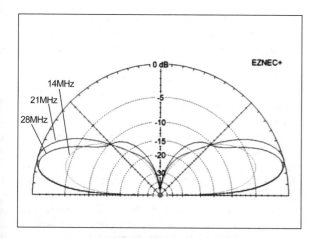

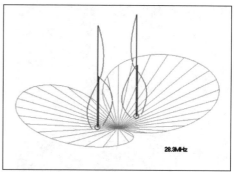

Fig 5.30: Elevation diagrams of the M3KXZ phased array for 14, 21 and 28MHz.

Fig 5.31: Three-dimensional diagram of the M3KXZ phased array on 28.3MHz showing the current amplitude and phases, together with an azimuth polar diagram, with the antennas connected 180° out of phase.

a given frequency range, adding to their neighbourhood acceptability. The challenges presented by the antenna and the array revolve around the matching and the feed system. Increased attention to these details may result in a very serviceable wide-band vertical array."

Peter Dodd, G3LDO, modelled this antenna using *EZNEC 5*. The antenna appears to produce some very low angle radiation on all the upper HF bands. Comparison diagrams of the 14, 21 and 28MHz are shown in **Fig 5.30**. A three-dimensional diagram of the M3KXZ phased array on 28.3MHz is shown in **Fig 5.31**. The current amplitude and phases, together with an azimuth polar diagram, are shown with the antennas connected 180° out of phase.

A full description of this antenna can be found on M3KXZ's website at www.outsideshack.com

G0KYA EFHW WIRE VERTICAL

Steve Nichols, G0KYA, described the end-fed half-wave (EFHW) vertical antenna in the October 2010 *RadCom*. The antenna is a half-wave length of wire taped to a fibreglass 'fishing rod' type pole. As an end-fed half-wave has a very high impedance of around 3000 - 4000Ω, the secret is in the matching unit: if you just connect the wire to your coax or rig you will be very disappointed!

G0KYA acknowledges the idea for this antenna came from the website of Steve Yates, AA5TB (www.aa5tb.com), which has a lot of information on the EFHW and much more besides.

The basic EFHW is shown in **Fig 5.32**. G0KYA first built an EFHW for 10m. First, you need a half-wave length of wire. Using the formula length (in feet) = 468/frequency in MHz, cut a piece of wire to 16ft 5in (precisely 5.00m). Next you need a T200 (red) toroid, available in the UK from JAB Electrical Components (www.jabdog.com), among other sources, and often available at rallies. Wind 17 turns of enamelled copper wire on the toroid as the secondary winding - each time the wire passes through

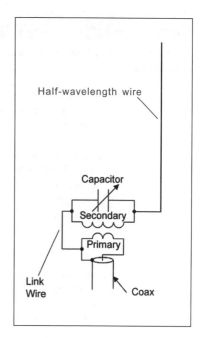

Fig 5.32: Basic principle of the end-fed half wave antenna. The capacitor is a short length of RG58 coax - see text.

The transformer is wound on a T200 (red) toroid. The coax capacitor is connected to the upper terminal block.

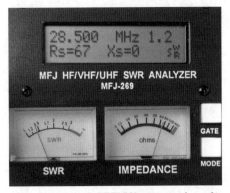

At resonance the EFHW antenna is quite well-behaved.

the toroid counts as one turn. The wire used by G0KYA was about 1.25mm diameter (18SWG): this can also be supplied by JAB if necessary. Leave a little at the end for connections and then wind two turns over this for the primary, again leaving a little spare.

Across the 17-turn winding you need to connect a capacitor. Approximately 24pF is required and a short length of RG58 coax can be used. As RG58 has a capacitance of about 28.8pF per foot cut off about 10in and connect that across the ends of the winding: an electrical screw connector block ('choc block') makes life easier. Then connect your coax across the two turn primary, connect your antenna to one of the secondary wires and connect another piece of copper wire from the other secondary wire back to the braid of the coax (the link wire in the diagram).

An end-fed antenna normally requires an earth or ground plane to work and the usual way of feeding one is against a short counterpoise. But with the EFHW vertical there is very little current flowing in the ground and it becomes almost unnecessary to have an earth connection. G0KYA found that this antenna can be fed without any earth stake, counterpoise or radials. The impedance is so high that little current actually flows down the braid. If you do get any RF problems, a coax choke of 8 - 10 loops of coax in a 6in coil about a foot or two from the antenna should fix them.

Setting up is easiest with an antenna analyser but can also be done at low power using a transmitter and SWR meter.

Connect the antenna analyser to the end of the coax and see where the antenna resonates. It will probably be lower than 10m. Snipping off half-inch lengths of the coax will reduce the capacitance and move the resonant frequency higher. If you get down to about four inches and are still not there, try removing a turn off the secondary coil. G0KYA ended up with 15 turns on the secondary and a piece of coax about four inches long - it is better to remove turns than snip too much off the coax. The end result was an SWR across the entire 10m band of less than 2:1. In fact, at resonance it was about 1.2:1.

A 20m version

The EFHW vertical is easily scaled to other bands. By doubling the length of the wire radiator to 10.05m (33ft) you have an effective low-angle half-wave radiator for 20m. A couple of minutes with a pen and paper and the equation for the resonant frequency of an LC network:

$$f = \frac{1}{2\pi\sqrt{LC}}$$

shows that halving the frequency means that the value of capacitance must be multiplied by four to make the antenna system resonant. G0KYA says, "I cut another piece of coax at four times the length of the original piece, hooked it all up and plugged it into the MFJ analyser. I couldn't believe it - the instant result was an SWR of 1.1:1 on 14.150MHz, rising to only 1.5:1 at the edges of the band."

The matching network should be built into a plastic box to waterproof it.

Results

While there was no long-distance propagation on 10m at the time, CB stations over 20 miles distant were heard on 27.6MHz that were completely inaudible on a 10m half-wave dipole, which indicated that the EFHW was working well. The angle of radiation of a vertical half-wave is quite low, so it should be quite a DX performer.

The 20m EFHW was at least as good as a half-wave 20m dipole at 30ft and US stations were romping in during the afternoon on SSB. It outperformed a regular quarter-wave vertical with radials lying on the ground by a couple of S-points and is also a lot easier to put up. The antenna was used for Jamboree On The Air, when it outperformed a G5RV at 30ft by about 1 S-point. Later, the same 20m EFHW was used at an International Marconi Day special event station, where it functioned very well and stations around the world, including VK4, KP2 and numerous US and EU stations were worked.

The 14MHz version of the EFHW wire vertical, supported by a 10m (33ft) fibreglass fishing rod.

A VERTICAL ZEPP

In the October 2006 *QST*, Gary Davis, KD9SB, described the 20m end-fed half-wave antenna he has used successfully from on board his yacht. The design is, in effect, a vertical Zepp, an antenna originally used on the Zeppelin airships in the early part of the 20th century. A similar configuration is often used on VHF and is then normally called a 'J' antenna. While implemented here for use on a sailing boat, the design should work equally well on land.

The Zepp antenna consists of a λ/2 of wire end-fed by an electrical λ/4 of open-wire or ladder type transmission line. It is a very simple and inexpensive antenna to build. The antenna is matched to the transceiver by a small antenna tuner. The configuration is shown in **Fig 5.33**. KD9SB chose the Zepp design as it can be difficult to obtain a good sea water RF ground on fiberglass or wooden boats.

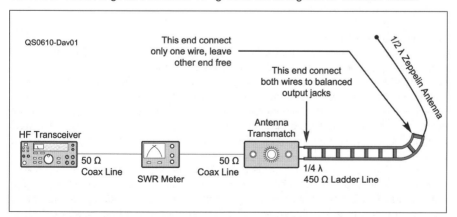

Fig 5.33: Antenna and tuner configuration. A separate tuner may not be needed depending on the radio configuration (images reprinted with permission of the American Radio Relay League).

The lower end of the configuration. Note that the balanced line is kept away from railings and other metal objects: don't be tempted to tie the line to the stern rail or stanchions - let it hang free.

For the λ/2 antenna, KD9SB used 13-gauge 19-strand Variflex insulated wire. A lightweight plastic egg insulator is attached to each end of the antenna. To support the antenna, he used a monofilament plastic line of the type used on small grass trimmers. This line is 0.065in in diameter. The monofilament line is used to reduce antenna detuning, caused by wet support lines. A 6ft line is used at the masthead end of the antenna to prevent detuning effects, due to the convergence of the stainless steel rigging at the masthead. A 2ft line is used at the stern rail end. The grass trimmer lines are attached at both ends. The top end is attached to a spare masthead halyard and raised aloft. The stern rail end is attached to the outermost corner of the stern rail, keeping it as far from the backstay and boom as possible (see photo). KD9SB also added a lightweight Dacron line from the halyard to a deck level cleat. This forms a downhaul so he can retrieve the halyard in case the antenna wire or support line breaks aloft.

Matching an end-fed λ/2

The λ/4 matching section is made from ladder line. KD9SB used 450Ω line made from 18 gauge solid wire. Ladder line is also available in 14 gauge stranded wire, a more durable choice for offshore or longer term use. One wire of the ladder line is soldered to the stern rail end of the antenna, and covered with heat shrink tubing. The other wire is left unconnected and hanging free. At the antenna tuner end of the ladder line, both wires are connected to the balanced line output jacks via a dual banana plug. Remember, a jumper wire is often used to enable the balanced line output.

The λ/4 matching section serves not only as the antenna feed line, but is also used as the impedance matching device between the antenna coupler and the antenna itself. A λ/4 transmission line transforms the high impedance of the end of the λ/2 antenna to a low impedance. The impedance should be close enough to operate into a transceiver's internal tuner through a short section of coax, or an external antenna coupler may be needed, depending on the transceiver.

The antenna interface needs to make the transition from the balanced line to the coax connector at the radio. One way to do that is with directly connected coax with a common mode choke, another is with a balanced antenna tuner and a third is to use an unbalanced tuner with a balun at the output. KD9SB uses a small MFJ-901B 'Versa Tuner'.

For the antenna, use the usual formula, 468/frequency in MHz. This results in a length of 32 feet 8 inches for 14.3MHz. The feedline length requires consideration of the relative propagation velocity, 0.91 for typical window type line. This results in a length of 15 feet 8 inches for the matching section. The antenna is broad enough to achieve a good match over the whole band.

If the feedline is too short to reach the antenna tuner, a length of 0.75λ can also be used, but the bandwidth will be reduced. The bottom of the matching section can also be connected directly to coax. In that case, it is best to use a choke coil of about six turns, about 6 to 10in in diameter, in the coax adjacent to connection. The SWR will be low enough that a run to the transceiver or tuner should not incur significant losses on any reasonably sized craft.

SINGLE AND DUAL-BAND J-POLES

Most antennas in this book are designed for the HF bands, but there is nothing to stop wire antenna being used, and successfully too, on the VHF and even UHF bands. This design for a dual-band 2m / 70cm wire 'J-pole' antenna was published in the March 2007 *QST* and is by Edison Fong, WB6IQN.

The conventional single-band J-pole antenna for 2m is shown in **Fig 5.34**. Unlike a quarter-wave ground plane, it does not need ground radials and it is easy to construct using inexpensive materials. The basic J-pole is a half-wave vertical. It works by matching a low impedance (50Ω) feedline to the high impedance at the end of a λ/2 vertical dipole by using a λ/4 matching stub shorted at one end and open at the other. Between the shorted end and the high impedance end of the λ/4 shorted stub, there is a point that is close to 50Ω. Although this point is slightly inductive, it is still an excellent match to 50Ω coax and at resonance the SWR is below 1.2:1. By experimenting, this point is found to be 1.25in from the shorted end on 2m. The 15.25in section in **Fig 5.34** serves as the quarter-wave matching transformer.

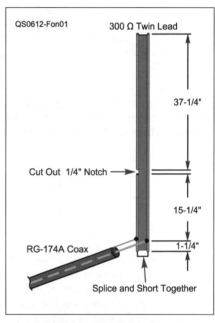

Fig 5.34: The original 2m ribbon J-pole antenna (all diagrams reprinted with permission of the American Radio Relay League).

Adding a second band to the J-pole

Almost all antennas will resonate at their third harmonic and a 2m antenna *does* resonate at UHF, but the key word here is *resonate*. Resonating is one thing; working well as an antenna is another. Unfortunately the performance at the third harmonic is poor when the antenna is used as a vertical. This can be best explained by 2m quarter-wave vertical over a ground plane. At 70cm (450MHz) it is a 3/4λ vertical but unfortunately the additional λ/2 at UHF is out of phase with the bottom λ/4 which means cancellation oc-

Right: Fig 5.35. *EZNEC* elevation plane pattern comparing 2m J-pole on fundamental (grey) and on 70cm (black) at height of 8ft above ground. Most of the energy at the third harmonic is launched at 44°.

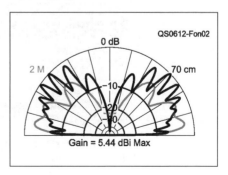

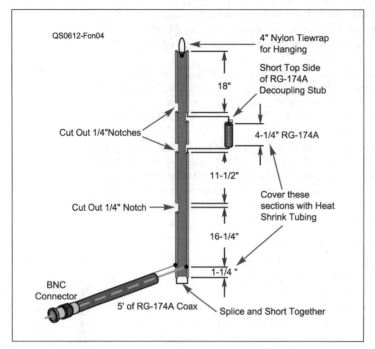

QS0612-Fon04

4" Nylon Tiewrap for Hanging

Short Top Side of RG-174A Decoupling Stub

18"

Cut Out 1/4"Notches

4-1/4" RG-174A

11-1/2"

Cover these sections with Heat Shrink Tubing

Cut Out 1/4" Notch

16-1/4"

1-1/4 "

BNC Connector

5' of RG-174A Coax

Splice and Short Together

Fig 5.36: The dual-band J-pole. Note that the exact dimensions will vary with the manufacturer of the 300Ω line, especially the exact tap point where the RG-174A coax feed to the radio is connected.

curs in the radiation pattern and the majority of the energy is launched at a take-off angle of 45°. This results in a 4 to 6dB *loss* in the horizontal plane, compared with a conventional λ/4 vertical placed over a ground plane (see **Fig 5.35**).

So although a vertical can be made to work at its third harmonic, its performance is poor. What we need is a method to decouple the remaining λ/2 at UHF of a 2m radiator, but have it remain electrically unaffected at VHF. We want independent λ/2 radiators at both VHF and UHF frequencies.

The design shown in **Fig 5.36** does this. To disconnect sections of the twinlead, quarter-inch notches are cut out to achieve the proper resonances, leaving the insulating backbone of the 300Ω twinlead in place. A short length (4.25in) of RG174A coax is used as a λ/4 decoupling stub for the UHF band. Heat shrink tubing is used to cover and protect the UHF decoupling stub, the four quarter-inch notches and the RG174A coax interface to the 300Ω twinlead. A small Teflon tie strap is attached to the top of the antenna so that it may be conveniently attached to a nonconductive support string. The photograph shows the λ/4 UHF matching stub inside the heat shrink tubing.

The antenna can easily fit inside a pouch or a large pocket, is less complex than a single band ground plane, yet will consistently outperform a ground plane using three or four radials. Set-up time is less than a minute.

The top of the antenna is a high impedance point, so objects (even if they are non-metallic) must be kept as far away as possible for best performance. The other sensitive points are the open end of the λ/4 VHF matching section and the open end of the λ/4 UHF decoupling stub. As with any antenna, it works best as high as possible and in the clear. To hoist the antenna, use non-conducting string. Fishing line also works well.

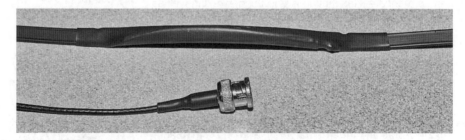

The λ/4 UHF decoupling stub made of RG-174A, covered with heat shrink tubing. This is shown next to the BNC connector that goes to the transceiver.

146MHz				445MHz			
VHF λ/4 GP 4 radials	Flexible Antenna	Standard VHF J-Pole	Dual-Band J-Pole	UHF λ/4 GP 4 radials	Flexible Antenna	Standard VHF J-Pole	Dual-Band J-Pole
0 dB reference	-5.9dB	+1.2dB	+1.2dB	0 dB reference	-2.0dB	-5.5dB	+0.5dB

Table 5.11: Measured relative performance of dual-band J-pole on 2m and 70cm.

Measured results

The dual-band J-pole was measured in an open field using an Advantest R3361 spectrum analyser and the results are shown in **Table 5.11**. The antenna gives a 7dB improvement over a flexible antenna at VHF. In actual practice, since the antenna can be mounted higher than the flexible antenna on a handheld, results of +10dB are not uncommon - the equivalent of giving a 4W handheld a boost to 40W. There was no measurable degradation in performance by incorporating the UHF capability into a conventional J-pole.

At UHF it outperforms the single band 2m J-pole operating at UHF by about 6dB. Also notice that at UHF the loss for the flexible antenna is only 2.0dB compared with the ground plane. This is because the flexible antenna at UHF is 6in long, which is a quarter wave, so the major difference for the flexible antenna at UHF is the lack of ground radials.

THE 'JUMBO-JAY' VERTICAL

The J-pole antenna has a long history, which certainly goes back to the mid-1930s, and is normally used for VHF work on 50MHz and up, as described above. The J antenna can of course also be used on HF, and the one described here is for 29MHz operation.

It is a full-sized half-wave vertical radiator which has at its base a quarter-wave matching section. A half-wave vertical antenna is a vertically polarised and omnidirectional radiator which can give excellent low-angle radiation. Its efficiency is 50% which is greater than virtually all quarter-wave vertical ground-plane antennas and it does not need radials or any special earth arrangements.

Centre feeding a vertical half-wave antenna will mean that its low-impedance feeder would normally come away horizontally from the dipole centre for some distance before dropping to ground. If this is not done, the radiator will be unbalanced and its feed impedance will not remain close to the usual 75Ω. The feed problems are overcome by using a quarter-wave matching section at the foot of the half-wave.

The design of this 'jumbo-jay' antenna is shown in **Fig 5.37**. It is made from wire and the lengths are designed for operation on 29MHz. A non-metallic support (or suspension from a horizontal rope) which is at least 9.1m (30ft) high is needed to hold up the 'J', and a 4.87m (16ft 1in) vertical half-wave length of wire is dropped down from this point. The matching section is arranged to lie along a strip of weatherproofed plywood or similar material so that the base of the 'J' is about 2m (6ft) above the ground. This is low enough to allow an easy adjustment of the matching when setting up the antenna.

The insulation must be good at the top of the antenna and also where the lower end of the radiator joins the matching section. The latter is a non-radiating, end-shorted, quarter-wave length of twin feeder which has a wire spacing of about 75mm (3in). Ceramic or other suitable stand-off insulators can be fixed to the plywood strip to support this matching section.

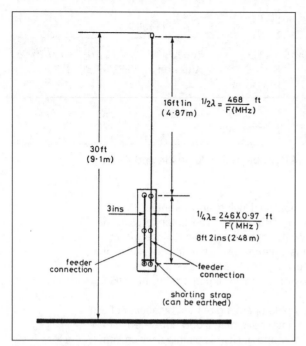

$$\tfrac{1}{2}\lambda = \frac{468}{F(\text{MHz})} \text{ ft}$$

16ft 1in
(4·87m)

30ft
(9·1m)

3ins

$$\tfrac{1}{4}\lambda = \frac{246 \times 0·97}{F(\text{MHz})} \text{ ft}$$

8ft 2ins (2·48m)

feeder
connection

feeder
connection

shorting strap
(can be earthed)

Fig 5.37: The 'jumbo-jay' vertical antenna. It is a half-wave radiator which is matched to a low-impedance coaxial feeder by using a quarter-wave stub.

The 'jumbo-jay' must be tuned to resonance before the 50Ω coaxial feeder is connected. A small shorting bar made with a pair of crocodile clips with a half-turn coil of wire between them can be easily loosely coupled to a dip oscillator. Starting at the lower end of the matching section, the shorting bar should be moved up slowly while continually checking the resonant frequency with the dip oscillator. When the correct setting is found (i.e. 29MHz in this example), the temporary shorting bar can be replaced with a wire soldered across the matching section and the unwanted remainder cut away.

The coaxial feeder is connected temporarily (again using crocodile clips) across the lower end of the matching section, a few inches above the shorting bar. Then using a low power signal tuned to a frequency near the resonant frequency, check the SWR at various points around this frequency using an SWR meter in the feedline. The tapping points must be adjusted to get the lowest SWR reading and then permanent soldered connections may be made. A perfect match showing an SWR reading of 1:1 may not be attainable but if the reading is 1.5:1 or better the losses will be very small. The centre of the shorting bar can be earthed and this will prevent any build-up of static charge on the antenna.

The 'jumbo-jay' will not have such a wide operating bandwidth as a similar sized antenna constructed with tubing, but it will allow operation over the FM and upper SSB segments of the 28MHz band. It also provides an excellent low angle of radiation that is suitable for both short range FM contacts that generally use line of sight propagation along the earth's surface, and for long haul communications where low angles are needed for the greatest distances.

The commonly found screening factors at some locations caused by buildings, trees and rising ground etc will distort the theoretical omindirectional radiation pattern of this antenna, particularly as its high-current section is only about 6.7m (22ft) from the ground. When the antenna has been set up and matched it could of course be relocated to a more elevated position and then its performance will be enhanced.

PHASED VERTICALS

Any pair of verticals can be phased to give additional gain, as described in *QST* in November 2009 and again in February 2010. By having multiple monopoles spaced some distance apart and fed in appropriate phase, the energy can be maximised in particular directions around the antenna.

A popular arrangement is to feed two monopoles in the same phase, spaced λ/2 to 5/8-λ apart, as shown in **Fig 5.38**. The energy will be focused in directions in which the distance to each antenna is the same: this is called a *broadside array*. A typical azimuth pattern is shown in **Fig 5.39**.

Maximum gain occurs at about 5/8λ spacing and is a bit less than 5dB more than that of a single antenna. **Table 5.12** shows the effect of spacing on gain. Spacing at λ/2 has the cleanest pattern with no side lobes, perhaps best if you are trying to reject

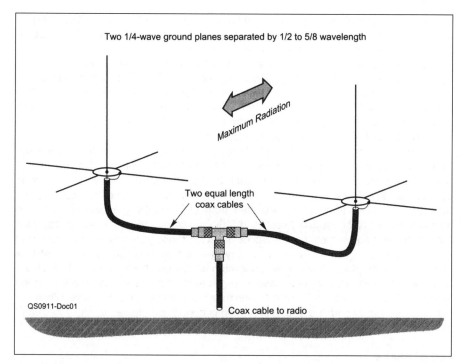

Two 1/4-wave ground planes separated by 1/2 to 5/8 wavelength

Maximum Radiation

Two equal length
coax cables

QS0911-Doc01

Coax cable to radio

Fig 5.38: The λ/4 ground planes in phase. The two antennas are fed in parallel through identical lengths of th same type of coax to ensure the signals arrive at both antennas in the same phase (diagrams reprinted with permission of the American Radio Relay League).

interference from the sides. Spacings wider than 5/8-λ have progressively stronger radiation towards the side until a full wave, at which point the side radiation is actually in phase, resulting in a four leaf pattern.

To feed the antennas in phase, the lengths of coax from the two antennas need to be the same, as shown in the diagram. The impedance of the two in parallel will be around half that from one element with the same length of coax. This is likely to result in an SWR of about 2:1: more about how to fix this in a moment.

When phasing two verticals, the first thing you need to do is to make sure that the two antennas each still match 50Ω. The mutual coupling of the an-

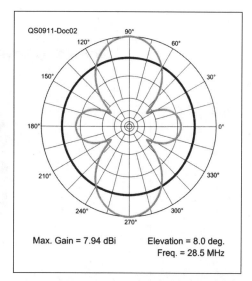

QS0911-Doc02

Max. Gain = 7.94 dBi   Elevation = 8.0 deg.
                             Freq. = 28.5 MHz

Fig 5.39: The azimuth pattern of two λ/4 ground planes about a half-wave apart and fed in phase (grey), compared with the omnidirectional pattern of a single ground plane (black).

Spacing	Peak gain
3/8-λ	2.30dB
1/2-λ	3.75dB
5/8-λ	4.60dB
3/4-λ	4.50dB
1.0λ	2.80dB

Table 5.12: Effect of spacing on gain of two element broadside array, compared with a single element.

tennas can detune them - less so at wider spacings. To adjust, put a 50Ω load on one antenna and adjust the other for a match at the required frequency. Then reverse them and repeat. Now you have two 50Ω systems.

However, if you ran 50Ω coax from each to the T connector, the two loads in parallel will yield 25Ω at the T connector. That will be a 2:1 SWR, probably higher than you want. To match that to 50Ω line, you can use a λ/4 section of 37.5Ω coax (two 75Ω cables in parallel) as shown in **Fig 5.40**. The actual impedance will be 56.25Ω, a 1.12:1 SWR, which is close enough. (Note that in this diagram the antennas shown are vertical dipoles: the same principle applies.)

Alternately, you could use λ/4 of 75Ω coax from each antenna to the T connector. That will result in each antenna showing 112.5Ω at the T, also resulting in 56.25Ω after the parallel connection, a good match to 50Ω for the run of coax to the shack. The only problem with this method is that, due to the velocity factor of the coax, the two antennas will need to be closer together than λ/2, and the gain will therefore be somewhat less. (While a 3/4-λ section will theoretically work in the same way as a λ/4 length, and some have used it successfully, it is not generally recommended to use this approach, for two reasons. Firstly, the cutting to length is three times as critical and, secondly, the operating bandwidth is only one third as wide.) If you want to use wider spacing between the elements the method is to use a short section (any length) of 50Ω coax, then a λ/4 of 75Ω, and then the T, as shown in **Fig 5.41**. Whatever you do, the lengths from the T to both antennas need to be the same, and you cannot reverse the transmission line sequence.

Out of phase

Another method of phasing two verticals is to feed them *out of phase*. By spacing the antennas λ/2 apart and feeding them 180° out of phase, the maximum radiation will

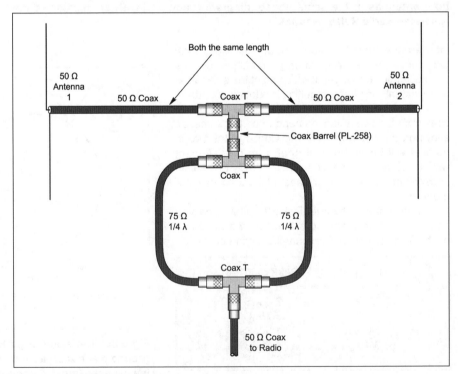

Fig 5.40: Matching two parallel 50Ω antennas to a 50Ω line using a single quarter-wave section of 37.5Ω coax made from two 75Ω cables in parallel

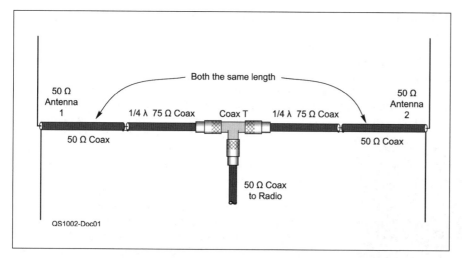

QS1002-Doc01

Fig 5.41: Transforming each antenna system to 112Ω so the parallel combination will equal almost 50Ω.

be in both directions along the line of the antennas. This is called an *end-fire array*.

By making them λ/4 apart and feeding them 90° out of phase, a pattern in a single direction will result along the line of the antennas. This is a bit more complicated to achieve, though, because the mututal impedances between the antenna elements make it non-trivial to force equal currents into both antenna elements.

THE VERTICAL MOXON ARRAY

The Moxon Rectangle is a 2-element beam originally developed by the late Les Moxon, G6XN. It is normally configured as a horizontal wire beam supported by fibreglass spreaders, but Nigel Ramsey, G6SFP, has turned the Moxon Rectangle on its side to produce a 2-element vertical array. The wire beam is supported by two 10m fibreglass fishing poles. The strength of the structure is a result of crossing the two poles and fastening them together.

Peter Millis, M3KXZ, also uses a vertical Moxon array close to the sea. He has described his version on a website dedicated to the Moxon Rectangle: see www.moxonantennaproject.com

M3KXZ gives the following dimensions for his 14MHz version of this interesting antenna:

♦ *Driven element:* 7.26m vertical, 1.15m horizontal;
♦ *Reflector:* 7.26m vertical, 1.42m horizontal;
♦ *Spacing* (between driven element and reflector ends): 0.11m;
♦ *Height of base above ground:* variable, up to 1.00m.

As with all vertical antennas, locating the vertical Moxon array by the sea will give a great low-angle signal. By directing the array out to sea, the parasitic element will provide even more low-angle gain, while rejecting signals from the land side.

G6SFP's vertical Moxon array, located close to the sea. The feedpoint and vertical wires can just be seen in this photo.

THE DK7PE 'JUMPER BEAM': A VERTICAL WIRE YAGI

Rudolf Klos, DK7PE, developed this antenna while operating from various locations in Africa in the 1980s. He often found himself staying in high-rise hotels, which were ideal for supporting sloping wire antennas for the low bands. On the higher bands he usually put up a sloping Windom antenna. However, the results were not entirely satisfactory as it favoured only two directions, while others directions were attenuated to varying degrees. In 1984, while operating as XT2CW from Burkina Faso, the 10m band was wide open but to cover all directions north of the building, from west to east equally, he needed a different system. Having no access to the hotel roof, the only solution was a vertical dipole fixed to a 40ft fiberglass pole hanging out of the balcony, about 90 ft above ground.

Comparing the two antennas confirmed the great advantage of the vertical dipole compared with the Windom. It covered a 180° sector in the directions not blocked by the building, and produced a much stronger signal.

Back in Germany DK7PE improved the system by making it operational on multiple bands. The resulting antenna, which he called the 'Jumper Beam', was described in the October 2011 *QST*.

A 40m half-wave dipole was cut into smaller dipoles up to the 10m band, with connectors from the automotive industry (jumpers) to select the particular band - see photo. Fixing this vertical dipole in front of a big building made of concrete and steel must have an advantage of at least a little additional gain, as any rear energy that isn't absorbed must be reflected somewhere - even though the properties are hard to predict. So why not put a real, accurately cut, reflector behind the vertical dipole and a director in front of it? It was easy to do.

The result was a full size three-element wire beam that covered all bands between 40 and 10m simply by opening or closing the jumper connectors and winding up any spare antenna wire. The 40ft fiberglass pole was long enough to

Detail of the jumper connection. The connector is an automotive push-on type. The plastic insulator position is adjusted to keep the weight off the connection (all photos by DK7PE and reprinted with permission of the American Radio Relay League).

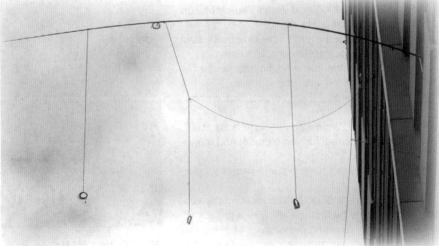

The DK7PE 'Jumper Beam', looking up from ground level.

Details of balcony attachment. Adjustable locking straps or 'bungee' cords are used to secure both the bottom of the pole and the fulcrum on the balcony rail.

build a three-element beam for any band from 30 to 10m. On 40m the ideal spacing between each element is around 30ft, making it too large for the 40ft pole. On 40m, however, a two-element Yagi with driven element and director can be made.

To keep this antenna as light as possible 20AWG copper wire is used. This is a good compromise between breaking strength and weight. The lengths that have been found to work best are shown in **Table 5.13**.

Originally a balun was used to feed the antenna with coax but, apart from the greater weight, no difference in performance was noticed so these days a balun is no longer used and the antenna is directly fed with light-weight RG58 coax as shown in the photo. With a matched antenna RG58 can easily handle up to 700W and attenuation, even on the higher bands, isn't an issue as the length seldom exceeds 50 or 60ft between balcony

Feed point details. The direct coax connection seemed to work as well as a balun and reduced the weight.

Band (m)	Director	Director Spacing	Driven Element	Reflector Spacing	Reflector
10	15.61	3.51	16.30	7.02	17.09
12	17.61	3.97	18.37	7.90	19.25
15	20.86	4.70	21.71	9.35	22.83
17	24.27	5.44	25.29	10.89	26.54
20	31.23	7.02	32.54	14.04	34.14
30	43.85	9.74	45.23	19.48	47.46
40	62.45	14.00	65.08	N/A	Not used

Table 5.13: Element dimensions (in feet).

and room.

Even though this is a lightweight antenna, the pole must always be properly secured on to the balcony railing and on the inner end with an appropriate counter weight or locking straps, as shown in the photograph. An armchair or something similar is usually available and by moving this object the beam's direction can be changed from Japan to Europe and then to North America, depending on the building's orientation. Tension belts or 'bungee cords' can be used to give the system the required stability. Light winds are not a problem as the elements move with the wind. In a strong wind, the system can be taken down within a few minutes.

Even though he has been unable to measure the gain, DK7PE reports that he has found the performance of this antenna to be far better than that of the single element antenna.

KITE-SUPPORTED VERTICALS

Before looking at some practical arrangements for kite-supported verticals, some rules and safety notes. The Civil Aviation Authority is the regulator for kites in the UK. No permission is required for heights of up to 60m above ground level, *unless* you are in aerodrome traffic zone (ATZ), where the maximum height is 30m. The CAA can advise if your proposed location is within an ATZ. If you wish to fly your kite higher, you must seek permission to do so a minimum of 28 days in advance - see www.caa.co.uk *Safety warnings:* Do *not* fly your kite near power lines or where it will fly over roads. Remember that the wind can change direction! Be *especially* vigilant about lightning – check the weather forecast before you go out and cancel kite trips if thunderstorms are forecast.

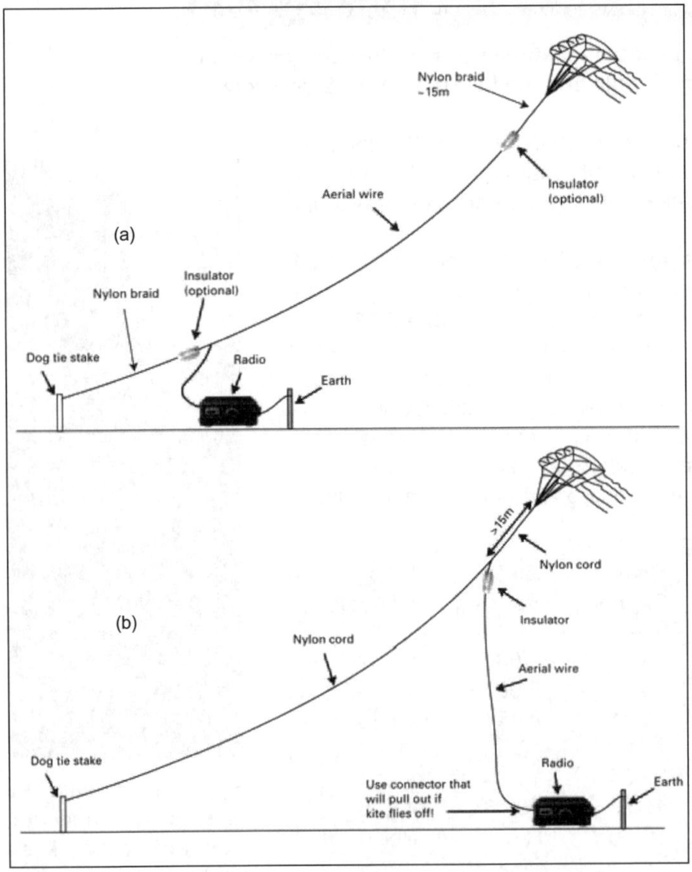

Fig 5.42: The two main methods of flying kite antennas.

Kite antennas

There are two main varieties: either a sloping wire or a vertical. The first and most obvious way is to use the antenna as the kite line. Use a header of at least 15m of normal kite cord before attaching the antenna wire; this will help you to launch the kite. Use a light stranded wire. **Fig 5.42(a)** shows the general arrangement. Note the use of a post at the ground end to give strain relief for the connection to the radio equipment – it is inconvenient to have to chase your radio across a field. Stakes sold for dogs are particularly suitable here. Another tip is to include a connector in the antenna near the radio that will easily pull apart, such as a banana plug and socket. This will also help to stop the radio being dragged away should something go wrong.

The second method is to

drop a vertical down from the kite line. Again use a substantial header (at least 15m) as this will help the kite to fly better and keep the antenna more stable. Although this method can result in a perfectly vertical antenna, Richard Newstead, G3CWI, commented (*RadCom*, November 2008) that when the wind drops a little you end up with a lot of wire on the ground. **Fig 5.42(b)** shows this arrangement. Both these arrangements work best when fed against some radials laid out on the ground.

The bands where kites give the best results tend to be 80 and 160m. Favourite antennas are a 5/8-λ wire for 80m or a 3/8-λ for 160m. If flown using the method shown in Fig 5.41(a), they will (just) fit within the height restrictions.

Choice of kite

Traditionalists will wish to follow in the footsteps of Marconi and use a box kite. Also popular is the Cody Kite, designed by the famous Wild West showman Samuel Cody. However, G3CWI recommends using a 'Parafoil'. Invented in the mid-1960s, these kites have no rigid parts, are easy to fly even in light winds, are stable in flight and they fly at a high angle. Look for one with a single line and with an area of between 0.75m^2 and 1.5m^2. Don't be tempted to use anything much larger as it will be difficult to control in a medium to strong breeze. Parafoils are readily available in kite shops.

Aerostats use lighter-than-air gas (usually helium) to provide the lift. A combination kite / aerostat is useful for supporting antennas and is easier to launch than a conventional kite, with the helium providing the initial lift and the kite taking over once up in the air.

A combined kite and aerostat used to support a wire antenna.

Precipitation static

Precipitation static occurs when snow or raindrops (or occasionally sand particles) pick up a charge by passing through a naturally occurring electric field. They then discharge when they strike your antenna. Each discharge causes a small popping sound in the receiver and, with a large antenna, they can be many thousands of particles hitting the antenna each second. In bad cases, the intensity of the noise caused by the precipitation static will drown out all but the strongest signals. Not only that but there will be very large voltages present on your antenna that could damage your receiver or, worse still, you! G3CWI notes that he found that precipation static is worst in summer conditions when there is very fine rain being blown by a brisk warm breeze.

A partial solution is to bleed the static discharge to earth. This can be done in a variety of ways but all require a good earth connection for best results. One simple way is to connect a 1MΩ resistor between the end of the antenna and earth. Another method is to use an RF choke that is constructed to have an impedance of about 10 times the expected impedance at the end of the antenna.

Neither of these methods will stop all the RF noise but they should protect you and your equipment from serious damage. An earth system consisting of one or more metal stakes in the ground and / or a few radials will be required to bleed the static to ground effectively. It is safest to cease flying in such conditions.

6 Loops

LOOPS, OR MORE CORRECTLY 'closed circuit' antennas, are a popular form of antenna that can be used to good effect on the HF bands as well as other frequencies. These antennas fall into two basic categories, namely those that contain a total conductor length which is small when compared to a wavelength, and those which use a wavelength or more of conductor.

Small loops can be likened to large coils, as they have a current distribution similar to that found in a coil: it is in the same phase and has the same amplitude in every part of the loop. To achieve this end, the total length of the conductor in such a loop must not exceed about 0.1λ. Small loop antennas that are used for transmitting are generally of a single turn. The idea of having a small yet effective antenna is very attractive to those who have very limited space for their antennas. Small loop antennas have a very low radiation resistance and a very high Q, which in turn implies a very narrow bandwidth. To overcome the low radiation resistance very careful construction techniques are required to ensure that losses are minimised. To achieve this, copper pipe is generally used as the basis for the antenna and, in view of their construction, small loops do not fall into the category of 'wire antennas' and therefore - with one exception - they are not covered here.

Antennas that are termed large loops are characterised by the fact that the current is not the same in all points around the loop. This gives rise to an entirely different set of properties and these can be exploited in a different way to those of small loops.

Loops may be constructed in either the horizontal or the vertical plane and we will look at both in this chapter. The loop can be more or less any shape: the ideal shape would be a perfect circle, as for a given length of wire around the outside it encompasses the greatest area, but as this is mechanically difficult to construct most loops are either rectangular (preferably square or nearly square) or triangular in shape. A square (or diamond-shaped) loop is called a *quad loop* whereas a triangular one is called a *delta loop*. However, there is nothing to stop the creative constructor from making a pentagon or hexagon shaped loop.

FULL-WAVE QUAD LOOPS

The basic loop antenna is a full-wave of wire in a square shape: the so-called quad loop. Full-wave quad loops have been popular antennas for many years. They can be considered to be derived from a 'pulled out' folded dipole. As such, the quad loop retains the RF current characteristics of such an antenna (see **Fig 6.1**), with in-phase currents along both its top and bottom sections. Each side of a quad is a quarter-wavelength long, and the antenna may be arranged either as a square or as a diamond. The two examples illustrated in Fig 6.1 are fed at their bases and they both provide horizontal polarisation. If fed at a point half-way up either of their sides the polarisation would be vertical.

The length of conductor used to achieve resonance in a quad is greater than just two half-wavelengths (285 / f(MHz) metres or 936 / f(MHz) feet), and instead the formula 306.3 / f(MHz) metres or 1005 / f(MHz) feet must be used when designing

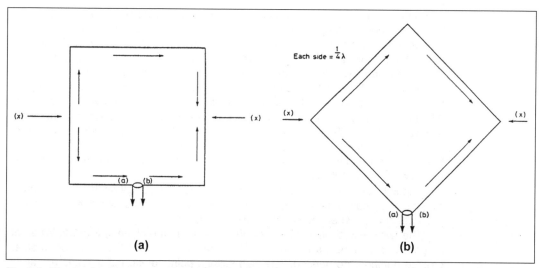

Fig 6.1: The instantaneous current distribution along the sides of a full-wave quad loop, (a) in a square formation, and (b) arranged as a diamond. When the loop is bottom-fed, as is shown in both these examples, its radiation will be horizontally polarised. The points 'x' are at high impedance and voltage which means that the quad in (b) must have very good insulation at these two corners.

this type of antenna. Practical conductor lengths for quad antennas for use on the HF amateur bands are given in **Table 6.1**.

Unlike a folded dipole, the feed impedance of a quad is only about 100Ω. The antenna exhibits some slight gain over a half-wave dipole. The distance that the two current maxima are apart means that it acts like a pair of stacked dipoles. The

Freq (kHz)	Overall length delta loop or quad	Length of each side	
		Quad	Delta
3600	85.00m 279' 1"	21.25m 69' 8"	28.33m 93' 0"
7100	43.14m 141' 7"	10.79m 35' 5"	14.38m 47' 2"
10125	30.25m 99' 6"	7.58m 24' 10"	10.1m 33' 2"
14150	21.64m 71' 0"	5.41m 17' 9"	7.13m 23' 8"
18100	16.92m 55' 6"	4.23m 13' 10"	5.64m 18' 6"
21200	14.44m 47' 5"	3.61m 11' 10"	4.81m 15' 10"
24940	12.28m 40' 3"	3.07m 10' 1"	4.09m 13' 5"
28300	10.82m 35' 6"	2.71m 8' 11"	3.61m 11' 10"

Table 6.1: Practical conductor lengths for quad loop and delta loop antennas.

direction of maximum radiation is at right angles to the plane of the quad loop, i.e. looking through the loop shows the directions of greatest radiation. The gain should be about 1dBd, which represents a power gain in two directions of 1.26 times, a useful feature of the single-loop quad antenna. There are quite deep nulls in the plane of the loop, which are more pronounced than the nulls off the ends of a dipole.

A further advantage of the quad is that being a closed loop it is less susceptible to the effects of the ground than a half-wave dipole. At a height above the ground of a 0.5λ the main radiation lobes of a quad antenna are about 4° lower than those of a half-wave dipole at the same height. At 3/8-λ the radiation angle is almost 10° lower. At λ/4 above ground most of a dipole's radiation will be upwards, but a full-wave quad has its main radiation lobes 40° above the horizon. This represents a 'first skip' distance of about 400 miles.

The influence of nearby objects such as trees or buildings on the characteristics of quad antennas is small. This means that such antennas can often be used to good effect even when located in house roof spaces etc.

The two basic configurations for quad antennas are given in **Fig 6.2**. When arranged as a square, as in Fig 6.2(a), 'spreaders' made of fibreglass or weatherproofed bamboo are needed. The high-voltage points along the antenna are at the centre points of the vertical wire sections, and therefore well away from the ends of the spreaders at A, B, C and D. The impedance at these corner points is not high and therefore little in the way of insulation is needed where the wire is tied to the spreaders.

The arrangement in Fig 6.2(b) requires more space, for its height and width are the diagonals of a square. Furthermore, the RF voltages and impedances will be high at points B and C. This means that there must be good insulation at these positions. Small ceramic 'stand-off' insulators or similar can be used at points A, B and C. The feedpoint insulation is not critical, as it is at a relatively low impedance.

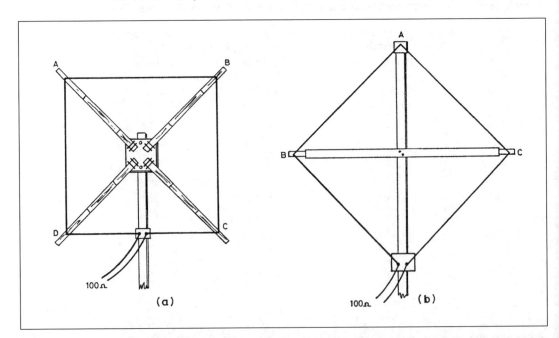

Fig 6.2: (a) A square quad arrangement using bamboo spreaders. The RF voltages will not be high at the points where the wires are fixed to the bamboos, so no special insulating arrangements are needed. (b) With this arrangement point A is at low impedance but points B and C will require good insulation.

The quad loop's feed impedance is about 100Ω. Open-wire tuned feeder (or 300Ω ribbon) can be used as the feeder with an ATU.

The 1dBd gain of a single-element quad loop makes it a useful and simple bi-directional antenna, and it only need be turned through 90° to realise all-world coverage. Its deep nulls are also useful and can be utilised to reduce the strength of unwanted signals.

THE ZS6AAA MULTI-BAND HF QUAD LOOP

The undoubted pioneer of multi-band loop and quad elements was the late Les Moxon, G6XN. He covered various multiband loop elements in his classic book *HF Antennas for all Locations*. In particular, Moxon brought to notice the use of a loop plus stub configuration, comprising about 144ft of wire, that resonates at 7, 14, 21 and 28MHz. It is made up of a square loop with 17ft sides with some 36ft of open twin-wire matching stub: **Fig 6.3**. This forms a 1λ loop at 14MHz, λ/2 at 7MHz, 3/2-λ at 21MHz and 2λ at 29MHz.

Andrew Roos, ZS6AAA, in 'The Compact Quad Multiband HF Antenna' (*QST*, August 2006), presents full details of a similar arrangement, described as an easy-to-build loop with a simple matching section that offers four-band HF coverage. In effect, the antenna comprises a 1λ loop on 14MHz fed through a matching 0.5λ stub with a characteristic impedance of some 800Ω and then, at ZS6AAA, with some 100ft of RG213 coax. As the loop impedance is about 120 - 140Ω, the SWR on the coax is about 3:1, well within the range of most auto or manual ATUs. On 7MHz, the high feed-point impedance is transformed by the 0.25λ stub and then directly into the coax. Similarly on 21MHz the 1.5λ loop high impedance is transformed down by the 0.75λ stub. On 28MHz, the 1λ stub reflects the low impedance of the 2λ loop.

The method of attachment of the transmission line to the loop is shown in **Fig 6.4**. ZS1AAA recommends the use of a 1:1 current (choke) balun to connect the coax to the 800Ω matching section with both loop and stub formed from a con-

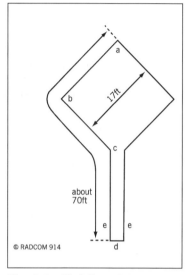

Fig 6.3: Multiband loop and matching stub as used by ZS6AAA. It can be fed from balanced low-impedance line at point 'd', or by 600Ω open line at about point 'e'.

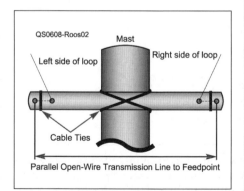

Fig 6.4: Details of compact quad loop transmission line attachment (reprinted with permission of the American Radio Relay League).

The ZS6AAA four-band compact quad loop.

tinuous 140ft length of wire. The configuration is reported to provide an acceptable SWR of 5:1 or less on all four bands, with good low-angle radiation. The loop can be square or more conveniently diamond shaped, though not too squashed. For the open-wire stub ZS6AAA uses 8in spreaders with the wire spaced about 6.75in apart.

DELTA LOOPS

For home-made wire antennas, the delta loop is probably more popular than the square or diamond-shaped quad loop. One reason for this is that only one high support is required for it in the the 'apex up' configuration.

A delta loop is a closed-loop antenna and it contains one wavelength of wire. It has several features which are common to the quad loop. A delta loop is normally arranged in the form of an equilateral triangle, having either one side at the top or at the base.

Delta loops are popular for use on the low bands (1.8, 3.5 and 7MHz) because they are easier to set up mechanically than a quad loop, and this is particularly

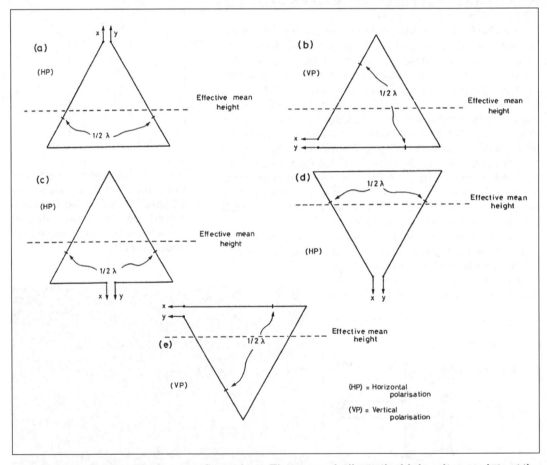

Fig 6.5: Five different delta loop configurations. The arrows indicate the high-voltage points at the ends of each half-wave. Versions (d) and (e) provide the best effective height above ground for a given mast height. The two vertically polarised versions shown in (b) and (e) are the best for long-distance work, for they both have their maximum radiation at low angles to the horizon. Types (a) and (c) have high-angle radiation (80°) and would be more suitable for short-distance communications. The delta loop at (d) has a radiation angle of about 47° and will normally have a first-skip range of about 400 miles (650km).

important at these frequencies in view of their size. However, they have a smaller internal area than a quad, which reduces slightly their comparative gain.

There are five basic arrangements for the orientation and feeding of delta loops. These are shown in **Fig 6.5**. Types (a), (c) and (d) will give horizontal polarisation and (b) and (e) will have vertical polarisation. The half-wave ends (i.e. the points of high voltage and impedance) are indicated in each of the five arrangements.

The geometry of a delta loop, which may be used with either a horizontal side at its top or its base, determines the effective mean height of the antenna. This effective height is greatest when one of the delta sides is positioned at the top. When one side is at the top, the effective height is the height from ground to the highest point of the antenna minus a 12th of a wavelength. When one side is at the base, the effective height is the height from ground to the highest point minus a quarter-wavelength.

The total conductor length in a delta loop is the same as an equivalent quad loop at the same frequency, i.e. 306.3 / f (MHz) metres or 1005 / f (MHz) feet . Like a quad loop, the maximum radiation from a delta loop is at right angles on both sides of the plane of the loop. Its feed impedance will range from about 70Ω in the case of an equilateral delta loop to more than 100Ω when the antenna is flattened somewhat. Another similarity to a quad is the delta's pair of radiation nulls in the plane of the antenna.

Performance

The performance of quad and delta loop antennas is largely determined by their height above ground. Each of these antennas has an 'effective mean height', and this equates with the height of a half-wave dipole above ground when it is cut for the same band. In the case of a quad antenna the effective mean height will be at a point half way up its vertical wires. For long-distance communications a half-wave dipole should ideally be at least a half wavelength above ground and this distance will still apply when considering the effective mean heights of loops.

The radiation angles of delta loops are also greatly influenced by their physical arrangement and the positions of their feedpoints. Only two of the five delta loops illustrated in Fig 6.5 are really useful for DX working. Type (b) has its maximum radiation at 27° and type (e) has an angle of only 20°. Both of these loop types are vertically polarised.

The horizontally-polarised versions shown at (a), (c) and (d), however, have radiation angles to the horizon of 80°, 80° and 47° respectively. This means that types (a) and (c) are really most useful for short-range communications only. Type (d) will have a 'first skip' range of about 650km (400 miles), whereas the two vertically-polarised delta loops (b) and (e) will have first skip ranges of 950km (about 600 miles) and 1500km (almost 1000 miles) respectively.

Unfortunately, type (e) - which is the best for DX work - needs two supports and it also has an inconveniently positioned feedpoint. Type (b), which only requires a single support and has its feed at one lower corner, is probably the best configuration for ease of construction when a large delta loop is contemplated for use on one of the low bands.

Practical delta loops

Two of the several ways to set up a delta-loop antenna are given in **Fig 6.6**, with both of these being 14MHz designs. The example shown in (a) has a mean effective height of almost a half-wavelength, and is arranged to provide low-angle radiation. The rather awkward position of the feedpoint is overcome when it is placed not too distant from the house. The feeder should *not* drop down vertically when using this arrangement or it will unbalance the system and detune the antenna.

In Fig 6.6(b) a single 10m (33ft) support pole is all that is needed. The lower ends of the delta are held in position by nylon cords. In this antenna arrangement the

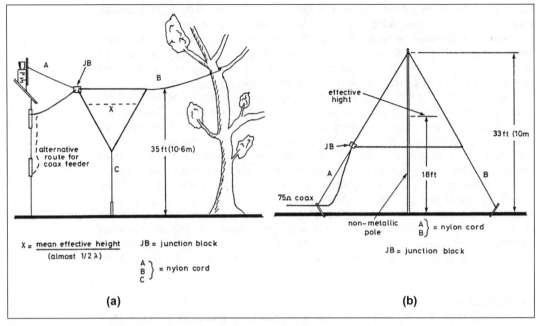

Fig 6.6: (a) A practical delta-loop antenna for 14MHz based upon the type shown in Fig 6.5(e). It is suspended from two supports. Its radiation angle is only 20°. (b) This version uses a single support mast and is the arrangement shown in Fig 6.5(b). Its effective height is, however, only 18ft (5.5m) whereas the antenna shown in (a) has an effective height of almost a half-wavelength.

feeder can safely drop down and run along at ground level or be buried. Conventional insulators are not required as the voltages at the corner angles of delta-loop antennas are not high. Nylon or Terylene cords are fine as both insulators and supports. The junction blocks are also located at points of low RF potential and as a result they can be made from almost any insulating material that will shed moisture.

A variation of the antenna shown in (b), which can be used when the physical size of the loop and its support are very large at the lower frequencies (7 or 3.5MHz), is one where the two upper sides of the loop come down from the centre support at

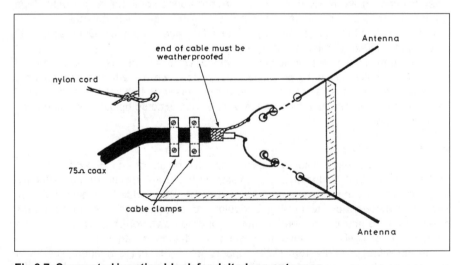

Fig 6.7: Suggested junction block for delta-loop antennas.

an angle of about 45°. This will allow the use of a shorter support mast and on 7MHz a mast height of about 15m (50ft) will suffice.

Trees can also be employed as delta loop supports, and some amateurs have had fine operating results when the complete loop was positioned actually inside the branch system of large trees. Such antennas virtually disappear through the summer months and fortunately the leaf growth does not seem to affect their performance to any great degree.

Fig 6.7 illustrates a suitable junction or connection block for delta loop antennas. Almost any insulating material which is weatherproofed will do for this - the actual end of the coaxial feeder cable and the soldered connections must also be thoroughly weatherproofed. The use of 75Ω coaxial feeder is not essential, and, like many other antennas so far described, a tuned feedline can be employed.

COLLINEAR DELTA LOOPS
The 'base up' (upside down) delta loop configuration shown in Fig 6.5(e), with its low angle of radiation of 20°, lends itself well to being used in an interesting antenna design. Two such delta loops can easily be phased together to give a couple of decibels gain over a single loop (and thus even more gain over a dipole). The antenna is shown in **Fig 6.8**.

A 'base up' delta loop can be constructed by having the top wire taut and allowing the other two 'sides' simply to hang down beneath it in a 'U' shape instead of the usual 'V' shape of the delta loop. (In fact, this is a slightly more efficient shape than the standard 'V' shaped delta loop, though the difference in actual performance is so small it probably cannot be measured.)

A second identical 'base up' delta loop is then placed next to the first, so that their two 'corners' are almost touching, and the two are fed together in phase. In practice, instead of making two identical antennas, one single length of wire 2λ long can be used. Suggested wire lengths for several HF bands are given in **Table 6.2**, although the antenna will probably need to be trimmed to length *in situ*. The impedance is close to 50Ω and the SWR at resonance should be around 1.5:1 or better.

The top wire should ideally be horizontal but it may also be sloping if you only have one tall support and if that support is high enough to allow the lower of the two 'U' shapes to hang below the sloping wire and still have a reasonable clearance above the ground – at least 2.0m (6ft 6in) is suggested.

One of your editors, 9M6DXX, used this antenna in its sloping configuration while on a work assignment in the 1990s in Papua New Guinea, from where he was active as P29DX. A 40m version was built, with the high end attached at the top of a profes-

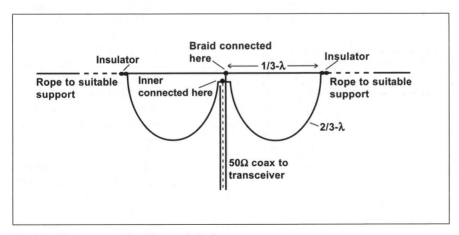

Fig 6.8: Close-spaced collinear delta loops.

Freq.	1/3-λ (half-top length)		Length of 'U' section		Total wire length	
7100	14.38m	47ft 3in	28.76m	94ft 4in	86.28m	283ft 1in
10125	10.08m	33ft 1in	20.17m	66ft 2in	60.51m	198ft 6in
14200	7.19m	23ft 7in	14.38m	47ft 2in	43.14m	141ft 7in
18140	5.63m	18ft 6in	11.25m	36ft 11in	33.77m	110ft 9in
21270	4.80m	15ft 9in	9.60m	31ft 6in	28.80m	94ft 6in
24940	4.09m	13ft 5in	8.19m	26ft 10in	24.56m	80ft 7in
28300	3.61m	11ft 10in	7.21m	23ft 8in	21.64m	71ft 0in

Table 6.2: Approximate wire lengths for collinear delta loops.

sional lattice tower about 120ft high. The far end was tied off to a distant tree with a long rope and the whole antenna system sloped from about 110ft down to about 70ft. Any antenna that high should work quite well, but it was compared with a 40m sloping dipole with the top also at 110ft, and the collinear delta loops regularly provided nearly one S-point of gain in their favoured directions (broadside to the antenna).

HORIZONTAL LOOPS

The horizontal loop is a simple multiband antenna that is easy to make and erect, works on all bands, gives a good DX performance on the HF bands and excellent local coverage on the lower bands.

Fig 6.9 shows a typical full-wave horizontal loop antenna (known in the US as a 'Sky Loop' or a 'Loop Skywire'). The loop shape can be modified from, say, square or rectangular to whatever fits in your plot.

The horizontal loop should be at least one full wavelength long on the lowest frequency of operation, but precise dimensions are not critical. It is fed with open wire 'ladder line' or ribbon feeder: once again the precise impedance is not critical as the antenna must be matched with an ATU.

On the lowest frequency of operation, where the loop is a full wavelength, its maximum radiation is straight upwards. It is therefore a very effective NVIS (Near-Vertical Incidence Skywave) antenna, ideal for local communications on 80, 60 or 40m.

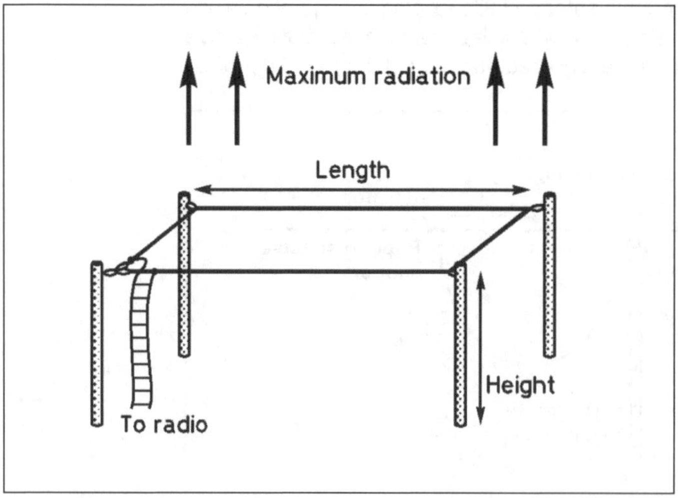

However, on higher-frequency bands, the horizontal loop can produce some very useful gain at low angles. Fig 6.10 shows the azimuth-plane responses at a 10° elevation angle of a 7MHz (142ft long) horizontal loop antenna at 40ft above ground. It is compared with half-wave dipoles at 30ft above ground on 40m, 20m and 15m respectively.

It will be seen that at 7MHz the loop shows some loss compared with the dipole. At

Fig 6.9: The full-wave horizontal loop: a great 'cloud-warmer' antenna.

Right: Fig 6.10. Azimuth-plane responses at 10° elevation of a 7MHz (142ft long) 'Loop Skywire' (horizontal loop) compared with: (a) a 40m half-wave dipole at 7200kHz, (b) a 20m half-wave dipole at 14200kHz, (c) a 15m half-wave dipole at 21200kHz. (Reprinted with permission of the American Radio Relay League).

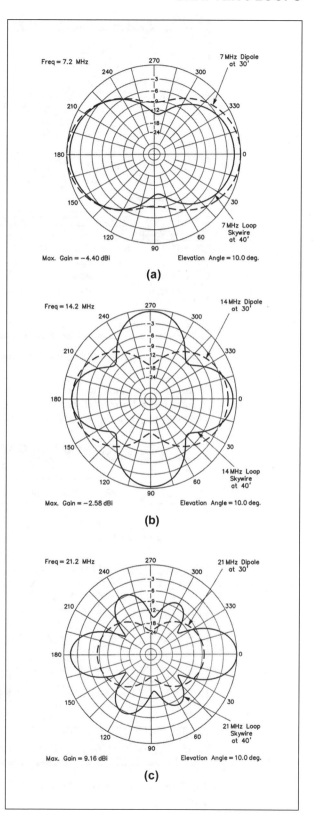

(a)

(b)

(c)

14MHz the loop has some advantage in certain directions, whereas at 21MHz the horizontal loop has more gain in almost all directions than a half-wave dipole.

G3MGW HORIZONTAL LOOP

Roger Wheeler, G3MGW, wrote about horizontal loop antennas in the May 2009 *RadCom*, describing them as the "best kept secret in amateur radio"!

Fig 6.11 shows a typical square loop, but the shape can be modified from, say, square or rectangular to whatever fits in your plot. G3MGW's loop is triangular, i.e. it is a horizontal delta loop. Horizontal loops do not even need to have *all* parts in the horizontal plane: several stations use what they call a 'Hori Ver', i.e. parts are horizontal whilst other parts slope up or down.

A useful feature is that the horizontal loop will work well even at moderate heights such as 25ft above ground - a doublet might not work so well at this height.

G3MGW used the free *MMANA* (Method of Moments ANAlysis) program

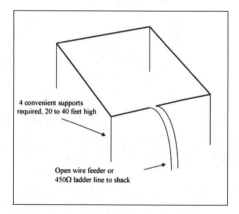

Fig 6.11: General form of a square horizontal loop antenna. The loop should be at least one wavelength long at the lowest frequency of operation.

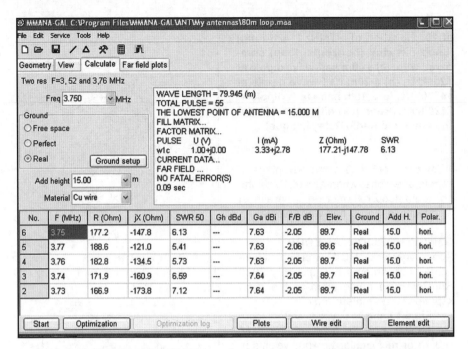

Fig 6.12: Results of horizontal loop analysis across some 80m frequencies.

(*MMANA* is available to download from http://mmhamsoft.ca) to analyse an 80m full-wave square horizontal loop, 15m above 'real' ground (other types of gorund are available to use). **Fig 6.12** shows the results of the analysis on 80m. The antenna

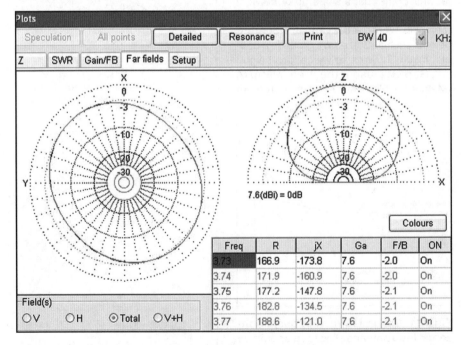

Fig 6.13: Far field plots of horizontal loop on 80m - left: horizontal, right: vertical plane.

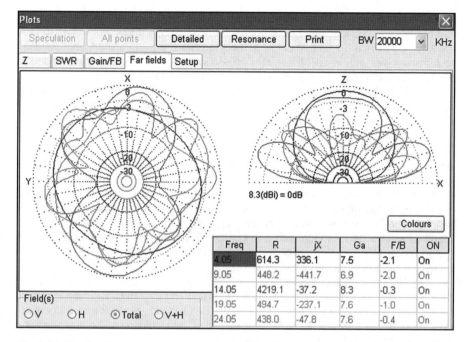

Fig 6.14: Far field plots and data for same horizontal loop at around 4, 9, 14, 19 and 24MHz.

impedance, at the antenna feedpoint, is a reasonably low resistance and has a capacitive reactance. Changing the leg lengths would alter both: increasing the overall length will make it resonant within the 80m band. Note the gain, 7.63dBi, which is perhaps a little more than a half-wave dipole at this height above ground. The azimuth and elevation far field plots are shown in **Fig 6.13**. Again, note the similarity to a half-wave dipole, although the loop is rather more omnidirectional, predominantly firing straight up.

The reason this antenna is rather special, though, is shown in **Fig 6.14**. Here, we are analysing the same 80m loop over a range of frequencies from 4 to 24MHz. The table of results shows that the resistance, R, and the reactance, jX, elements of the feedpoint impedance change with frequency. However, note that they are never very large, nor very small values, and this means that they are well within the range of most antenna tuners. Moreover, looking at the elevation plots on the right, as we go higher in frequency we get a lower radiation angle, e.g. at 14.05MHz the radiation angle is 20°, and the gain is also greater than a half-wave dipole. Both of these facts are very good for DX working. Both plots show that the responses break down into small lobes just as a dipole does.

G3MGW's horizontally-mounted delta loop is configured as an equilateral triangle with sides of 100ft and at a height of about 25ft. Analysis of his antenna shows only a slightly lower vertical gain, down a couple of dB, but with fewer lower angle side lobes. The fact that this antenna is relatively insensitive to having its shape moulded to fit the environment is a real advantage for a restricted plot.

G3MGW's antenna was constructed with multi-strand copper cable obtained from a rally, but almost any antenna wire would suffice. At each support point, he passed the antenna cable through one hole in a 'dog bone' insulator. He tied a rope to the other hole, which then went to a pulley mounted on a support mast.

Experience of finding antennas lying unexpectedly on the ground taught G3MGW to use multistrand wire for antennas rather than single strand as it survives coastal winds so much better. For the same reason, he used 450Ω ladder line with stranded, rather than solid conductors. About 40ft of line and an MFJ tuner were used to feed the loop. Open wire feeder to a balun, at the shack end, fed with a short length of coax to a transceiver with in-built tuner should also work well. It is not recommended to feed the loop directly with coax as the feeder loss could be high.

G3MGW reports excellent results working Europe and the UK on 80m. Similar results apply on 40m to Europe. On the higher bands the antenna is about 3 to 4 S-points down on his main antenna, a 2-element cubical quad, as one might expect.

THE 'LAZY QUAD'

Although it is superficially similar to a quad antenna in that it is a full-wave loop, the 'Lazy Quad' is in fact a close relative of the Kraus, W8JK, beam. Unlike a quad it is held in a *horizontal* plane and **Fig 6.15** shows a *plan* view of the antenna. The centre of the loop is broken by an insulator so it therefore becomes two half-waves, each of which is end-fed. The feed impedance is very high, typically about 9000Ω, and as a result a low-impedance feeder cannot be connected directly to it. The antenna has its maximum radiation in two directions and is horizontally polarised. The gain over a half-wave dipole at the same height is 4dB.

The length of each half-wave element in this antenna (i.e. half the length of the perimeter) is 7.03m (23ft 8in) when cut for operation on 21.2MHz. Dimensions for all bands from 10 to 40m are given in **Table 6.3**. The insulation at the four corners is not very important as they are not high voltage points. The insulation at the feedpoint and also at the other ends of the half-waves must be good.

A 'lazy quad' for use on 10m has sides that are only 2.63m (8ft 7in) long, and a rotatable version using fibreglass spreaders would be sufficiently compact for many locations. Even on 21MHz the diagonal spreaders could be made with four 2.6m (8ft 6in) lengths of fibreglass tubing.

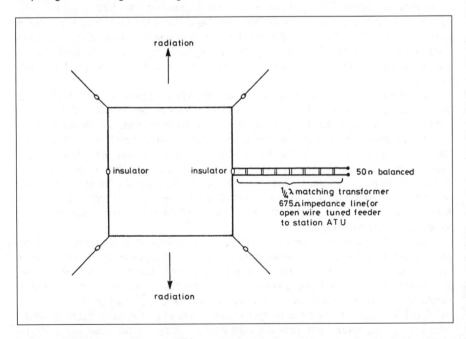

Fig 6.15: The 'lazy quad', which is a 'split' full-wave loop arranged to lie horizontally. Its very high feed impedance makes matching to a 50Ω feeder difficult: open-wire tuned feeder can be used instead of the quarter-wave matching transformer shown.

Freq (kHz)	Length of each λ/2 wire metres	feet	λ/4 matching stub (675Ω) metres	feet
28300	5.26	17ft 3in	2.55	8ft 4in
24940	5.97	19ft 7in	2.90	9ft 6in
21200	7.03	23ft 1in	3.42	11ft 3in
18120	8.22	27ft 0in	3.99	13ft 1in
14150	10.53	34ft 7in	5.11	16ft 9in
10125	14.72	48ft 4in	7.14	23ft 5in
7100	20.99	68ft 10in	10.18	33ft 5in

Table 6.3: Dimensions for 'lazy quad' half wavelength wires (half perimeter) and quarter-wave 675Ω open-wire line matching transformers.

The ideal method of feeding the 'lazy quad' uses a quarter-wavelength long matching transformer, as described in the chapter on antenna matching (see Chapter 8). As the 'lazy quad' has a feed impedance of about 9000Ω, the matching transformer should be made from 675Ω impedance open-wire line, and it will provide a 50Ω balanced output impedance. At this point a 1:1 balun must be used which will allow the connection of any length of standard 50Ω coaxial cable.

For operation on 21.1MHz the length of such a quarter-wave matching transformer will be 3.42m (11ft 3in). A 675Ω impedance line is easily made using 18SWG wire with a spacing of 180mm (7in).

One way to tune the antenna is to use a dip meter. A shorting bar made with two crocodile clips is connected across the end of the 675Ω matching section and coupled to the shorting bar to measure the resonant frequency of the antenna. By moving the crocodile clips along the line, a point will be found which indicates resonance at the required frequency; the unwanted wires can then be cut and removed. If open-wire or ribbon feeder is used as a tuned line to feed this antenna there is no need to tune the antenna to resonance as any discrepancy will be taken up within the feeder system.

The SWR should be better than 1.5:1 over a bandwidth of 400kHz centred on the design frequency of 21.2MHz. This bandwidth will be greater for antennas centred on 29MHz.

THE BI-SQUARE ANTENNA

The bi-square antenna is a two-wavelength broken loop that is set up in the vertical plane. Dimensions for the five bands from 10 to 20m are given in **Table 6.4**. It has gain in two directions at right angles to the plane of the loop (broadside) of about 4dB over a half-wave dipole and it only needs a single support. This needs to be 11m

Freq (kHz)	Total wire length (metres)	(feet)	λ/4 matching transformer (300Ω) (metres)	(feet)
28300	20.71	67ft 11in	2.28	7ft 6in
24940	23.50	78ft 0in	2.59	8ft 6in
21200	27.64	90ft 8in	3.04	10ft 0in
18120	32.34	106ft 1in	3.56	11ft 8in
14150	41.41	135ft 10in	4.56	15ft 0in

Table 6.4: Dimensions for bi-square antenna and quarter-wave 300Ω ribbon matching transformers.

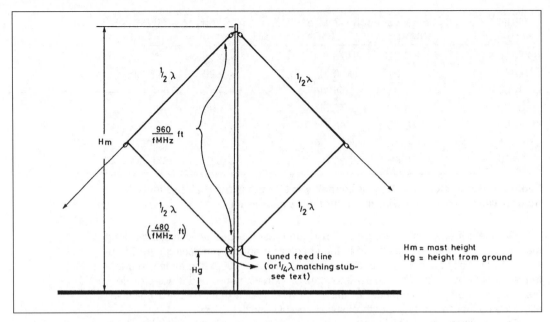

Fig 6.16: The bi-square antenna provides useful gain. It is a broadside two-wavelength loop set up in the vertical plane.

(36ft) high for an antenna designed for 21MHz and only 8.6m (28ft) high for a 28MHz version.

The basic arrangement is shown in **Fig 6.16** above. The total loop wire length is 2 x 960 / f (MHz) feet or 2 x 293 / f (MHz) metres, and the antenna is set up in the form of a diamond.

Fig 6.17 shows that each side of the bi-square has equal horizontal and vertical radiation components. The latter cancel and leave four horizontal sources which are in phase. This means that the antenna is horizontally polarised at the design frequency, but when it is used at half the design frequency there is end-fire directivity and vertical polarisation. At half-frequency the gain is reduced to about 2dBd and the antenna will not have its normal 1000Ω feed impedance. To get the best results this antenna must be at least a metre (3ft) above ground and preferably from 3 to 3.5m (10 to 12ft) above electrical ground.

The bi-square is best fed with a tuned line, but for single band operation a quarter-wave matching transformer can be employed. If a length of 300Ω ribbon feeder is used as the stub or matching section the impedance will be transformed to the region of 80Ω to 90Ω and a reasonable match to 75Ω coax will be achieved. A 1:1 balun should be connected between the quarter-wave transformer and the 75Ω coax.

A 21.2MHz bi-square has two sides of equal length, each

Horizontal radiation components, a,b,c, d(add)
Vertical radiation components e,f,g,h(cancel)

Left: Fig 6.17. The instantaneous current distribution along a bi-square antenna. The horizontal radiation components add and the vertical components cancel. Radiation is therefore horizontally polarised and is in two directions, i.e. looking through the loop.

one being 13.78m (45ft 3in) long. If slotted 300Ω ribbon with a velocity factor of 0.88 is used to make up the matching transformer, it will be 3.04m (10ft) long.

As a final note it is necessary to remember that good insulation is needed at all the four corners of a bi-square because these points carry high voltages and represent a high impedance.

MFJ WIRE LOOP TUNERS

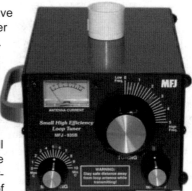

All the loop antennas described so far in this chapter have been *large loops. Small loops* are generally built of copper tuning and are therefore not within the scope of this book. The US company MFJ, however, has developed a series of ATUs designed specifically to tune indoor *wire* magnetic loops. The increased losses introduced by using wire instead of copper tubing can be decreased somewhat by making the wire loop larger than would typically be the case with a rigid copper loop for the same frequency band. MFJ recommends the use of 4mm wire, but the tuners will also work with somewhat thinner wire. The units will tune loops of approximately one-sixth of a wavelength to one-quarter of a wavelength long. The coverage of any one length of loop is about 0.75 of an octave, so different size loops must be used to cover the various bands. The units can operate from 80 to 10m, depending on the length of the wire loop used, and they are rated at 150W.

The present models (2011 / 2012) are the MFJ-933, which contains the ATU tuning mechanism only, the MFJ-935B which has an added antenna current meter, and the MFJ-936B which further adds an SWR bridge and power meter.

The circuit of the MFJ-935B is shown in **Fig 6.18**. VC1 adjusts the coupling from the transmitter to the loop and VC2 tunes it. VC2 is a butterfly capacitor with the centre grounded, so there is no voltage on the shaft. One of the output connections passes through a toroidal pickup coil, L1, which senses the current flowing in the loop. This is rectified and fed to a moving coil meter via a potentiometer, which indicates the relative value of that current.

A plastic socket is fitted to the top of the unit, on to which PVC 'spreaders' can be fitted and used to support wire loops for the 20, 17 and 15m, or the 17, 15, 12 and 10m bands. For best performance the loops should be configured to contain the largest symmetrical inside area. A circle is optimum and a square comes next. As the loop is distorted into a rectangle, so the efficiency drops. The PVC spreaders, which are an optional extra from MFJ (or you can easily make

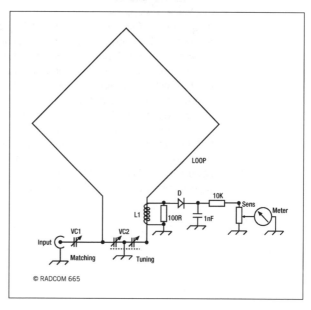

Fig 6.18. Circuit diagram of the MFJ-935B wire loop tuner.

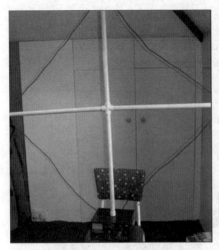 

Left: Although many signals could be heard on the higher bands, this arrangement was not particularly successful with the loop in the middle of an upstairs room. **Right:** Wrapping a 26ft long wire around the window frame produced good results on 40 and 20m, with signals only 1 - 2 S-units down on well-sited outdoor half-wave dipoles.

your own), allow the loops to be made into a proper square.

When tested independently it was found that the location of the loop within the room was important. Initial trials with the loops located in the middle of a room proved disappointing. They were successful when the antenna wire was placed around a window frame, suggesting that the performance might be better still when used outdoors. On both 40m and 20m, good contacts were made easily during the day on SSB using power levels from 10W to 50W. Using a 26ft length of wire around a window frame signals were generally 1 - 2 S-points down on full-size outdoor half-wave dipoles - see photos.

Many amateurs do not have the space to put up outdoor antennas, particularly for the lower frequency bands, where a dipole for 40m is around 65ft long. Even the ubiquitous half-size G5RV is over 50ft long. Flat-dwellers may not be able to put up *any* external antenna at all. The MFJ wire loop tuners allow such people to get on the air and radiate a signal that can be within a couple of S-points of a well-sited outdoor dipole. Frequent travellers who often stay in hotels will also find a use for these units, as they will allow amateur radio operation to take place from locations that might otherwise have seemed to be impossible.

Safety note: MFJ quite correctly points out that high voltages and high currents exist on the wire loop while transmitting. Therefore, it is important that no-one is able to touch the loop when you are transmitting. A second precaution is associated with the field strength that exists near short loop transmitting antennas. It is imperative to keep a safe distance - MFJ suggests a minimum distance of 2 metres for all bands when operating at 100W, but a greater distance would be safer still.

7 End-fed wires

A SINGLE LENGTH OF WIRE fed from one end is perhaps the simplest antenna type available to the radio amateur. In their simplest terms the longest piece of wire that can be strung up as high as possible usually produces some reasonable results. An ATU can then be used to ensure a good match to either the feeder or the transmitter or receiver that is to be used. However, like most things in this world, all is not quite as simple as it first seems, and this presents some interesting points and challenges to the would-be end-fed wire user.

One of the major points when using an end-fed wire is that the wire radiates as soon as it leaves the ATU. This means that high levels of RF may exist in the vicinity of the radio shack. This has disadvantages from two viewpoints. The first is that there is a growing awareness of the possible dangers of radio frequency radiation from a health standpoint. Secondly, high levels of RF can give rise to feedback if the radiation is picked up by power leads, microphone leads and the like.

As such it is best to adopt one of a number of strategies. It may be that the ended wire is only needed for receiving, or for low power transmissions. Otherwise it may be possible to have a remote ATU which is fed from the shack by coax. In this way it is possible to remove the regions of the antenna carrying the high levels of RF away from inhabited areas, thereby avoiding health risks and much reducing the possibilities of EMC problems.

WIRE LENGTH AND IMPEDANCE

The impedance of the wire is of particular importance because ultimately a good match will need to be presented to the transmitting and receiving equipment. It is possible to look at what the impedance of a random length of wire might present at its feedpoint. All wires display a high impedance at their far ends at any frequency. This fact makes it a simple matter to work forwards along the wires in half-wavelengths or quarter-wavelengths to determine the approximate impedance at the feedpoint. A quarter-wavelength back from the remote open end will have a low impedance, and a half-wavelength back will have a high impedance.

Some impedances are difficult to match with an ATU, particularly those which are very high or low, so it is prudent to arrange that such conditions are not present at the ATU end of an end-fed wire. Lengths of wire which are close to odd multiples of a quarter-wavelength (or just less than this) are particularly bad, and the latter lengths will display a capacitive reactance which needs to be tuned out. When a long end-fed wire is used as a multi-band antenna it is almost impossible to determine a length which will avoid some reactance on one or more bands, but this reactance can be quite easily tuned out by using either an inductor (for capacitive reactances) or a capacitor (for inductive reactances) between the wire end and the ATU.

PRACTICAL END-FED WIRES

Two physical arrangements for end-fed wire antennas are shown in **Fig 7.1**. The wire in Fig 7.1(a) is virtually horizontal along its length, and will show little if any radiation which is vertically polarised. Also, being relatively high, there will be challenges in

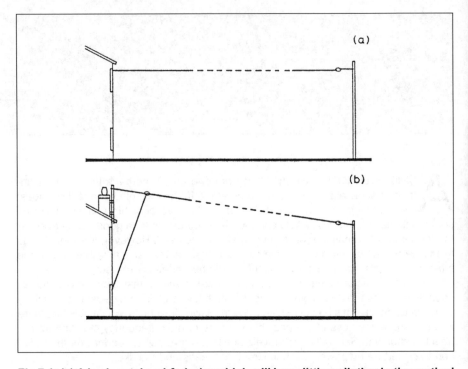

Fig 7.1: (a) A horizontal end-fed wire which will have little radiation in the vertical plane. On its harmonic frequencies there will be pronounced nulls at right angles to the wire. (b) A similar wire but the sloping section will allow some vertically polarised radiation and tend to spoil the expected radiation pattern of an end-fed wire operating on its harmonic frequencies. The nulls at right angles to the wire will not be so pronounced.

ensuring a good earth arrangement, as discussed later.

In Fig 7.1(b) the wire slopes up from a downstairs window to a high point and then runs down at a small angle to the end support. If the near-vertical part of such an antenna is just a small proportion (say, 1/10) of the main top length, it will have little effect upon performance, although there must be some vertically polarised radiation from the descending 'feed' wire. This vertically polarised section will fill in the nulls in the radiation pattern but additionally may produce some TVI or other EMC problems. The gradually sloping top will lower the angle of radiation towards the far end of the antenna and most of the radiation will also be in that direction.

End-fed wires which are 9 to 12m (30 to 40ft) above ground will be very effective on 14MHz and the other bands higher than this frequency. Their DX performance on the higher bands will not, however, be matched on lower bands such as 7 and 3.5MHz. Here, they will have much higher angles of radiation and will therefore be more suited for medium distance and short-haul communications.

USING COUNTERPOISE WIRES

Counterpoises and RF earths were discussed in Chapter 1. However, because end-fed wires need to be operated with a good ground system, we return to the subject here. In an ideal world a 'good ground system' would mean using a very short earth wire to a particularly good earth. This may not be a viable option in many instances, leading to even higher levels of RF in the vicinity of the station (which end-fed wires are prone to in any case), with all the attendant problems that suggests.

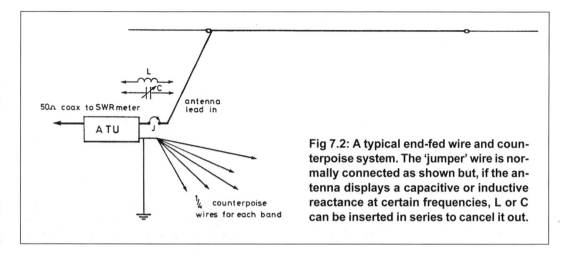

Fig 7.2: A typical end-fed wire and counterpoise system. The 'jumper' wire is normally connected as shown but, if the antenna displays a capacitive or inductive reactance at certain frequencies, L or C can be inserted in series to cancel it out.

An upstairs shack can be particularly bedevilled by earthing problems, for often the run of the earth wire, even when made with heavy-gauge wire or flat strip, has a considerable inductance and will be long in terms of wavelength on the higher-frequency bands. When used for transmitting this could give rise to "hot' equipment, a nasty phenomenon where supposedly earthed metal cases can give the operator an unpleasant RF burn when touched during transmission.

A method for reducing these effects is by using counterpoise wires connected to the ATU, although RF levels could still remain high. The arrangement shown in **Fig 7.2** is adequate for many situations (low power and receiving) and it includes an inductance L (with tap points) and a variable capacitor C, either of which may be used in series with the antenna wire to remove unwanted reactance at the feed point end of the wire. The jumper (J) will be used on those bands where reactance does not present a problem.

Reactance problems are usually revealed when it seems almost impossible to bring down the SWR between the ATU and the equipment to a sensible figure. It also may show as very 'sharp' tuning of the ATU. (A 'sensible' SWR reading means one which is something between unity and 1.5:1.)

The counterpoise wires are cut to a quarter-wavelength for each band, and are best made with PVC covered multi-strand flexible wires. Such counterpoise wires will have a considerable RF voltage at their ends when the band they are cut for is in use and if the output power is in excess of 50 watts or so it is suggested that wires, and particularly their ends, are well insulated.

THE W3EDP ANTENNA

The W3EDP antenna is a simple yet effective multi-band design that has been around for many years. It uses a 25.9m (85ft) wire with a 5.1m (17ft) counterpoise connected when used on some bands. The antenna wire may be bent to suit typical suburban locations without any marked degradation in performance.

The W3EDP antenna is shown in **Fig 7.3** and can be thought of as an end-fed Zepp with a 20.7m (68ft) top and a 5.2m (17ft) feedline. The feeder is rather unusual in that the wires which make it up need not be parallel: the counterpoise (half the feeder line) can be run outside in any direction.

On 3.5MHz the counterpoise is not connected and the antenna behaves as an end-fed wire about 5.8m (19ft) longer than an electrical quarter-wave. An advantage here is that the point of maximum radiation (the high current point) is almost 6m (20ft) along the wire. This additional length from the basic quarter-wave also en-

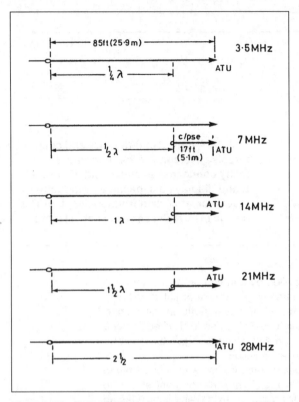

Fig 7.3: The 85ft W3EDP single-wire antenna will behave rather like an end-fed Zepp on 7, 14 and 21MHz. The counterpoise wire, although not positioned close to the antenna, will nevertheless act like one wire of an open-wire Zepp feed system.

sures that the impedance at the lower feedpoint end is not too low, so there will be easier matching to the ATU with some inductive reactance which can easily be tuned out.

For operation on 7MHz the counterpoise is connected and the antenna becomes a half-wave with a wide spaced 'feeder' which is about an eighth of a wavelength long. At the feedpoint the impedance will not be very high, but nor will it show the very low impedance (approximately 36Ω) that is present a quarter of a wavelength from the end of a half-wavelength top. Instead there is a medium impedance which can be matched without difficulty.

On 14MHz the antenna wire is within a few centimetres of being a resonant full-wavelength for this band, and the 'feeder' is just 15cm longer than an electrical quarter-wavelength. The impedance at the ATU end is low, but not so low as it might be were the 'feeder' an exact quarter-wavelength.

On 21MHz the antenna wire now becomes almost 1.5λ long. The high impedance at the shack end of this 1.5λ section connects to the final 5.6m (17ft) which then becomes a part of the feeder which is about 3/8-λ long. This length presents a medium impedance at the feedpoint and again is easy to match.

The counterpoise is not required when the antenna is used on 28MHz, so the antenna then behaves as a 2.5-λ end-fed wire. This band is one where there may be matching problems, for the feed end of 2.5-λ wire is at quite a high impedance. The introduction of a series capacitor between the antenna and the ATU might help to reduce matching problems, as it will electrically shorten the antenna.

The W3EDP is perhaps one of the simplest and cheapest of all multi-band antennas, being simple and inexpensive to construct and then easy to install. As a result it is a favourite with some of the QRP fraternity, and with just a few watts it is easy to obtain contacts over reasonable distances on all the bands on which it will operate.

LONG WIRE ANTENNAS

The definition of a 'long' wire is one that is a wavelength or more long at the frequency of operation. So a wire that is 140ft long would not be considered a true 'long wire' on 1.8 or 3.5MHz, but it would on 7MHz and on all the other HF bands. A wire shorter than one wavelength long is more properly referred to as simply an 'end-fed' wire, or sometimes a 'random' wire.

True end-fed long wires exhibit some interesting directional radiation patterns. A single wire antenna which is two half-wavelengths or more long will have alternate half-wavelengths out of phase. When wires are very long in terms of wavelength, the half-wavelengths along their length will also have different amplitudes of current,

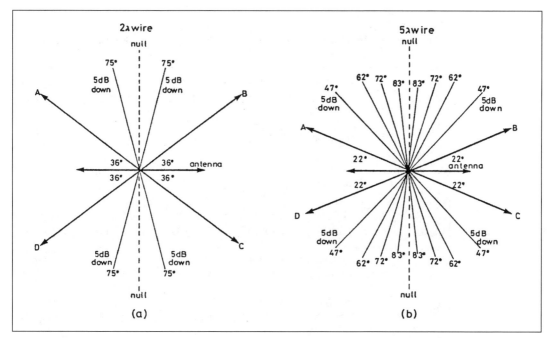

Fig 7.4: (a) The expected horizontal radiation pattern of a wire that is two wavelengths long. (b) A five-wavelength wire has its four main lobes closer to the line of the wire and has more minor radiation lobes.

these currents diminishing along the wire.

Long wires produce quite complex multi-lobe radiation patterns, unlike the simple radiation lobes produced by collinear antenna systems. The longer the wire is made in terms of wavelength the more the main lobes tend to align with the axis of the antenna. The number of minor lobes in other directions also increases as the wire length becomes greater. **Fig 7.4(a)** shows the horizontal radiation pattern for a horizontal wire, two wavelengths long. The four main lobes are marked A, B, C and D, and their effective power is about 5dB greater than the radiation from the four minor lobes. When the wire length is increased to five wavelengths - **Fig 7.4(b)** - there are still four main lobes but these are aligned closer to the line of the antenna wire, each being 22° from this line. There are additionally 16 minor lobes, the weakest of which are almost 10dB down from the main lobes. In both these examples, and with all long-wire antennas, there are deep nulls at right angles to the wire.

If a long-wire antenna is at least half a wavelength above the ground at its lowest frequency, the angles of radiation in the vertical plane will be low, usually between 10° and 15° above the horizon.

A single wire which is five wavelengths long when used on 14MHz will have power gain over a dipole (22° from the line of the long wire) of more than two times (4dBd). The same wire, when used on the 28MHz band, will become 10 wavelengths long and will show a gain of 7.4dBd. The maximum gain will then be in directions closer to the run of wire.

Wires which are 10 or more wavelengths long radiate mostly from their ends and they should therefore be aligned towards the preferred direction. In terms of gain for money spent, a long single wire antenna can have an advantage over a multi-element Yagi beam, but of course cannot be rotated. To achieve world coverage, the long wire enthusiast will need several wires running in different directions to provide the necessary coverage and this may require a very large area - obviously the gain is of no use if it is not aligned in the required direction.

Number of wavelengths long	14.15MHz	18.12MHz	21.2MHz	24.94MHz	28.5MHz
1	20.66m 67' 9"	16.14m 52' 11"	13.79m 45' 3"	11.73m 38' 6"	10.25m 33' 8"
2	41.86m 137' 4"	32.70m 107' 3"	27.90m 91' 8"	23.76m 77' 11"	20.78m 68' 2"
3	63.00m 206' 10"	49.25m 161' 7"	42.00m 138' 0"	35.79m 117' 5"	31.30m 102' 8"
4	84.25m 276' 5"	65.81m 215' 11"	56.20m 184' 6"	47.81m 156' 10"	41.83m 137' 3"
5	105.40m 345' 11"	82.37m 270' 3"	70.37m 230' 11"	59.84m 196' 4"	52.35m 171' 9"
6	126.60m 415' 6"	98.92m 324' 7"	84.50m 277' 4"	71.87m 235' 8"	62.87m 206' 4"
7	147.80m 485' 0"	115.48m 378' 11"	98.67m 323' 9"	83.90m 275' 3"	73.40m 240' 9"
8	169.00m 554' 7"	132.04m 433' 3"	112.80m 370' 2"	95.93m 314' 9"	83.90m 275' 4"

Table 7.1: Resonant lengths for end-fed long wire antennas.

Lengths of long wires

The individual wavelengths away from the ends of a long wire do not join on to insulators, so their calculated lengths do not have to take into consideration the 'end effect' and they will therefore be closer to the theoretical free-space lengths.

The lengths in metres, and feet and inches, of wires up to eight wavelengths long on the five higher-frequency HF bands are given in **Table 7.1**. On other frequencies the lengths can be calculated by using the expression:

$$\text{Length (metres)} = \frac{300 \, (N - 0.025)}{\text{Freq (MHz)}}$$

where N is the number of full wavelengths in the antenna. To calculate the lengths in feet use:

$$\text{Length (feet)} = \frac{984 \, (N - 0.025)}{\text{Freq (MHz)}}$$

A long wire must be at least two wavelengths long to show noticeable gain over a half-wave dipole (about 1.3dBd), and until it is four wavelengths long its gain remains small. It is only when eight or more wavelengths are used that the power gain becomes really significant, e.g. 6.3dBd for eight wavelengths.

Wave-lengths	Angle (°)	Gain (dBd)
1	54	0.5
1.5	42	0.9
2	36	1.3
2.5	33	1.8
3	30	2.2
4	26	3.0
5	22	4.0
6	20	4.8
7	19	5.5
8	18	6.3
9	17	6.9
10	16	7.5

Table 7.2: Gain of a long wire relative to a half-wave dipole.

The angles (from the run of the antenna wire) at which radiation is at a maximum for different antenna lengths, together with the expected gain, are given in **Table 7.2**. In practice it will be found that the radiation from the end of the antenna which is farthest from the feedpoint is greater than that from the feed end. This is because the radiation lobes towards the far end are due to the forward-going wave along the wire, whereas from the feed end the radiation can only be due to the wave that is reflected from the far end. Loss by radiation, together with any resistive losses, will make the returning and reflected wave weaker than the forward-going one. It is therefore best to direct long-wire antennas *towards* the preferred direction of radiation or reception.

NON-RESONANT LONG WIRES

The simple end-fed long wire is a resonant antenna and it has standing waves along its length when in operation but, if such a wire is correctly terminated at its far end by the use of a suitable and non-inductive resistor, it becomes non-resonant and additionally unidirectional.

A single horizontal wire can be likened to one half of a two-wire transmission line, when the other wire has been replaced by the ground. The characteristic impedance of such a 'single-wire' transmission line, when using normal wire diameters and at a height of between 6 and 9m (around 20 to 30ft) will lie between 500 and 600Ω.

The radiation away from the far end of a very long single-wire antenna results in a smaller proportion of the radiation being reflected back towards the feedpoint. If a resistor with a value equal to the characteristic impedance of the wire is fitted between the far end of the wire and ground, as shown in **Fig 7.5(a)**, there will be little or no reflected wave. There will be a travelling wave along the wire but no standing waves, and the antenna will be similar to a correctly terminated transmission line - but with one important difference. Because of the very wide spacing between its conductors (the wire and the ground) it will radiate much of the energy applied at the feedpoint. Approximately half of the power will be dissipated by the terminating resistor but this is not too important as the radiation is only needed in one direction.

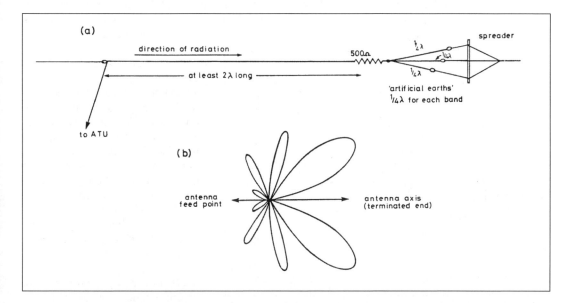

Fig 7.5: (a) A terminated end-fed wire which uses 'artificial' quarter-wave earth wires to terminate the 500Ω non-inductive resistor. This antenna is shown for three-band use. (b) The horizontal radiation pattern of a typical terminated long-wire antenna showing its two main lobes.

The gain of a non-resonant wire is similar to that of a resonant wire of the same length so it needs to be at least two, and preferably more, wavelengths long. The radiation pattern in the horizontal plane is similar to that of a resonant long wire but is modified by the unidirectional characteristic. **Fig 7.5(b)** shows the radiation pattern for a two-wavelength, non-resonant, terminated wire antenna. The angles of maximum radiation relative to the direction of the wire are almost the same as the angles for resonant wires. The antenna feedpoint will show an impedance of about 500Ω and this can be easily matched to 50Ω by using a simple ATU of the L or pi section type.

The most obvious problem when making an antenna of this type is the termination resistor's connection to earth. If the far end of the antenna was dropped to a resistor at ground level, there would then be about 9 to 12m (around 30 to 40ft) of vertical wire which would radiate in all directions and so ruin the unidirectional property of the non-resonant wire. If instead the resistor was left at the top and a wire was then taken down to ground, the wire would most certainly not be 'earthy' at its top end. The resistor would then present a reactive load to the antenna. One way to overcome this problem is shown in Fig 7.5(a) where several quarter-wavelength wires are arranged to behave as 'artificial earths' for each frequency to be used. The resistors used to make up the terminating resistance should be mounted on an insulating block so that the weight and tension of the long wire does not damage them. The terminating resistor must be able to dissipate just under a half of the transmitter power which, assuming a 100W transceiver, will mean about 45W key-down. The duty cycle for CW or SSB mean that a 25 - 30W resistor should suffice.

V-BEAMS

When two end-fed long wires are arranged as a horizontal 'V' and fed out of phase, they make a very effective bidirectional beam antenna that will work on several bands (see **Fig 7.6**).

The feed to the 'V' can be of open-wire tuned line, 300Ω ribbon used as a tuned line, or simply a pair of wires of equal length that come down to the ATU. These wires can be spaced at any distance up to as much as about 2m (6ft) on the lower-frequency bands, and there will be no significant radiation from them, although it is more usual to space the wires by around 15cm.

The apex angle of the 'V' is arranged so that the radiation lobes from each leg of the antenna reinforce each other within the 'V' and the outside lobes will cancel. To get this reinforcement, and therefore the maximum gain, there are certain necessary criteria, the most important being the apex angle, which itself depends upon the number of wavelengths contained in each leg of the antenna. The ideal apex angles for different leg lengths are given in **Table 7.3**.

It will be seen that the apex angle reduces by a small amount as the number of wavelengths increases, and this means that a compromise angle can be used which will provide useful gain over

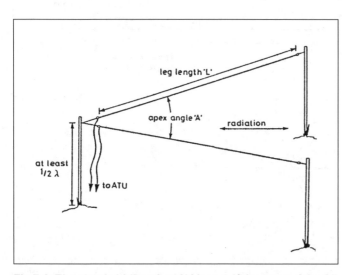

Fig 7.6: The simple bidirectional V-beam. If the apex of the 'V' is not far from the shack, two wires of equal length can be used as a twin-wire feeder. Their spacing is not important.

several bands. A V-beam with five-wavelength legs on 14MHz (about 106.6m or 350ft) will need an apex angle of 44°. This legs of this antenna will each be 7.5-wavelengths long on the 21MHz band and 10-wavelengths long on 28MHz. The optimum apex angles on 21 and 28MHz are 36 and 32° respectively, so a compromise angle of 35° will give an antenna which should work well on three bands. On 14MHz the vertical radiation angles will be raised from the very low angles obtainable when the apex angle is optimum but it will still be at or below 15° above the horizon.

Such an antenna can also be used on the 7 and 3.5MHz bands, although on these bands the gain is reduced and the vertical radiation angles will be higher. This is because the leg lengths are shorter in terms of wavelength and the apex angle is too small.

Leg length (wavelengths)	Apex Angle (degrees °)
2	73
3	58
4	50
5	44
6	40
7	36
8	35

Table 7.3: Apex angles for various V-beam leg lengths.

Gain and performance

The theoretical gain of a simple V-beam antenna which uses the correct apex angle is 3dB greater than the gain of a single wire as long as one leg of the 'V'. This means a gain of 7dBd for a five-wavelength V-beam. However, in practice the gain realised can actually be greater than this figure, because it is modified by the mutual impedance between the wires which make up the 'V', and is as much as an additional 1dB with a five-wavelength antenna. At eight-wavelengths per leg this additional gain will be almost 2dB, making a total gain for such an antenna as much as 11dBd.

Gain of this magnitude is very difficult to achieve with multi-element Yagi beams and represents a power gain of more than 10 times. Even more gain can be achieved by the stacking of two identical V-beams, one above the other, or by using two which are broadside, to form a 'W'. However, such complexities put these varieties outside the scope of this book.

The three supports which hold up the wires of a V-beam should be at least half a wavelength high at the lowest operating frequency. However, if such an antenna with supports at 11 to 12m (around 35 to 40ft), about a half-wavelength on 14MHz, is used on 7 and 3.5MHz, its performance on these bands will be similar to that of any horizontal antenna which is relatively close to the ground, and there will be mostly radiation at high angles.

Although leg lengths in terms of wavelength have been given for the determination of apex angles and antenna gain, the wires can be of any convenient length just as when single long wires are used. It is only important that both legs of the antenna are of equal length.

THE NON-RESONANT V-BEAM

A standard V-antenna, made with a pair of equally long resonant wires, has a bi-directional radiation pattern. However, a V-beam can also be made with two terminated non-resonant wires and such a beam is unidirectional.

If only one support mast is used (at the feed end) the two wires may be sloped down to their terminating resistors at ground level. This greatly simplifies the construction of a V-beam, and it will have a maximum gain midway between the wires and in the direction away from the feedpoint.

The non-resonant V-beam is shown in **Fig 7.7**, where the leg lengths L must be a minimum of one wavelength long at its lowest operating frequency. The apex angles for the different leg lengths are similar to those which are optimum for the resonant V-beams. Each terminating resistor has a value of 500Ω but, because the power is distributed equally between both wires, the power ratings of the resistors can be halved from what would be necessary when using a single terminated wire.

Being non-resonant, this V-antenna can be fed with a non-resonant feeder which should have a characteristic impedance of 500 to 600Ω. Such a feeder is easily

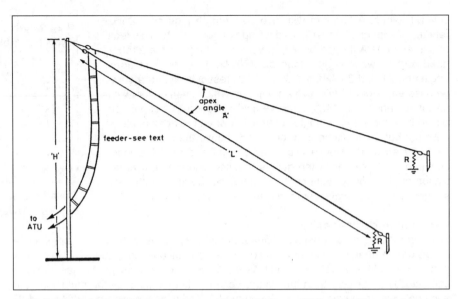

Fig 7.7: A terminated V-beam antenna. This is very useful for reliable point-to-point long-distance working. As the antenna wires tilt down to ground level their terminating resistors can connect to earth directly.

made from 18SWG wires which are spaced 7.5mm (3in) apart, but any open-wire feeder or 300Ω ribbon can be used instead as a tuned line. Another alternative would be to use a 9:1 step-up balun at the antenna apex which could then be connected to 50Ω coaxial cable. There would not be a perfect match, but the SWR would not be high and the losses would be insignificant.

This antenna will work over a frequency ratio of about 3:1 and give several decibels of gain across this range. Leg lengths of 30.5m (100ft) to give 1.5-wavelengths on 14MHz, with a support height of around 18m (60ft) and an apex angle of 80° will make a useful point-to-point antenna for long-distance work on the 14, 21 and 28MHz bands. The dimensions can be reduced to half-size (using the same apex angle) for operation on 28 and 50MHz, making a compact antenna to fit into most average sized gardens.

The earth system for the terminated ends should not be neglected as they form an essential part of the radiating system. A system of six radials, each extending for about 10 to 12m would ensure that the performance of the earth is satisfactory.

THE 'HALF RHOMBIC'

First described by J Mullaney, W4HGU, in *QST* way back in January 1946, the 'half rhombic' antenna has not received much attention in amateur radio publications since. It was brought back to our attention by Joel R Hallas, W1ZR, in two short articles in the March and July 2010 issues of *QST*.

If a span of 200ft (61m) is available, a wide-band unidirectional antenna can be achieved as shown in **Fig 7.8**. With the 9:1 transformers shown, and only a few short ground radials at each end, a 50Ω 1.2:1 SWR is realised from 7 to 56MHz, avoiding the need for a tuner. The gain goes up and the radiation angle goes down with increasing frequency. It's at its best from 20m and up, see **Figs 7.9** and **7.10**, but works as well in its forward direction as a monopole on 30 and 40m. Note that the gain on 20m is just 2dBi (fractionally less than that of a half-wave dipole) but the front-to-back ratio is a useful 20dB.

The 9:1 transformers may be difficult to source, so an alternative method of

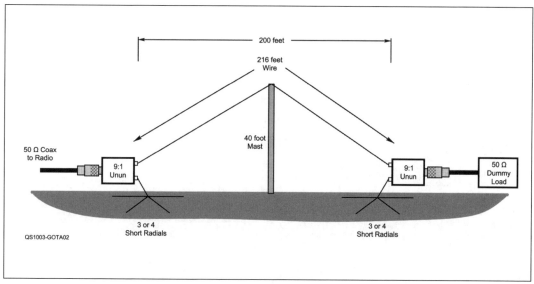

Fig 7.8: The half rhombic unidirectional vertical antenna for 20m - 6m (method 1). If the termination is removed it becomes a bidirectional resonant half rhombic (diagrams reprinted with permission of the American Radio Relay League).

construction is shown in **Fig 7.11**. The termination needs to be in the range of 450 to 600Ω. While special termination loads designed for rhombic use are available, they are usually quite expensive. The other method made use of a readily available 50Ω dummy load for the termination through a 9:1 transformer. The load needs to handle 50% of the transmitted power so, for a 100W station, a 50W 450 to 600Ω resistive load will work fine. Caddock resistors are non-inductive power resistors (they must be non-inductive to work properly) and Mouser (www.mouser.com) lists a 75Ω 15W Caddock resistor at $3. Six such resistors in series will make a 450Ω, 90W dummy load.

The other end may be even easier. All you need is to be able to couple a 450 to 600Ω mostly resistive load to your radio. If you have a tuner designed to work with a single wire or unbalanced antenna with a 10:1 SWR, you're done. If you want the tuner to be some distance from the antenna,

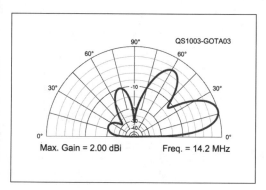

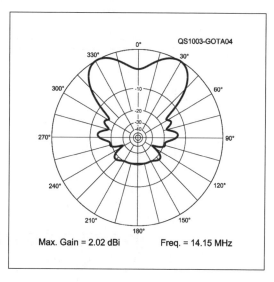

Fig 7.9: Elevation pattern of the half rhombic at its peak azimuth on 20m.

Fig 7.10: Azimuth pattern of the half rhombic at its peak elevation on 20m.

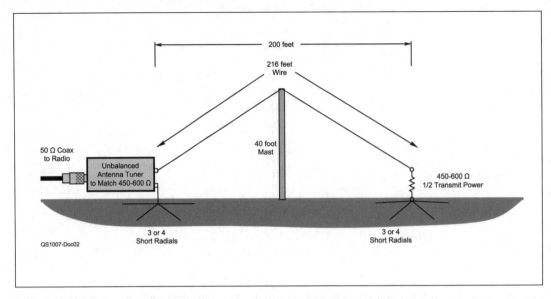

Fig 7.11: Method 2: the half rhombic antenna configured for use without the 9:1 transformers.

a 4:1 balun and a run of coax to your tuner and radio should work just fine, even with an internal tuner rated for a 3:1 SWR.

OTHER END-FED WIRE DESIGNS

Virtually any end-fed wire can be made to radiate if fed through a wide-range ATU and one possible arrangement is given here. It was described as the 'Skymiser' antenna by John Ellerton, G3NCN, in the June 1999 *RadCom* and represents the results of his search for an adequate 1.8MHz antenna for use in a housing estate area.

The antenna is shown in **Fig 7.12** and consists of a vertical section, fed at the top by a horizontal wire, the whole being tuned at the end by a conventional ATU. It will

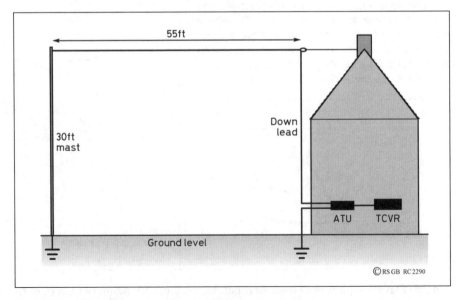

Fig 7.12: Basic arrangement for the 'Skymiser' antenna.

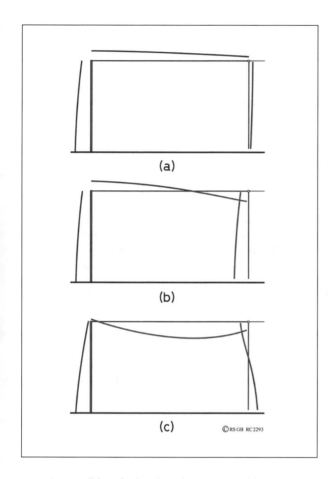

(a)

(b)

(c)   ©RS GB RC2293

Not too obtrusive at the far end of the garden, the vertical mast which forms the far end of the 'Skymiser'.

Left: Fig 7.13. The assumed current distribution for (a) 1.8MHz, (b) 3.5MHz and (c) 7MHz.

operate on all bands, but is only a reasonably true vertical on 1.8MHz and possibly 3.5MHz. The secret of its successful operation lies not so much in the antenna itself, but rather in the earthing. Ideas mentioned in Chapter 1 can be implemented to ensure a good arrangement is adopted.

This antenna is of true 'plumber's delight' construction, being electrically continuous from the base of the mast to the shack. The horizontal wire is connected directly to the top of the mast, i.e. it is not insulated. At the base of the mast and at the shack are independent earth systems.

The assumed current distribution on 1.8, 3.5 and 7MHz is shown in **Fig 7.13**. The performance of the antenna tends to support the distributions shown in the diagrams. On 1.8MHz the antenna behaves as a top-fed vertical. Radiation tends to be omni-directional, although currents in the horizontal section and feed wire undoubtedly modify that. Similar behaviour is expected on 3.5MHz although modification of the omni-directional characteristic will be greater and some useful horizontally polarised radiation helps in more local operation. On 7MHz the vertical feed wire and the mast team up to emulate two verticals out of phase. Results obtained from using the antenna support this idea. The antenna gives good results along the alignment of the mast and download. Some radiation is also expected from the top section, but this is higher angle.

Modifying the length of the top to be 66ft and the masts to be 33ft long can be expected to enhance the phased vertical behaviour on 7MHz and increase the gain along the direction of the axis of the mast download. On 3.5MHz the feed impedance should become lower.

RECEIVE ANTENNAS

Although the Beverage antenna is normally fed by coaxial cable, and thus cannot really be considered to be an end-fed wire antenna, it is certainly very much a 'long wire' and therefore both it and a couple of other receive-only antennas are included in this chapter.

You will generally find that your transmitting antenna is the optimum one for receiving from around 10MHz up, and often somewhat lower. At those frequencies, you want to get all the signal you can from a distant station - and that means taking advantage of the gain of your transmitting antenna. Below that frequency, the signal you're trying to receive is often masked by the combination of natural noise from our galaxy and man-made noise from your neighbourhood. If you could make the signal stronger than the noise you'd be better off, even if you lost some antenna gain. In fact, you can hear the station just about as well with lower receive gain as long as the external noise is at least 10 times that generated within your receiver.

Reception on the lower-frequency amateur bands (160, 80m and sometimes 40m) is different from that on the higher bands for a couple of reasons:

♦ There is generally more external noise. All other things being equal, external noise tends to reduce with frequency. At some point - often at 20 or 15m, depending on the time of year, the external noise starts to become a factor in signal-to-noise ratio (SNR), compared with internal receiver noise.

♦ Antennas at lower frequencies tend to have coverage over wide azimuth and elevation ranges. Thus noise (and interference) comes in from many directions that don't include our desired signal.

For these reasons, a low-gain receive-only antenna that is focused in the direction of our desired signal can be beneficial, even if we are not able to transmit on it. Here are a few possibilities.

THE BEVERAGE ANTENNA

During and after WWI, Harold Beverage, 2BML (later W2BML), worked on many projects intended to improve trans-oceanic reception of radio signals. At that time, operations were conducted at frequencies typically below 500kHz and therefore noise levels were even higher than they are at 1.8MHz and above. Beverage noted that signals received from long low wires had significant directivity, such that noise from many directions was reduced. He was awarded the first of many patents for the antenna that still bears his name on 7 June 1921. The Beverage antenna is shown in **Fig 7.14**.

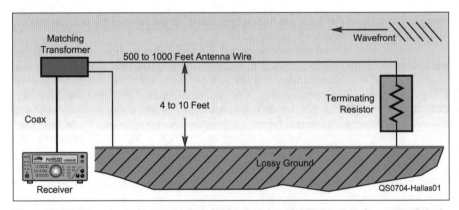

Fig 7.14: The Beverage antenna. Note that the wavefront coming from the right is tilted due to the lossy ground. The resultant horizontal component of its electric field is coupled to the antenna (reprinted with permission of the American Radio Relay League).

The Beverage antenna is probably the best known version of what is termed a 'wave antenna'. It is used by many 'low-band' (160 and 80m) enthusiasts because it enables weak signals to be received with lower levels of noise than many other antennas, including directional loops. Although excellent for receiving, the antenna is very inefficient and therefore not used for transmitting.

The antenna consists of a length of wire longer than a wavelength supported at a low level, typically around 3m (10ft) above ground, and terminated at the far end in a resistor with the same value as the characteristic impedance of the antenna.

Terminating one end of the wire in a resistive load causes the antenna to receive from only one direction. The resistor should be a carbon type of approximately 600Ω, and rated at about 2 watts. The matching transformer should have a ratio of around 9:1 and the antenna can be fed with 50 or 75Ω coax.

A nice characteristic of the Beverage antenna is that, unlike many other types, it works best when it is close to the ground: about 10ft is optimum. It also works best with *lossy* ground.

A vertically polarised wavefront coming from the right (in the drawing) across lossy ground will be slowed by its interaction with the ground so that the wave will tilt as shown. This results in a portion of the electric field becoming horizontal and coupling to the wire as the field progresses towards the receiver. Wavefronts coming from the opposite direction result in signals being delivered to the terminating resistor instead of the receiver. Signals from other directions have the horizontal component of their electric fields in a direction that does not couple well to the wire. The effect becomes more and more pronounced as the antenna is made longer, providing significant improvement in signal-to-noise ratio for lengths above 1 or 2λ and heights from a few feet up to an optimum of about 10ft, depending on ground conductivity. Longer lengths provide even sharper directivity, although gain tends to decrease.

A practical Beverage

By 'practical' we are assuming that you have the prime requisite, i.e. the necessary space, to put up this antenna! The wave antenna is most responsive to signals that have a very low angle of reception that maintain a constant vertical polarisation. On 160 and 80m, and often 40m, long-haul signals often have these characteristics and this makes the Beverage an ideal antenna for those who have the space to erect one.

A Beverage may work best over a poor earth, but the earthing to which the terminating resistor is connected must nevertheless be very good. This suggests that a number of radials or buried wires should be used.

The transformer steps down the high impedance of the Beverage wire to a low value which is suitable for a match to coaxial cable. The secondary of this transformer should be electrostatically shielded from the primary winding, and this is most easily managed by the use of a two or more turn link winding at the end of the coaxial cable and arranged as a Faraday screen. See **Fig 7.15**.

In operation the Beverage antenna acts like a long transmission line with one lossy conductor and one good conductor. The good conductor is the antenna wire whereas the lossy conductor is the earth. In Fig 7.15 the Beverage antenna is shown running along a line from east to west and a transmitting station is assumed to lie to the east. The travelling wave from this station, when it reaches the antenna wire, will move along it from east to west and induce currents in the wire which then travel in both directions. The current travelling east moves against the motion of the wave and it reduces to almost zero when the wire is one wavelength or more long. The currents travelling west, however, travel at almost the velocity of light and will therefore move along with the wave. These currents moving west all add up in phase at the west end and produce a strong signal there.

If the eastern end of the wire was either grounded or open-circuit, the induced

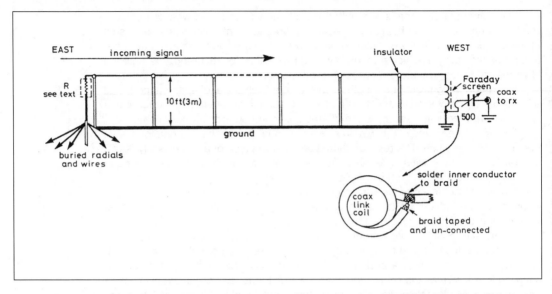

Fig 7.15: The terminated Beverage receiving antenna for use on 1.8 or 3.5MHz. The Faraday screen is made from one or two turns of coaxial cable. To be effective a Beverage antenna must be at least one wavelength long.

currents generated by signals from either the east or the west would be reflected back to the western end of the wire. The antenna would then become bidirectional.

The terminating resistor R absorbs the RF energy reaching the far end of the wire, so preventing any reflection, and gives the antenna a unidirectional property. A value of 400 to 600Ω is usually recommended.

Length and performance

One wavelength must be regarded as a minimum length for an effective Beverage antenna, and on 1.8MHz this will be about 160m or 500ft. Single-wire Beverages have an optimum length of from one to three wavelengths.

A terminated Beverage will have almost no pick-up at all from its sides. It also has a very low noise level with a considerable attenuation of atmospheric noise. There is no other antenna type its equal for the reception of DX on the 1.8MHz band. Loops are good but are really not in the same class as a Beverage wave antenna.

Of course the big disadvantage of the Beverage is that it takes up a *lot* of space: for 160m, a 2λ Beverage is nearly 1200ft long. Many will have trouble finding that kind of distance in a straight line that also happens to be in a useful direction but, if you have the property available, or have friendly neighbours, this can be a very effective receiving antenna for little more than the cost of the wire.

Point-to-point working is not often very important to amateurs, for they generally wish to contact different distant stations which may be located anywhere in the world - and several Beverage antennas would be needed to do this. Few amateurs are fortunate enough to have the ground which is needed to set up more than one Beverage antenna, so most workers on the low bands must use other low-noise systems. A couple of examples are given here.

THE 'EWE' ANTENNA

If you do not have the space necessary for a Beverage antenna, the 'EWE' may prove to be a suitable alternative. It was first described by Floyd Koontz, WA2WVL, in *QST* in 1995 and gets its unusual name from its resemblance to an inverted letter 'U'.

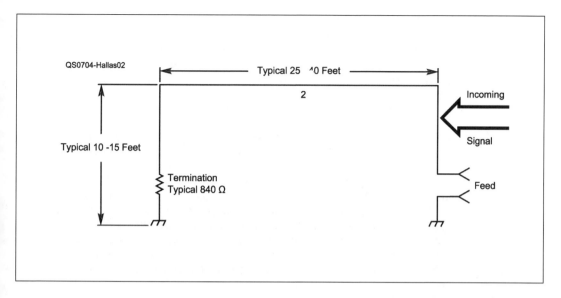

Fig 7.16: The 'EWE' receive antenna for 160 and 80m (all diagrams reprinted with permission of the American Radio Relay League).

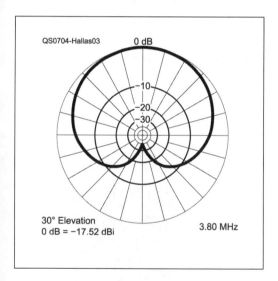

Fig 7.17: 3800kHz azimuth response of the EWE in Fig 7.16.

Fig 7.18: 3800kHz elevation response of the EWE of Fig 7.16.

The EWE is shown in **Fig 7.16**. As the impedance is about 820 - 840Ω, the antenna is typically fed via a 9:1 balun to 50 or 75Ω coax. Although it looks like a short Beverage, the operation of a EWE is quite different, making use of the two vertical portions to cancel the response from the rear. This trades a bit of height for a shortened length, but the antenna can be effective without being very high or long. The azimuth and elevation patterns at 3800kHz are shown in **Figs 7.17** and **7.18**.

Note that the direction of maximum response is *opposite* to that of the Beverage. The EWE has also been shown to work best with poor ground conductivity.

TWO-ELEMENT HORIZONTAL 'EWE'

The standard EWE antenna is erected in the vertical plane. However, in the December 2006 *QST*, Floyd Koontz, WA2WVL, described a *horizontal* version of the EWE that he developed in order to solve a particular reception problem he had. He wanted to maximise the received signal-to-noise ratio in Florida of 80m SSB European signals.

With the standard vertical EWE, a single element has a deep null off the back. A single horizontal EWE, however, would have that null at 0° elevation instead. Over real ground, the single horizontal EWE has a front-to-back ratio (F/B) on 80m as shown in Fig 7.17 for 30° elevation. The low-angle gain increases with height above ground, as with most horizontal antennas, but the pattern remains nearly the same at 10 to 30ft heights. The size can be chosen to fit the available space but four supports (trees, towers, house, etc) are needed to hold up the corners.

Of the different sizes and shapes that can be used, one is optimum. It is a square, λ/8 on a side (a total of λ/2 around). For this size (30 x 30ft for 3.8MHz), the feed is non-reactive and can be matched with a simple broadband transformer. The calculated feed impedance was 1337Ω and it was matched with a 26:5 two-winding transformer. The F/B was more than 11dB on 80m and 15dB on 160m.

Two-element design

As noted, a single EWE antenna gives a modified cardioid pattern with a usable, but not dramatic, front-to-back ratio. The front-to-side ratio is only about 4dB, so a two-element design was established to improve the back and side rejection. Available trees allowed a spacing of 100ft. **Fig 7.19** shows the layout of this array including the location of the feedpoints and terminations.

Fig 7.20 is the modelled pattern of the two-element array, again at 3.8MHz and 30° elevation. As is evident, the two-element array resulted in a sharpened beamwidth and a significantly improved F/B. While the pattern for 30° elevation is shown, it is similar with lower output at lower elevations.

The antenna was to be 25ft off the ground. This was determined to be the maxi-

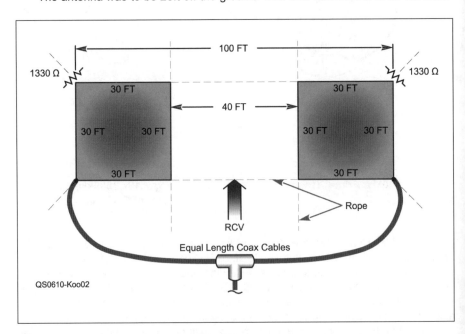

Fig 7.19: Orientation of the two-element horizontal EWE antenna array.

mum height that could be safely reached from a 24ft extension ladder. Vinyl insulated 14 gauge speaker wire was used, but any wire strong enough to be pulled tight without stretching could be used. The loops were tied at the corners (every 30ft) by one-eighth inch Dacron ropes. The knots were taped with black electrical tape to prevent the knots from coming untied.

After all the soldering was completed, the connections were coated with silicone window sealant except for one of the 50Ω transformer connections. The two loops must be fed in phase to develop the pattern and there is a 50% chance of getting it right. If you guess wrong, the pattern will have a 30dB null off the front and receiving performance will be poor. If that is the case, simply reverse the connections, and then coat those with sealant as well.

During the assembly process the wire is lying on the ground in the space where it will be pulled up. A piece of the eighth-inch Dacron

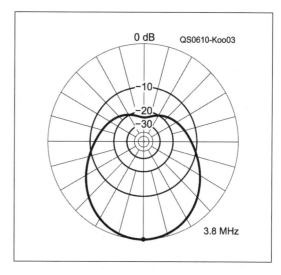

Fig 7.20: *EZNEC* modelled pattern of a two-element horizontal EWE, configured as in Fig 7.19, at 3.8MHz and 30° elevation.

line was fed through each screw eye and pulled back to ground and tied to another screw eye at 4ft. After doing this on eight trees, the antenna is now ready to be lifted in place without further climbing.

Both feedpoints had equal length coax cables attached. The length was determined by the location of the ninth tree to which both coax cables would go (100ft was used for each run length). The cables were run overhead at about 12ft from tree to tree. A BNC 'T' connector was used to parallel the 100ft coax cables and the third port connected to the coax that went to the shack.

Antenna output level considerations

The calculated gain of the two-element horizontal EWE (at 20°) at 3.8 MHz was about -18dBi (a λ/4 vertical has a gain of about 0dBi). For a height of only 10ft the gain drops to -24dBi. Most modern receivers and transceivers have sufficient sensitivity so that even at this level there is sufficient gain that the signal-to-noise ratio is limited by external noise. If the noise level does not increase by at least 10dB when replacing a dummy load with the receive antenna, you will need to have additional gain to get full benefit from this antenna. In order to compare directly the performance of this antenna with your transmitting antenna, you may want to add gain so that the signal levels are similar and the S-meter moves in the same way. A preamplifier with a gain of 18 to 25dB should be just what you want for 80m, more if you use the antenna on 160m.

It also might be that switching your receiver's preamp on provides just the amount of gain required to bring the signal level up to that from your transmitting antenna, and that is a suitable way to equalise the gain. Whatever preamp option you take, make sure that the preamp is protected from pick-up of RF from your transmitting antenna. In many cases, the receive antenna will bring it directly into the preamp, if provisions are not made to the contrary.

Operation with this system has been gratifying with the SNR often being improved by 10 to 20dB on 80m compared with the reference antenna. On 160m, WA2WVL reported that many SSB stations could be copied that were previously below the noise.

8 Impedance Matching and Baluns

THIS CHAPTER COVERS matching the antenna to the feeder, as well as matching the feeder to the transceiver. Baluns are sometimes used as impedance transformers, so they are also included in this chapter, although in many cases their main function is to prevent the flow of unwanted common-mode currents.

Once an antenna has been designed and installed, it is necessary to ensure that it operates at its maximum efficiency. One key element of this is to ensure that the impedances in the system are matched. An Antenna Tuning Unit (ATU) is often used to provide a good match between the transceiver and the feeder and so ensure a maximum transfer of power, but they also provide other advantages. PA transistors are susceptible to damage if operated into a poor match, so modern transceivers use protection circuitry to reduce the output power if they operate into a mismatched load. The use of an ATU can prevent this happening. Another advantage is that, as an ATU consists of a resonant circuit, its use may help to limit spurious signals from a transmitter, or help to reduce the effect of strong out-of-band signals to the receiver.

When matching an antenna system there are two areas that need to be addressed: the matching of the antenna to the feeder, and matching the feeder to the transceiver.

ANTENNA TO FEEDER MATCHING

This problem of matching the antenna to the feeder has been discussed at some length in the various descriptions of antennas in earlier chapters, but it is convenient to review some points here as the focus in this chapter is on impedance matching.

In many cases there is little or no problem in matching an antenna to a feeder. When the antenna feed impedance is about 75Ω, as is the case when using a typical half-wave dipole, a coaxial or twin-wire feeder having this impedance can be used. If a 50Ω impedance coaxial feeder is used with a 75Ω impedance antenna, the additional losses induced by the mismatch are not very great and are quite tolerable. Other antenna systems which have a higher feed impedance can be fed with good quality 300Ω ribbon feeder or an open-wire line that has been specifically made to suit the antenna impedance.

Naturally there are many instances when the antenna impedance does *not* fall into one of these convenient situations. In particular where the antenna impedance is low and lies between 20 and 50Ω, for which standard coaxial and other cables are not readily available.

One way around this is to use two equal lengths of a standard coaxial cable in parallel. Two equal lengths of 75Ω coax may be connected in parallel to provide a 37Ω impedance, a close match to the base of a typical quarter-wave Marconi antenna (although in practice, when ground losses are also taken into account, a quarter-wave vertical will often match closely to standard 50Ω coax without resort to paralleling two lengths of cable).

Two pieces of 50Ω coax in parallel provide an impedance of 25Ω.

By using two equal lengths of 75Ω and 50Ω cable in parallel, an impedance of 37.5Ω is achieved (however, for this to work they must have the same velocity factor).

Even two lengths of 300Ω ribbon feeder can be taped together and, when connected in parallel, they will provide a 150Ω feeder.

QUARTER-WAVE MATCHING TRANSFORMERS

The quarter-wave transformer is a relatively easy way to provide impedance step-down or step-up ratios, and its own impedance, Z_t, can be calculated from the formula:

$$Z_t = \sqrt{(\text{Antenna impedance} \times \text{Feeder impedance})}$$

For example, if an antenna has a high feed impedance of 9000Ω and needs to be matched to a 50Ω, the impedance of a suitable quarter-wave matching transformer would be the square root of 9000 x 50 (= 450,000), which is approximately 675Ω.

A 675Ω impedance open-wire line is easily made using 18SWG wire with a spacing of 180mm (7in).

The length of the quarter-wave section is calculated from the free-space length of an electrical quarter-wave at the operating frequency, multiplied by the velocity factor of the line to be used. A well-constructed open-wire line will have a velocity factor of about 0.97, so the length of a suitable matching transformer can be found from:

$$\frac{246 \times 0.97 \text{ (feet)}}{f \text{ (MHz)}}$$

For operation on 21.1MHz the length of such a quarter-wave matching transformer will be 11ft 4in (3.45m).

Another example where a quarter-wave matching transformer is of great use is to match the approximately 100Ω impedance of a full-wave quad loop antenna to a standard 50Ω coaxial feeder. The square root of 100 x 50 (= 5000) is approximately 70.7, so a quarter-wave length of 75Ω coax would make a very effective impedance transformer.

THE HALF-WAVELENGTH LINE

The 'half-wave line' system is based on the fact that the impedance at any point along a wire or feedline is repeated at half-wave intervals, the actual line impedance having no influence upon this characteristic. For instance, if a half-wavelength of 300Ω feeder is connected at one end to the centre of a half-wave dipole (75Ω), it will present a 75Ω impedance at its other end.

On the higher HF bands, such as 10m, the half-wave line is rather short (e.g. 12ft of coaxial cable), and it might only be useful when the antenna is very close to the operating position. On the other hand, the use of half-wave feedlines can be impractical on the lower-frequency bands unless the antenna is located a long way from the operating position, although there is no reason why excess feeder (if coaxial cable) cannot be coiled up in some way.

In order to calculate the electrical half-wavelength of a feedline, the free-space half-wavelength of:

150 / f (MHz) metres *or* 492 / f (MHz) feet

must be multiplied by the velocity factor of the feeder or cable. Most of the commonly used coaxial cables have a velocity factor of 0.66.

When a half-wavelength line is used the antenna feed impedance will be translated to the end of the line where it can be matched to the equipment via a suitable ATU. The losses along such a line will depend upon the characteristics of the coaxial or whatever other type of feeder is used.

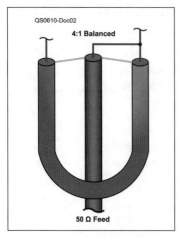

Fig 8.1: 4:1 coax balun (reprinted with permission of the American Radio Relay League).

4:1 COAX IMPEDANCE TRANSFORMER

For a single band, the half-wave coax 4:1 balun is hard to beat. If cut properly, it will provide a true 4:1 transformation at its resonant frequency for any impedance, although really it works best for either 200:50Ω with 50Ω coax, or 300:75Ω with 75Ω coax.

Fig 8.1 is drawing of a λ/2 balun. Be sure to take into account the velocity factor of the particular type of coax you select and multiply the calculated free space length by that factor. The number varies between about 0.67 for polyethylene dielectric coax to about 0.8 for foam dielectric cable, but if you have a manufacturer's catalogue number it is best to check on their website for the precise factor. Careful measurement with a ruler should work if you have the relative velocity.

You won't find a cheaper or better 4:1 balun anywhere. Such baluns are used successfully from HF into the microwave region. Their only disadvantage is that they are not broadband as are the ferrite based designs. They work fine on a single band (or odd multiples, for example 144 and 432MHz).

ANTENNA ELEMENT MATCHING

An alternative to matching the feedline to the antenna's impedance is to make changes to the antenna element itself so that instead it matches the impedance of the feedline. Many antenna designs make use of the beta match, the hairpin or the gamma to achieve the desired match. The gamma match was examined in detail by Roger Wheeler, G3MGW, in an article published in the September 2006 *RadCom*.

The major advantages of the gamma match are that it provides an *unbalanced* feedpoint which allows a direct connection to the coax, and that it is of simple construction with inherently low losses. The function of the gamma match is to change the antenna's impedance to be the same impedance as that of the feedline. The constituent parts of the gamma match are shown in **Fig 8.2**.

To achieve a 1:1 match the variables C, S, l, d1 and d2 need to be adjusted. In practice, d2 is fixed by the antenna design, and d1 is usually smaller than d2 to keep the overall weight down. If the antenna is constructed with wire elements, e.g. a quad, it is convenient to make d1 = d2.

Antenna handbooks usually suggest initial values such as setting S to 0.007λ and l to between 0.04λ and 0.05λ. Gamma capacitor C should be around 7pF per metre of wavelength (so for 20m C would have an initial value of 140pF). So by setting sensible, empirically derived, defaults for d1, d2 and S we have eliminated three of the five variables.

To 'tune' the gamma match you need to alternately adjust the two remaining variables C and l until you achieve the required match at the chosen frequency. The match is usually monitored by observing the SWR. You may be fortunate and achieve an acceptable match by changing just l followed by C. If not, S has to be changed and the whole process repeated.

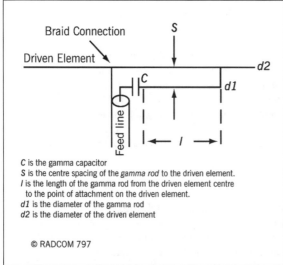

C is the gamma capacitor
S is the centre spacing of the *gamma rod* to the driven element.
l is the length of the gamma rod from the driven element centre to the point of attachment on the driven element.
d1 is the diameter of the gamma rod
d2 is the diameter of the driven element

© RADCOM 797

Fig 8.2: The constituent parts of the gamma match.

SWR AND LINE LOSS

The Standing Wave Ratio (SWR, also known as Voltage Standing Wave Ratio or VSWR) is related to the forward and reflected power on a transmission line and is given by the following formula:

$$SWR = \frac{1 + \sqrt{P_r / P_f}}{1 - \sqrt{P_r / P_f}}$$

where P_r is reflected power and P_f is forward power.

An SWR meter measures the forward and the reflected voltage or current on an antenna feeder and it is the ratio of these two readings that is indicated by the meter. If a feeder with a characteristic impedance of 50Ω is connected to an antenna load of either 100Ω or 25Ω, there will be a mismatch and in both these instances the SWR meter will read 2:1. However, the SWR reading does not tell you which of the two possible conditions actually exists.

Such a level of mismatch is not really serious, unless the losses in the feeder are also large. There is a multiplication factor of line loss which applies when there is a non-unity SWR on the line. When the SWR becomes 2:1 this factor is 1.25. For example, at 10MHz a 100m or 300ft coaxial line which has an inherent loss of 1.8dB has a total line loss of 2.25dB when the SWR becomes 2:1. When an SWR is a poor 3.7:1 the total loss on the feeder rises to 3.6dB. In fact a standing wave ratio of 3.7:1 will always result in the doubling of the inherent line loss - a factor worth noting.

Losses of 1dB or thereabouts can be insignificant on their own. A change in level of 1dB is the smallest change that is noticeable by the human ear. Even a 3dB loss (half power) represents little more than a half of an S-point of signal level. It is necessary to keep the level of losses and gains in proportion, seeing the overall picture. However, this should be balanced by the fact that several small gains or losses soon mount up. But it is not worth spending large amounts of money to reduce a loss by 1dB when it is unlikely to have any major impact on the performance of the station as a whole. It is quite likely that these losses could be counteracted by small change elsewhere that might cost far less to implement.

Bearing this in mind, a standing wave ratio of 2:1 will result in a loss of only 1.3dB along 100m (300ft) of 300Ω impedance ribbon used as a 'flat' untuned feeder at 10MHz. The same length of an open-wire feed line has a loss of just 0.56dB when the SWR is 2:1 at the same frequency.

A given SWR reading does not give any indication of the reactive components on the feeder, and it will not be accurate unless the load is a pure resistance.

This short discussion on SWR and the examples given may help to reassure those who feel anxious when their SWR meters read 2:1, as this will not cause a noticeable reduction in radiated power on its own. It is only when the levels start to rise above this and the transceiver output level is reduced by the protection circuitry

Two modern SWR meters. Left: The Daiwa NS-660P. Right: The Watson WCN-200.

SWR reading	% reflected power	Comments
0 - 2.5	0 - 18	Solid-state rig SWR protection starts to operate, try looking for an improvement at the higher SWR value
2.5 - 5.0	18 - 45	Valve equipment probably OK, start looking for a problem or improve the SWR to get closer to 2:1
5.0 - ∞	45 - 100	Check the feed / antenna system, there *is* a problem!

Table 8.1: Guidelines for various SWRs (by GM4FZH).

that there is a need for concern. Clive Smith, GM4FZH, writing in *Test Equipment for the Radio Amateur* (4th edition, RSGB, 2011) compiled a useful commentary on the values of SWR and their meaning (**Table 8.1**).

THE ATU
A good introduction to ATUs was given by Eamon Skelton, EI9GQ, in his 'Homebrew' column in the September and October 2007 issues of *RadCom*. What follows is an edited summary.

An ATU is an impedance matching device which is used between the RF input / output connector of a transmitter / receiver and an antenna system. Most transmitters and receivers are designed to use a 50Ω unbalanced coaxial connection for the

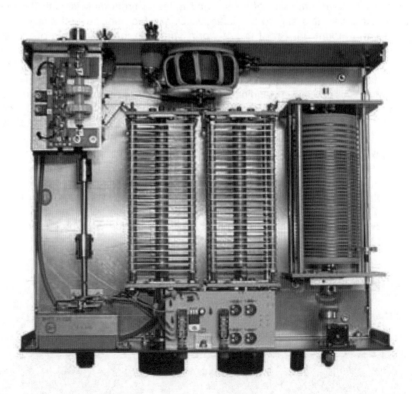

Inside the Palstar AT1500CV, a commercially-made wide-range (20 - 1500Ω resistive) ATU covering 1.8 - 30MHz and capable of handling up to 1500W. Note the large size of the air-spaced capacitors and the 'roller coaster' inductor.

Inside the MFJ-901B ATU. The tiny transformer balun at the output of the ATU is able to handle 100W without stress.

antenna input / output. The ATU allows us to match an antenna system of arbitrary impedance to 50Ω, 75Ω or any other value that we require. Pi (π), T and L networks are all widely used in ATUs. In fact, it would only be a slight exaggeration to say that any random collection of inductors and capacitors could be connected together in any random configuration to make some form of ATU.

Note that there are many situations where an ATU is *not* required. Some antennas have a feedpoint impedance which is reasonably close to 50Ω. A quarter-wave ground plane or a centre-fed half-wave dipole are typical examples. Other antennas that might have a feedpoint impedance radically different from 50Ω include a built-in matching system so that the impedance seen at the feedline is nevertheless close to 50Ω. This matching system can be made from sections of transmission line, as used with the G5RV doublet and the J-vertical, or from lumped LC components. Some matching systems like the gamma-match use a combination of transmission line and lumped LC components.

One of the best ways of feeding a multi-band doublet is to use low-loss balanced line between the transmitter / receiver and the antenna feedpoint. The impedance seen at the shack end of the line will vary widely from band to band and might be several thousand ohms when the antenna is one wavelength long. We will have to use some kind of matching network to match our 50Ω transmitter / receiver to this unknown line impedance. Because the doublet and feedline are balanced with respect to ground, we will need to use a matching system that provides a balanced connection to the feedline. The unbalanced to balanced transformation can be performed by the ATU or alternatively, we can use an unbalanced ATU in combination with a *balun* (balanced to unbalanced transformer), of which more later in this chapter.

ATUS FOR SINGLE-BAND USE

If you only have to cover one band, you do not need to have all the features of a versatile all-band ATU. You can do it much more simply with just two components, as Ian White, GM3SEK, described in the June 2006 'In Practice' column in *RadCom*. The objective of the ATU is to transform the impedance of the antenna (or the impedance at the bottom of the feedline) to 50Ω, the load impedance your transceiver is designed to work into. To build a single-band ATU:

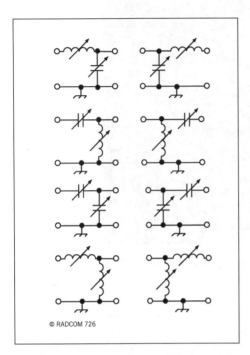

Fig 8.3: There are eight possible L-matching networks.

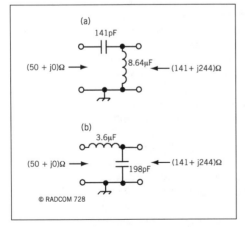

Fig 8.4: The two possible L circuits (see text).

1. Measure the impedance that you're trying to match.
2. Choose a suitable matching network - which can be just one coil and one capacitor - and calculate the component values. A computer program will do this for you.
3. Wind the coil - another program will design it for you - and either choose a suitable capacitor or make your own out of coaxial cable.
4. Put it all together and install it, preferably outdoors, right next to the antenna.
5. Give the L and C values a final tweak for minimum SWR. The network will then cover most of an HF amateur band without needing any further adjustments.

As a design example, let's look at a matching network for a 12m high vertical on the 7MHz band. Step 1 is to find out the value of the complex impedance (R ± jX) that you are trying to transform to 50Ω. The MFJ-259B antenna analyser will do this: although it is not a full vector network analyser - it can measure the magnitude of the reactance, but cannot tell you whether it is positive (inductive) or negative (capacitive). For the 12m vertical, the MFJ-259B indicates 141Ω resistive, in series with 244Ω of reactance, which could be either positive or negative. The instruction manual explains how to find out which one it is, but we can supply this information from background knowledge about antennas. The height of this particular antenna is greater than a quarter-wavelength at 7MHz, but less than a half-wavelength, so its feed impedance at the base is inductive: we can say straight away that the impedance we're trying to match is actually (141 + j244)Ω.

Step 2 is easy too, thanks to the program L_TUNER.EXE from Reg Edwards, G4FGQ (available to download free from www.wireless.org.uk/g4fgq). The family of eight different L networks in **Fig 8.3** allows you to match any complex impedance to any other, but you have to pick the right one. Reg's program narrows the choice to two possible networks, and then you only need choose the one that is easier to build.

Step 3 is to build one of the two networks shown in **Fig 8.4** (either network will work, so your choice can be based entirely on ease of construction.)

The 3.6μH coil can be calculated but the SOLNOID3.EXE program, also available on G4FGQ's website, makes life easier. About 14 turns of 45mm diameter and 100mm overall length will do the job. Add one or two extra turns to the calculated number, to give yourself some range of adjustment in step 5. The 198pF

An almost essential piece of test equipment for every antenna experimenter: an SWR analyser or antenna analyser. This model is the very popular MFJ-259B.

It doesn't have to look pretty; it only has to work! GM3SEK's single-band ATU for matching a 12m-long vertical on 40m.

capacitor also needs some degree of variability for step 5. To avoid possible problems with the RF current rating of fixed capacitors, the capacitor can be made from RG213 or RG58 coax, both of which have a capacitance of 100pF/m. This kind of capacitor can only be adjusted in one direction - downwards - by cutting pieces off the end of the coax, so start with a longer length than calculated.

The design and construction of the coil and capacitor can be very free-and-easy, and there is no need to be too formal about it. Step 5 will adjust both components to their correct values.

Step 4 is to find a box to put it in and step 5 is to connect the antenna and make the final adjustments to the inductor and capacitor. With an L-network, you won't see a perfect impedance match until both components have been adjusted to their correct values. An antenna analyser such as the MFJ-259 is ideal for this job, because you can sweep some way above and below the target frequency. Since both L and C are starting out above their required values, you will find the best match at some frequency below the 7MHz band. To get a feel for how the network behaves, try adjusting the inductor by stretching or compressing the turns, and you will find some frequency where the SWR dips to exactly 1:1. Now cut about 5cm off the open-circuit end of the coaxial capacitor, and adjust the inductor again to find the frequency of the optimum match. It will have moved up a little, so keep on repeating this adjustment cycle until you have moved the match frequency up to your favourite spot inside the band. As you get closer to the target frequency, take increasing care not to snip too much off the end of the coax. Finally, weatherproof both exposed ends of the coax with some hot-melt glue, and roll the coax into a coil.

TYPES OF ATU

The simplest ATU is an L-network consisting of a single capacitor and a single inductor, as discussed above. A low-pass type of L-network with a series L and shunt C or the high-pass equivalent with a series C and shunt L are both suitable. This type of matching network is often used in automatic ATUs, where banks of inductors and capacitors are switched by relays. One problem with the L-network is that it can only be used to match a low impedance to a high impedance or vice versa.

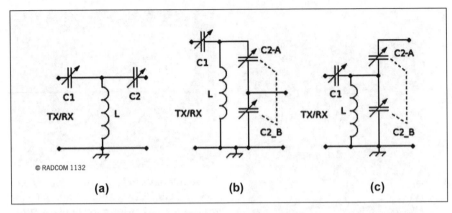

© RADCOM 1132

(a)　　　　　(b)　　　　　(c)

Fig 8.5: Different ATU configurations (see text).

To accommodate impedances that may be greater or less than 50Ω, it is necessary to use a relay or switch to swap the network low-Z and high-Z connections.

The addition of a third reactive element allows us to build a much more flexible matching network. The addition of a second capacitor allows us to make a low-pass Pi network or a high-pass (CLC) T-network as shown in **Fig 8.5(a)**. This type of T-network is very widely used in both home-made and commercially-made ATUs.

If you have a dual-gang capacitor, you could build the 'Ultimate Transmatch' as shown in **Fig 8.5(b)**, or the 'SPC Transmatch', as shown in **Fig 8.5(c)**. Both of these matching networks are derived from the T-network and offer greater selectivity than the simple T-network. The T-network acts as a high-pass filter and offers little or no suppression of harmonics.

Some types of ATU provide a balanced connection to the antenna. **Fig 8.6** shows a link-coupled tuner which is designed to work with balanced feedline. C2-A and C2-B are a dual-gang tuning capacitor. The capacitor body and rotor plates of C1 and C2 are grounded. This is very convenient when the tuner is built in a metal enclosure. There is no need to isolate the capacitors from ground as required by some other designs. Band switching of this type of tuner can be quite complicated because of the need to adjust the value of both L1 and L2 and to find the optimum tapping point for the balanced feeder on L2. This circuit was very popular in the days when open construction and crocodile clip connections were the norm.

Fig 8.7 shows a simpler form of balanced tuner. This circuit is also link coupled

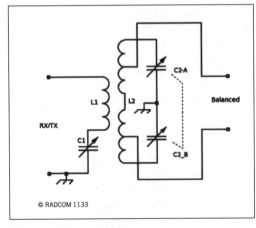

© RADCOM 1133

Fig 8.6: Link-coupled tuner.

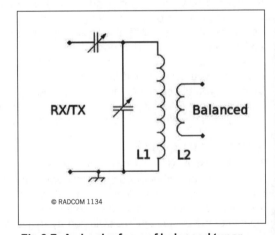

© RADCOM 1134

Fig 8.7: A simpler form of balanced tuner.

and it is easily adapted to unbalanced operation by simply grounding one end of the coupling link. Band switching is achieved by using a two-pole switch to connect to taps on L1 and L2.

PRACTICAL ATU CIRCUITS
L AND PI-SECTION ATUS

L and pi-section ATUs are easy to build and versatile in their operation, forming one of the simplest multi-band ATU designs. The circuit given in **Fig 8.8** shows the design. Capacitor C1 may be switched in as shown and this makes the circuit into a pi-section ATU, but when it is switched out the circuit it becomes an L-section system. Although the circuit shows a switch associated with C1, it does not actually need to be switched as it can be left in circuit and set to its minimum capacitance.

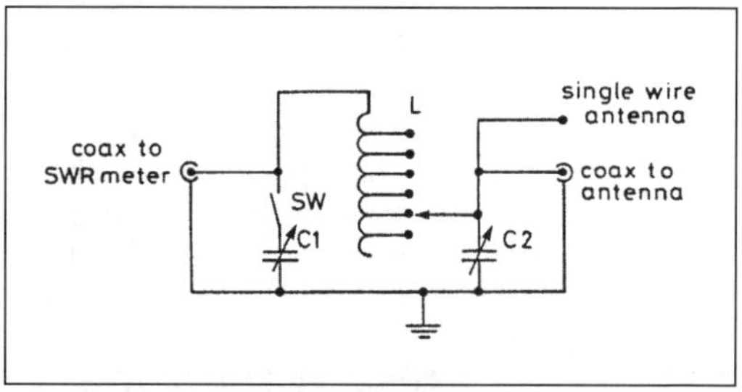

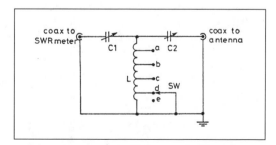

Fig 8.8: An L-section or pi-matching unit. This is a versatile ATU which does not require a coupling coil. A single coil with adequate taps can be used to cover a wide range of frequencies.

A wide range of impedance loads can be matched to 50Ω with this circuit and either a switched coil or a variable inductor ('roller coaster') may be used for the inductor L. It will be found that if the antenna is at high impedance the capacitance of C1 will be greater than that of C2. A low-impedance input from the antenna requires the converse of this, and then C2 must have the largest capacitance.

In effect this ATU also forms a simple low pass filter: the use of a considerable capacitance to ground via either C1 or C2 reduces the chances of harmonic radiation. It does not need a coupling coil and is also easy to adjust. The disadvantage of this type of ATU circuit is that it cannot match such a wide range of impedances as some of the more sophisticated circuits.

The component values for the pi-section ATU which will tune from 3.5 to 28MHz are as follows:

L = 15µH (20 turns of 14SWG, 76mm (3in) diameter and 95mm (3.75in) long. 10 turns are wound at four turns per inch (25mm) and 10 turns are at eight turns per inch. L is tapped every two turns. It may be wound on a former or air wound. If its diameter is reduced to 50mm (1in), it will need 38 turns of 18SWG at six turns per 50mm (1in).
C1 = 350pF (older-style valve or tube receiver type).
C2 = 200pF (wide-spaced high-voltage type).

T-NETWORK ATU

The T-network design is shown in **Fig 8.9** and in this design the inductor L is connected from the live or signal line to ground, effectively in parallel with both the input and the output. Capacitors are in the signal line and must be isolated from earth. This type of ATU is normally only used to match to a low impedance antenna or load. They are ideal when matching quite low values (typically 10 to 50Ω) to standard 50Ω coaxial cables. The voltages

Fig 8.9: A T-section ATU which is also a simple matching device. Its greatest disadvantage is that it is poor at rejecting high frequency transmitter harmonics. Its construction is also complicated by the fact that the rotors and stators of C1 and C2 are not at earth potential.

across the capacitors C1 and C2 are not high, so wide-spaced transmitting types are not necessary. The inductor L can be tapped for multi- band use and again no coupling coil is needed.

Unfortunately this circuit has a drawback: it has a very poor attenuation of transmitter harmonics and behaves as a high-pass filter, with L presenting a high shunt impedance. Nevertheless, it is useful and quite satisfactory if a good low-pass filter is used between the transmitter and the T-section.

Component values are not critical, but typical ones for this circuit are:

L = 22 turns of 16SWG enamelled wire 40mm (1.5in) diameter, close wound.
The taps down from the top of the coil are:
a = 8 turns (7 - 10MHz)   b = 5 turns (14MHz)   c = 5 turns (18 - 21MHz)
d = 3 turns (24 - 28MHz)   e = no tap (the complete coil is used on 3.5MHz).
C1 and C2 can both be 160pF maximum capacitance broadcast types.

PARALLEL-TUNED ATU

A parallel-tuned circuit can be used as an effective ATU. The circuit is actually similar to that used in the 'tank' circuit of old valve transmitters. The circuit, although simple as can be seen in **Fig 8.10**, can be used for many end-fed antennas and it can accommodate a wide range of antenna feed impedances.

An ATU should not have a high Q, otherwise energy transfer will be difficult to achieve and the tuning will be particularly critical. A Q of between 10 and 12 is ideal, and to achieve a value in this region the tuning capacitor C and the inductance L1 must each have a reactance of about 500Ω at the operating frequency. Even when designed within these parameters a very high antenna impedance might still present matching difficulties. To overcome this, the Q may be lowered further by increasing the inductance of L1 and reducing the value of C. A rough rule-of-thumb guide to the correct values of C and L is that the capacitor should be 1pF for each metre of wavelength and the inductor L1 should be 0.25μH for each metre of wavelength of the frequency in use. Calculated values are given in **Table 8.2**.

When using a transmitter output power of 100W the tuning capacitor should have a plate spacing of at least 1.5mm (1/16in). Capacitors with smaller spacing than this risk arcing over.

The link coupling coil L2 has one or two turns of wire which can be set at a variable distance from the tuning coil L1. L2 is wound or arranged to be at the 'earthy' end of L1 and the coaxial cable from L2 should reach the transmitter via an SWR meter. Tuning C, trying the different tap positions for the antenna along L1, and also varying the coupling between L1 and L2 are the three adjustments that must be made to secure the lowest SWR reading.

For multi-band work, L1 may use plug-in coils which should preferably be self-supporting and wound with heavy wire or thin copper tube. The same link winding may be used on most bands.

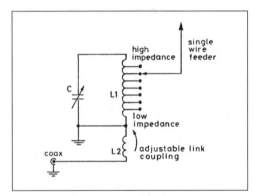

Fig 8.10: The parallel-tuned ATU which will match a fairly wide range of antenna impedances, but presents problems when the impedance is low. The capacitor C must be a high-voltage working type with wide plate spacing.

Band (MHz)	Capacitance value (pF)	Inductance value (μH)
1.8	180	40
3.5	90	22
7	45	12
10	33	8
14	20	6
21	16	4.5
28	11	3

Table 8.2: Table of values of capacitance and inductance for the parallel-tuned ATU.

ATUS FOR TWO-WIRE FEEDERS

A variant of the previous design is shown in **Fig 8.11(a)**, and it is arranged to match a two-wire feedline. In the configuration shown it can accommodate a range of medium to high impedances, and the inductance L1 is tuned by a split-stator variable capacitor. The capacitance across L1 is the effective capacitance of each half of C1 in series. No earth connection to the tuned circuit is shown but the junction of the two sections of the variable capacitor C1 may be earthed. The actual 'earthy' point along the coil will lie somewhere close to its centre and the link winding L2 is arranged over this part of L1.

Fig 8.11(b) shows another way to match a pair of feeder wires, but in this case it is assumed that the feeder impedance will be low. When this impedance is low a more effective match is made when series tuning is employed, using the two variable capacitors C1a and C1b. Again, no earth connection is required.

Both the circuits shown in Fig 8.11 use link windings L2 which are in series with a variable capacitor C2. This system is much easier to adjust and physically easier to arrange than the variable coupling shown in Fig 8.10.

The component values for L2 and C2 are found from the lowest frequency to be used in the band of intended operation and also the impedance of the coaxial line to the transceiver or transmitter. The capacitor C2 must resonate with L2 on this frequency, i.e. it will have a value of 1000pF at 3.5MHz when using 50Ω line if the reactance of L2 also equals this impedance. Some approximate capacitance values for six amateur bands are given in **Table 8.3**.

As the capacitances become rather large on the low bands, a larger link winding can be used on 3.5 and 1.8MHz, which means a 500pF broadcast-type variable can be used for C2. This capacitor will also be suitable for the other bands.

Band (MHz)	Value for C2 (pF)
1.8	1800
7	500
10	350
14	220
21	150
28	130

Table 8.3: Table of value for C2 as used in Fig 8.11.

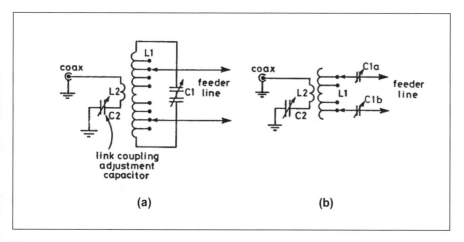

(a)

(b)

Fig 8.11: (a) A parallel-tuned circuit ATU that is suitable for use with tuned feeder lines, particularly when they present a high or medium impedance. A fixed link coil L2 can be used and the degree of coupling may be adjusted by C2. (b) This series-tuned ATU uses a pair of ganged (but not electrically connected) variable capacitors in the feed line and it can match low impedances without difficulty. The coupling link is as described for (a).

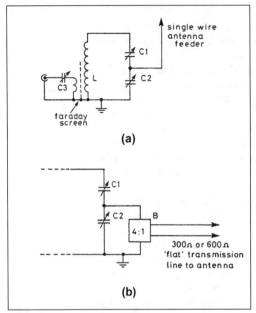

Fig 8.12: (a) A capacitive-tap ATU which can give an infinitely variable impedance match to the tuned circuit L, C1 / C2. C1 and C2 are separately tuned and the ratio of their capacitances determines the match. (b) A 4:1 balun may be used to present an unbalanced impedance to the capacitive-tap ATU. This can only be done when the transmission line is of the 'flat' untuned type, such as the feed from a folded dipole when employing a 300Ω ribbon feeder.

CAPACITIVE-TAP ATU

Instead of using an inductive tap arrangement such as that used in the previous designs, it is also possible to use a capacitive tap arrangement. This has proved to be popular over many years with a variety of operators and today it is still a favourite in many applications.

The design is shown in **Fig 8.12(a)**. It is similar to the parallel-tuned circuit but instead of using taps along the coil there are two variable capacitors. These are connected in series and they are used to provide impedance matching and additionally tune the circuit to resonance.

To understand the operation of this ATU, imagine that the antenna wire is at high impedance. It will match when C1 is large and C2 is small in capacitance. On the other hand, if the impedance of the wire is low, C2 will have to be large and C1 will be small. The normal rules of antenna matching Q still apply, so a pair of quite high-value capacitors are needed. Typically values of about 500pF maximum should be suitable for each. As they are always in series and tune across the inductor their plate spacings can be smaller than would be usual when just a single capacitor is employed.

In **Fig 8.12(b)** either a 300Ω or 600Ω 'flat' and non-resonant feeder line can terminate at a balun (either 1:1 or 4:1 ratio) which will present an unbalanced output to the ATU. A balun should not be used in this position when a tuned line is employed, as the unwanted reactances can give rise to balun heating with a wasteful loss of power and possible damage to the balun.

MODIFIED Z-MATCH

The Z-match form of ATU has been popular for many years, with a number of different versions appearing from time to time. The original Z-match was intended for use with valve transmitters, but a modified design (**Fig 8.13**), developed by Louis Varney,

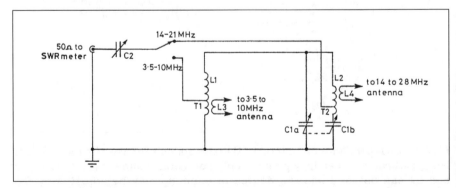

Fig 8.13: The popular Z-match as modified by G5RV. This ATU is well suited to matching both tuned and untuned feedlines, and will cover all the HF bands (3.5 to 30MHz) without band switching.

G5RV, is more suitable for solid-state transceivers. It can be seen that the 50Ω source is tapped down the main inductors L1 and L2 at T1 and T2. The variable input capacitor C2 is included in Varney's design, and it is a part of the series-resonant tuned input circuit which, when correctly tuned, presents a 50Ω non-reactive load to the transmitter.

The Z-match uses the multi-band tuner principle and can cover the 3.5 to 30MHz frequency range without coil changing. The inductance of the high-frequency coil L2 is small enough to be neglected at lower frequencies, which means that the two sections of the split-stator tuning capacitor C1a and C1b are then in parallel and tune the inductor L1 over the 3.5 to 10MHz range. At the higher frequencies (14 to 28MHz) L1 is large enough to behave like an RF choke and it has little effect upon the L2 tuned circuit. On these frequencies L2 is tuned by the small variable capacitance provided by C1a and C1b which are in series.

The output coils L3 and L4 are both tightly coupled to L1 and L2 respectively, and are usually arranged to be of a larger diameter than these so they can actually be positioned over them. No output switching is shown in Fig 8.13, but it will be needed in a working model and should connect either L3 or L4 to a twin-wire feeder system. Other switching arrangements, which will allow the connection of unbalanced low-impedance coaxial feeders or instead connect the transmitter output directly to an antenna or dummy load, can be incorporated in the final practical design.

An SWR meter in the line between the transmitter and the Z-match is needed when tuning this ATU. With C1a / C1b set to a median capacitance, the input capacitor C2 must then be adjusted for a minimum SWR reading. C1a / C1b should then be set to a different value of capacitance and the procedure repeated until the lowest possible SWR is obtained. This process will have to be carried out on each band (a written note indicating the various capacitor settings will allow for rapid adjustment to the correct match on each band as needed).

The Z-match has a rather restricted range of impedance-matching, and it may not always be possible to obtain a really low value of SWR on one or more bands with some antennas. However, the great advantage of the circuit is that there is no need for coil changing or switching even over a wide (often 8:1) frequency range.

Suggested component values for the modified Z-match are:

L1   10 turns at 40mm diameter close wound with 14SWG enamelled wire. The tap T1 is four turns from the earthy end.
L2   5 turns 14SWG enamelled wire with the tap T2 made 1.5 turns from the centre of the coil towards C1b.
L3   8 turns 50mm diameter 14SWG enamelled wire over the earthy end of L1.
L4   3 turns 14SWG enamelled wire arranged over the tap T2 on L2.
C1a / C1b   Split stator 250 + 250pF variable.
C2   500pF broadcast receiver type.

THE G5RV ATU

In 1966 Louis Varney, G5RV, wrote that there are various satisfactory forms of ATU that can be used with the G5RV antenna, but he had designed one that was extremely flexible electrically and yet did not require the coils to be tapped for optimum feeder loading. G5RV's ATU is shown in **Fig 8.14**.

C1 is a 200 + 200pF split-stator transmitter capacitor, the plate spacing being determined by the

Right: Fig 8.14. The ATU designed by Louis Varney for use with his G5RV antenna.

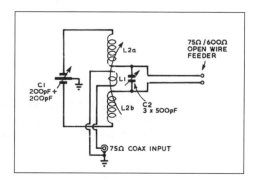

power it will have to handle. The coupling capacitor, C2, consists of three 500pF broadcast receiver variable capacitors connected in parallel. If necessary, this combination may be supplemented by a bank of switched high voltage mica capacitors.

THE SPC MATCHING CIRCUIT

For a number or years a modified version of the T-match circuit was used by many amateurs. Unfortunately, under some conditions of impedance transformation, the circuit shows a high-pass response and does little to attenuate high-frequency harmonics. To overcome this problem a new circuit, shown in **Fig 8.15(a)**, was devised by the late Doug DeMaw, W1FB, and is known as the W1FB SPC match.

The circuit in Fig 8.15(a) is arranged so there is always some capacitance in parallel with the balanced feeder inductor (L1 + L2). One half of a dual-section variable capacitor (C2b) tunes the inductance and its other section (C2a) is in series and connects the tuned circuit to the output connectors. It is the dual use of this capacitor that gives the name 'SPC' (Series-Parallel Capacitance) to this ATU design.

The harmonic attenuation is good and the bandpass response is maintained when the load impedances range from less than 25Ω to more than 1000Ω. This is because there is always a substantial capacitance in parallel with the inductor L1 + L2 and to earth.

A rotary inductor is frequently used for L1 and the smaller separate coil L2 is used at the high-frequency end of the range of the ATU. This is a self-supporting inductor which must be positioned at right angles to L1. When constructing this design it should be borne in mind that the common and normally 'earthy' spindle between the two capacitor sections of C2a / C2b will not be connected to earth, but to the 'hot' end of the coil. This means that this component should be well insulated from the chassis and have an insulated extension spindle between it and the front panel.

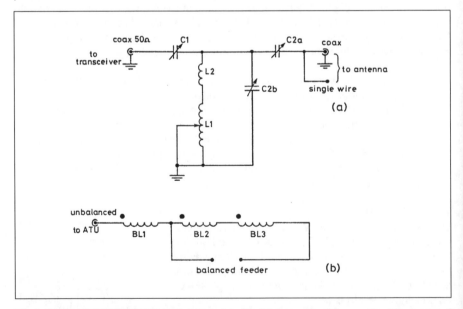

Fig 8.15: (a) The W1FB SPC matching circuit which can match a very wide range of impedances and also provide some considerable harmonic rejection. When using untuned twin wire feeders a balun is required. (b) A circuit for a trifilar airwound 1:1 balun which is suitable for high-power work. At 100W or less a ferrite core can be used.

As it is drawn in Fig 8.15, the SPC circuit can load into either a single wire or an unbalanced coaxial feeder. When a 'flat' untuned feeder is used to feed the antenna this may terminate at a suitable (1:1 or 4:1) balun. The unbalanced connection of the balun should be connected to the antenna coaxial cable connection of the ATU. It is not recommended to use a balun in conjunction with a feeder that has a high level of standing waves. Although in some instances it may work, on other frequencies there will be inevitable high reactances which cannot be tuned out. If the use of a tuned feedline is contemplated it is best matched with a Z-match circuit or one of the circuits shown in Fig 8.11.

A suitable 1:1 balun for use with the SPC ATU is shown in Fig 8.15(b). This has 12 trifilar turns close wound on a 25mm (1in) diameter former. A ferrite core could saturate with high powers but can be used for power levels below about 100W.

For construction of the SPC ATU, the inductor L1 can be a rotary inductance (25µH minimum) or a 28 turn coil of 14SWG wire about 65mm diameter (2.5in) wound over a length of 90mm (3.5in). This should be tapped every two turns. L2 consists of three turns of 10SWG wire with a 25mm (1in) coil diameter wound over 40mm (1.5in). This coil is self supporting, and can also be made from 6mm (0.25in) wide copper strip. With an inductance of this specification (L1 + L2) the SPC circuit will tune from 1.8 to 30MHz. For the capacitors, the value of C1 is 200pF and C2 is 200 + 200pF.

It is suggested that the wiring of an SPC matching unit should be made with thin flashing copper strips and that the stators of C2a / C2b are arranged so that they are well above the metal chassis. If this is not done the circuit might not resonate on 28MHz. If a metal cabinet or other enclosure is used it should be big enough to allow adequate spacing between it, the inductors and the variable capacitor stators (about twice the diameter of the coil L1. It is often easier to use a tapped coil rather than a rotary inductor as it provides for much faster band changing. Once the correct tapping points have been found for each waveband, the band switching is simply a matter of changing the position on a switch, whereas using a rotary coil it can be a far more lengthy process.

COMMERCIALLY-MADE ATUS

For anyone not wanting to build their own ATU, there is a very good selection of commercially-manufactured items that can be bought through the usual amateur radio retailers. Before an ATU purchase is contemplated, some care must be taken to ensure that it is going to be suitable for the antennas that are presently in use or are likely to be used in the future.

A first consideration must be the power-handling ability of an ATU: some are only suitable for receiving or QRP use. Many of those designated for transmitting are only suitable for use with a basic transceiver and can therefore safely operate with transmitter output powers of about 150W at the most. If a linear amplifier is to be used the ATU must be rated to somewhere between 500W and 2kW peak power; the variable capacitor plate spacing is probably the most important factor. It is the high voltage rating of the components used that makes such ATUs expensive.

Another most important feature is the ability of an ATU to match a very wide range of impedances. A good ATU (such as one based on the SPC circuit) will match a very wide impedance range but some of the small matching units will only match antenna (or feeder) impedances up to a maximum of 500Ω. These are certainly not suitable for end-fed wire antennas, for example, which may present an impedance of 1000Ω or more on some bands.

Most of the commercial ATUs now include several switch-

The MFJ-989D, a commercial wide-range ATU capable of handling 1.5kW.

Inside the MFJ-989D ATU.

ing options which allow a variety of co-axial inputs, end-fed wires or 'flat' untuned twin lines (using a balun) to be matched. They often also have a switched connection to an external dummy load and many have integral SWR and / or power output meters which can be switched to several power level ranges. These ATUs may be able to measure output powers from under 1W up to 2kW or even more. Automatic ATUs are becoming more popular but some of these may only have a limited imped-ance-matching range.

AUTOMATIC ATUs

Many amateurs, particularly those using wire antennas, cannot always install a per-fectly resonant antenna. However, by using a simple random length wire, or perhaps a doublet of any length fed by balanced line, one can often put out a very potent signal, provided the antenna can be correctly matched to the transceiver. The automatic ATU may be the best method of achieving this.

The reason for using any ATU is, of course, to provide maximum power transfer between your transmitter and the antenna. But this is only true as long as the ATU is located at the antenna feedpoint itself, or somewhere along a feedline that is matched to the antenna. If your antenna has an impedance very much different to 50Ω, such as just a few ohms in the case of a shortened mobile whip, and you use 50Ω coax to feed it with the ATU at the 'bottom end' of the coax, what you'll be doing - or what you'll be trying to do - is to match your transmitter to the 50Ω coax line with a different impedance antenna at the far end. What you need to do is to locate the ATU right at the antenna feedpoint and then run 50Ω coax from this to your transceiver, operating the ATU remotely.

Fortunately, virtually all automatic ATUs can accomplish this, electrically at least (you may need to weatherproof them) and some have a remote control or indicator facility

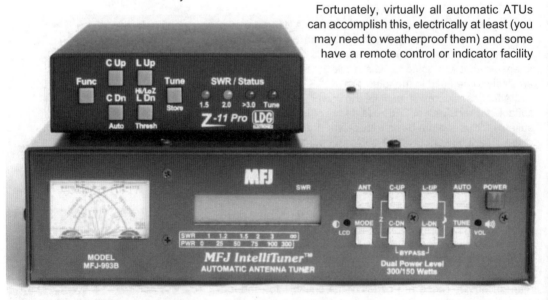

Two commercial automatic ATUs: top, the LDG Z-11 Pro and, below, the MFJ-944B 'IntelliTuner'. Both are L-match type tuners.

The Elecraft T-1, a tiny automatic ATU that covers 1.8 - 54MHz and is rated at 20W.

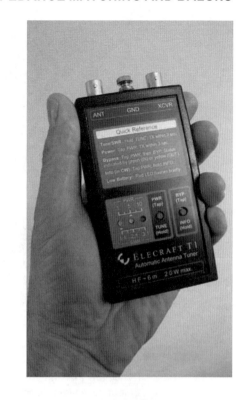

that lets you know the state of the tuner and when the antenna has been correctly tuned. For antenna installations at home you could also use balanced line feeder and use a tuner at your shack end if it has the capability of handling a balanced feed.

There are many commercially-made automatic ATUs on the market. How do they work? Early auto ATUs used continuously-variable capacitors tuned by motors, but these were large and mechanically complex. These days almost all auto ATUs are based on switched fixed-value capacitors and / or coils in a binary value combination depending on electronic feedback from the antenna impedance and phase, a method developed by Chris Lorek, G4HCL, as early as the 1980s. He described the operation of automatic ATUs in the June 2009 *RadCom*.

Let's say we need a change in capacitance value between zero and, say, 255pF. We could use a continuously variable capacitor for this, although this will always have some stray capacitance at its minimum setting. But instead we could use a bank of eight capacitors, switched in and out in parallel as needed, with values of 1pF, 2pF, 4pF, 8pF, 16pF, 32pF, 64pF and 128pF. This is a binary sequence, each value being twice the value of the preceding one. This way, depending on which individual capacitors are in circuit at any moment, we can have any value in 1pF steps from no capacitance (none switched in) and 255pF (the total capacitance of all of them switched into circuit in parallel). The same applies to inductance, with individual inductor values being switched in and out of series connection.

Automatic ATUs operate by sensing the impedance presented to the transmitter and switching in and out differing values of capacitance and inductance, under microprocessor control following a pre-defined tuning algorithm, until either the best possible SWR has been achieved or a pre-set SWR below a given limit, say 1.5:1, has been reached. This procedure usually takes a few seconds or so.

The tuner's microprocessor often also has a memory facility linked to an internal frequency coun-

The Chinese-made CG3000 automatic ATU is fully weatherproofed and is thus designed for mounting right at the base of the antenna.

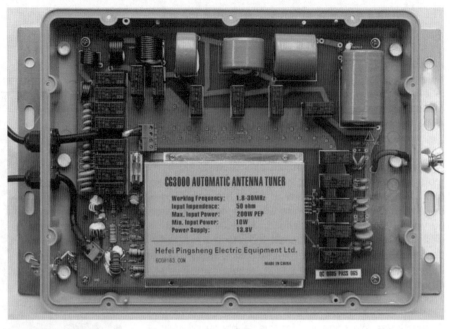

Inside the CG3000 remotable automatic ATU.

ter, where the transmit frequency is memorised along with the final tuning capacitor / inductor values needed for the best tuning combination for that frequency range. Then, when that frequency segment is identified again at some time in the future from the transmitter power going into the tuner, the microprocessor instantly switches in that pre-stored tuning combination rather than re-tuning each time.

BALUNS

The term 'balun' is an abbreviation meaning 'BAL-anced-to-UNbalanced'. Balanced means equal and opposite voltages and current in a signal source, transmission line or load. In addition, a balanced transmission line's conductors are required to be identical, such as in ladder line. Unbalanced lines and loads have voltage or current that is higher in one conductor or terminal than the other, with one terminal often grounded.

The baluns is a component that should be used whenever making a transition between balanced and unbalanced systems. For example, they should be used when feeding a dipole with coaxial feeder. The cost of some commercially-made items is one issue that deters many people from including them as part of the antenna system. While it is possible for the antenna to operate satisfactorily for many purposes without a balun, their use is to be advised.

Ward Silver, N0AX, gave a good introduction to the subject of baluns in the January 2007 *QST*. A balun is an electrical device used to transfer power between balanced and unbalanced loads or lines. Some are wound on cores in the manner of transformers while others are constructed from segments of transmission line. Baluns can be designed to work at a single frequency or over a wide range.

♦ A *balanced load* is a load that presents equal impedances at each terminal.
♦ A *balanced transmission line* is a symmetric transmission line whose conductors carry equal voltages and currents.
♦ *Common mode* refers to currents (or voltages) that appear equally on all conductors of a transmission line.

A coaxial transmission line, while balancing voltage and current between the centre conductor and inside of the shield, has a third conductor - the outside of the shield - carrying different voltages and currents and so it *cannot* be balanced. At RF, the outside and inside of the shield are effectively separate conductors due to the skin effect that causes AC current to flow very near the surface of a conductor. Coaxial feedlines can have completely independent currents flowing on the two surfaces of the shield.

CHOKE BALUNS

The *common-mode choke current balun* connects an unbalanced coaxial feed line to a symmetric, balanced antenna such as a dipole. The photo shows three types of choke baluns: ferrite bead, toroidal and coaxial. We will concentrate on baluns that use ferrite cores or beads. All of them suppress or 'choke' common-mode RF current flow on the outside of the coax shield by creating an inductance from the outside of the feedline shield. The resulting common-mode impedance prevents current from flowing along the outside of the shield. The equal and opposite currents inside the feedline are then transferred only to the antenna terminals.

Bead baluns are generally the most effective. By preventing current flow on the outside of the coax shield, currents are forced to be equal in each half of the dipole and the antenna's radiation pattern is not altered by currents radiating from the coax shield. It also reduces RF current on the outside of feedlines that can interfere with other signals and upset power and SWR measurements.

You can make bead baluns by placing ferrite beads over coaxial cable. The outside of the coax shield acts as a 'one-turn' winding inside the core while signals inside the coax are not affected. The bead balun in the photograph is made from seven Amidon FB-77-1024 beads over RG213 coaxial cable. Any similar bead made from type 31 or 73 ferrite will work on the HF bands. Use type 43 ferrite for VHF and UHF applications. Wrap the beads with good quality electrical tape, then install the connector or waterproof the exposed conductors.

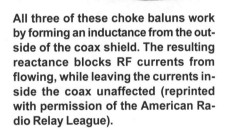

All three of these choke baluns work by forming an inductance from the outside of the coax shield. The resulting reactance blocks RF currents from flowing, while leaving the currents inside the coax unaffected (reprinted with permission of the American Radio Relay League).

CURRENT VS VOLTAGE BALUNS

There are two basic types of baluns. *Voltage baluns* force the voltages at their outputs to be equal and out of phase. *Current baluns* force currents at their output terminals to be equal and out of phase. The current balun is the most useful to radio amateurs because in antenna systems radiated power is determined by the currents in the antenna and not the feedpoint voltage. In addition, most antennas (even perfectly symmetrical ones like dipoles) are not electrically balanced due to the proximity of other conductors, so equal voltages at the feedpoint terminals do not guarantee equal currents.

Ian White, GM3SEK, explained the difference between current and voltage baluns in more detail in the December 2009 'In Practice' column in *RadCom*. You often see a perfectly 'balanced' antenna in a textbook but perfect balance is only a theoretical concept, one that is impossible to achieve in reality, and difficult even to approach. **Fig 8.16** shows that a truly balanced antenna requires perfect left-right symmetry, not only in the antenna and its feedline but also in the antenna's electromagnetic fields. Those fields interact with all other objects in the vicinity, so the requirement for

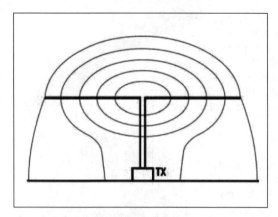

Fig 8.16: Highly idealised picture of electric fields around a symmetrical antenna.

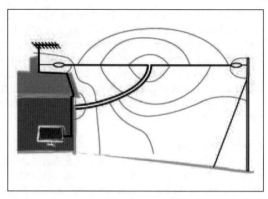

Fig 8.17: The typical reality: nothing is symmetrical and common-mode currents flow on the feedline.

perfect symmetry extends out into the antenna's surroundings. **Fig 8.17** is an example of how the fields around real-life antennas can be distorted by surrounding objects such as the house, metals masts and an asymmetrical feedline layout.

Also note that no vertical or sloping antenna can ever be perfectly balanced, simply because one side is closer to ground than the other. If the electromagnetic fields surrounding the antenna are asymmetrical, the same will apply to all the voltages and currents along its wires, so we can expect to find unequal voltages and currents at opposite sides of the feedpoint. Unequal currents at either side of the feedpoint will cause common-mode RF currents to flow on the feedline.

If this is the case, it will make the feedline radiate (effectively becoming an unwanted part of the antenna) and the current will seek pathways to earth through the shack, the domestic mains wiring, TV downleads, telephone lines and any other routes it can find. Most of our domestic wiring is already heavily polluted with noise from consumer electronics, and this noise can follow the same pathways in reverse, travelling up the outside of the feedline and then back down the inside of the coax into our receivers.

Fortunately, treatment is fairly simple: the antenna feedpoint is the trouble spot where common-mode currents begin and a good current balun can prevent this. RF from the transmitter is delivered up the inside of the coaxial feedline, which is completely shielded from the outside world. The shielding is largely due to the skin effect, which forces RF currents to flow only on the surfaces of metallic conductors. RF current inside the coax cannot get through the thickness of the shield, so it stays inside until it reaches the antenna feedpoint. This is where the shield ends and the trouble begins, because the skin effect also provides a path for RF current to spill over the end of the shield and flow back down the outside of the shield. This unwanted common-mode current is shown as I3 in **Fig 8.18**. I1 and I2 are the normal coaxial-mode currents, I1 on the centre conductor and I2 on the inside of the shield. The tightly coupled fields inside the coax ensure that I1 and I2 are always equal and opposite, so (I1 = -I2). I4 and I5 are the currents flowing in the

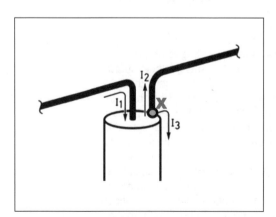

Fig 8.18: Currents at the antenna feedpoint. I3 is the troublesome common-mode current on the outside of the coax.

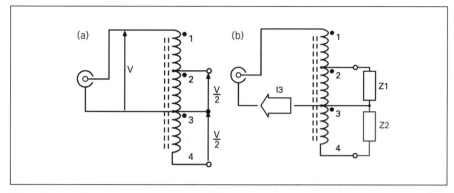

Fig 8.19: A 1:1 voltage balun, (a) showing voltages across three identical windings, (b) with unbalanced load impedance shown in two separate parts.

two legs of the antenna, which should be equal but often aren't. We also note that I4 = I1 because these are duplicate labels for the same current on the same wire. Point 'X' in Fig 8.18 is the junction of three separate conductors - the inside of the shield, the outside of the shield and the right-hand leg of the antenna. The total amount of current arriving at X is exactly equal to the total amount of current departing, so noting the direction of the arrowheads we can write (I5 = I2 - I3). Putting all that together, we get (I3 = I4 - I5). Or in plain words, if the currents at either side of the antenna's feedpoint are unequal for any reason, the difference between those currents will appear on the outside of the feedline as an unwanted common-mode current.

In the theoretical case of a perfectly balanced antenna, I4 exactly equals I5, which means I3 will be zero - but *only* in that theoretical perfect case! If there is the slightest trace of imbalance, I4 and I5 are no longer equal, and the difference between these two currents (I4 - I5) will be driven out on to the surface of the shield as an unwanted common-mode current I3. Deeper analysis shows that is *always* true, even when a balun is used. A balun should be aiming to make I4 and I5 more equal, and I3 smaller... but some baluns are better at this than others.

The *voltage balun* is shown in **Fig 8.19(a)** - there are several different types, this particular example being an autotransformer with three identical windings (trifilar) connected in series and in phase. To see how it works, imagine a voltage V applied across windings 1-2 and 2-3 in series. The voltage across each individual winding is therefore V/2. The balanced output is taken between terminals 2 and 4, and is V/2 + V/2 = V, balanced about the centre tap at terminal 3. Since the output voltage equals the input voltage, this example is a 1:1 balun with no impedance transformation.

Fig 8.19(b) includes the load impedance of the antenna, drawn as two separate impedances Z1 and Z2 on either side of the centre tap (terminal 3). If the antenna is not perfectly balanced, Z1 and Z2 are unequal... but the voltage balun will still *attempt* to drive both impedances with the same voltage. This causes unequal currents to flow in Z1 and Z2 (corresponding to I4 and I5 in Fig 8.18) and inevitably the difference between those two currents becomes the unwanted common-mode current I3. So instead of reducing the common-mode current when the load is unbalanced, the voltage balun actually *helps* that current to flow. Feeding an unbalanced antenna with a balanced voltage is clearly the wrong thing to do. Voltage baluns sometimes *do* seem to work, but only where the load was quite well balanced in the first place. And even there, they suffer from the problem that all the RF power is transmitted through the coupling of magnetic flux, so construction and selection of magnetic materials can be quite critical, and voltage baluns don't like mismatched load impedances. But the main criticism of voltage baluns is that they never do anything to improve the balance of the antenna itself. That is where the *current balun* scores.

The current balun directly attacks the real problem, the unwanted common-mode current, and that also helps improve the balance of the antenna itself. The easiest kind of current balun to understand is simply a length of the coaxial feedline wound into an RF choke. This winding has no effect on the currents I1 and I2 flowing inside the shield, but the choke places a large impedance in the path of the common-mode current I3, reducing the level of current and the problems it can cause. The other benefit of reducing I3 is that it forces the currents I4 and I5 on either side of the feedpoint to become much more equal, and this in turn improves the balance of the entire antenna.

A current balun cannot erase *all* the effects of an asymmetrical installation, but it goes a long way in the right direction. In contrast, the voltage balun does little or nothing because it is approaching the problem from the wrong direction. Even when the common-mode current has been choked off by the balun at the feedpoint, in practice it often tends to reappear further down the feedline due to electromagnetic coupling with the antenna. In stubborn cases you many need to add further chokes in other strategic locations, e.g. where the feedline enters the shack.

There is no difference between a feedline choke and a current balun, apart perhaps from the connectors or terminals; the only difference is where you install it and what you call it ('feedline choke' is always correct but the term 'balun' only applies at the antenna feedpoint).

Information about the deficiencies of voltage baluns and the advantages of current baluns has been available since the early 1990s, when those two terms were first coined by Roy Lewallen, W7EL, in a classic article entitled 'Baluns: What They Do and How They Do It' (published in the *ARRL Antenna Compendium Vol 1*, ARRL, 1985). The article is now on the web (at www.eznec.com/Amateur/Articles/Baluns.pdf) and is highly recommended reading. For the vast majority of antenna applications, the current balun is the right choice. The voltage balun does find applications in a few specific types of antennas but, even then, they should be used in combination with a current balun (or its identical twin, the feedline choke) to keep unwanted I3 currents off the feedline.

THE SEARCH FOR THE 'PERFECT' RF CHOKE / CURRENT BALUN

In the May 2010 *RadCom* Ian White, GM3SEK, described the challenges of making cost-effective RF chokes or current baluns, and then offered three highly effective designs. He also produced a longer article, with greater background information and more detailed winding instructions, which was published as an 18-page PDF on his 'In Practice' website (go to www.ifwtech.co.uk/g3sek/in-prac and follow the link). What follows here is a shortened version of the original *RadCom* feature.

Experience has shown that RF chokes need to have an impedance of at least a few thousand ohms which must be maintained across a wide bandwidth. Many types of cable choke fail to meet these criteria, and air-wound chokes and ferrite-loaded chokes each have different weaknesses.

Air-wound chokes are simple coils of cable that are often suggested as choke baluns. We tend to think of these coils as inductors, but their high-frequency performance is actually dominated by the distributed capacitance between the turns. Instead of an inductor, they are often actually a high-Q parallel resonant circuit, which does not constitute a dependable RF choke. The impedance is only high around the resonant frequency, and much lower elsewhere. Their performance is also very dependent on the situation in which they're being used, because the impedance of the choke consists almost entirely of either inductive or capacitive reactance at all frequencies except the very narrow region close to resonance.

In practice, air-wound chokes often *do* provide enough impedance to handle easy EMC problems, but they do not have the broad bandwidth that is often claimed, and they are not dependable.

The impedance of a *dependable* RF choke needs to be both large and predominantly resistive. The advantages of resistive impedance are that it cannot be cancelled out and that it also tends to broaden the useful bandwidth of a choke. The only way to create a high resistive impedance is to engineer a certain amount of loss into the choke, which is why ferrite is required (resistive loss in an RF choke is a *good* thing!) We are aiming for a value of several thousand ohms, rather than something like 500Ω which experience has proved to be inadequate. Ferrite chokes with a resistive impedance of less than 1000Ω are at much greater risk of underperforming and overheating. Many chokes are designed only to meet that inadequate target of 500Ω, and some commercial examples have also suffered cost-cutting by using smaller quantities of ferrite or failing to use the correct materials.

To make a really good ferrite choke, you need to:

♦ Choose the right grade of ferrite, one that has some loss at the operating frequency;
♦ Construct the choke to create just the right amount of coupling between the ferrite material and the magnetic field around the cable.

There are hundreds of different grades of ferrite with widely differing magnetic properties. They all *look* the same, so you need to buy 'named ferrite' from a reliable source and closely follow a proven design in order to achieve dependable performance. Most 'named' ferrite is manufactured by the Fair-Rite Corporation in USA but, when shipping and import duty are also taken into account, unfortunately it becomes prohibitively expensive to import.

Jim Brown, K9YC, has shown that it is possible to construct a balun with very high levels of resistive impedance (5000Ω or even more) and capable of handling power levels up to the US legal limit of 1500W. However, this superb performance comes at a cost: the use of large ferrite cores, sometimes four or five at a time, which are not affordable at European prices. The cost-effective way to achieve a high impedance is to use multiple turns through the *same* core, because the impedance increases with the number of turns *squared*. Multiple turns of thick cable once again requires expensive large cores. Ferrite beads are *not* cost-effective as they can usually take only one turn of cable. Each individual bead generates quite a low impedance, so a high impedance would require perhaps 40 or 50 beads in series.

PRACTICAL FERRITE CHOKE CURRENT BALUNS

The search, therefore, is for cost-effective RF chokes that have high performance but without using large and expensive ferrite cores. Some new designs for practical ferrite choke current baluns by George Cutsogeorge, W2VJN, were published in the 2010 *ARRL Handbook* and these were brought to our attention by Ian White, GM3SEK, in his May 2010 *RadCom* article.

The designs use a small number of relatively low-cost ferrite cores made by Fair-Rite which are also available from Farnell UK (http://uk.farnell.com) at just £2.52 each (January 2012 price). They are Fair-Rite 2643167851 or Farnell 1463420 - *note that no substitutes are allowed!* These cores have an oval central hole, 26 x 13mm, which will take several turns of coax such as RG8X or RG58.

Three separate designs cover all the bands from 160 to 10m. The key dimensions are given in **Table 8.4**, and further construction details are available on Ian White's website at www.ifwtech.co.uk/g3sek/in-prac

For the low bands (1.8 and

	Number of turns	Mean diameter	Number of cores
Low bands	5	125mm	3
Mid bands	4	85mm	3
High bands	3	Close wound	2 (glued side by side)

All ferrite cores are Fair-Rite 2643167851 = Farnell 1463420.
No substitutes allowed!

Table 8.4: Dimensions of the three HF ferrite chokes.

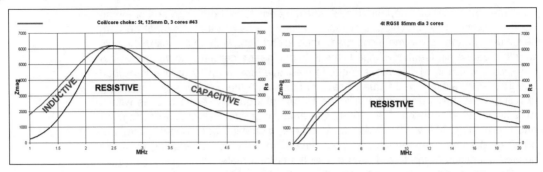

Fig 8.20: Performance of the low-bands choke.   Fig 8.21: Performance of the mid-bands choke.

3.5MHz), three of the ferrite cores are threaded on to a five-turn coil of cable with a diameter of 125mm. **Fig 8.20** shows the measured performance: the resistive part of the impedance is about 4000Ω on topband and 3000Ω on 80m. The total impedance includes some additional inductive reactance at lower frequencies and capacitive reactance at higher frequencies, which can be regarded as a bonus – nice to have, but we're not depending on it for good performance. As can be seen in **Fig 8.20** the two amateur bands are actually on the skirts of the resonance peak, so that peak needs to be positioned fairly accurately to produce similar performance on both bands. To obtain the correct amount of distributed capacitance between turns of the coil, you'll need to follow the detailed assembly instructions on the website with care.

To cover 5, 7 and 10MHz, reduce the coil diameter to 85mm and the number of turns to four, but still use three cores. **Fig 8.21** shows excellent performance across all three bands, and this same choke may also be usable for easier EMC problems down to 3.5MHz and up to 14MHz. For optimum wideband coverage it is essential that the turns of cable are stacked vertically inside the cores with no crossovers, exactly as shown in the photograph.

For 14 - 30MHz coverage, if two of the same cores are superglued together side by side as shown in the photo, three turns close wound will make a good choke. The

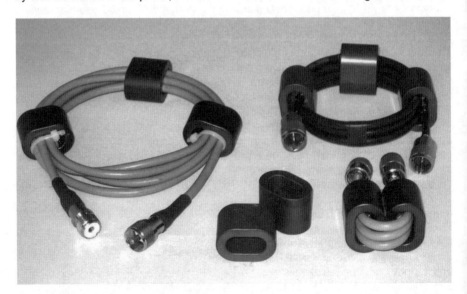

Clockwise from left: low-bands ferrite choke, mid-bands choke, high-bands choke, the ferrite cores.

impedance, shown in **Fig 8.22**, isn't quite as high as the lower frequency chokes at their very best, but it is substantially resistive across the whole 14 - 30MHz range. In terms of 'value for ferrite' this two-core choke will at least equal a straight string of 40 to 50 ferrite beads!

If you want more impedance or a wider bandwidth, you can cascade any of these chokes in series along the cable. The interactions are quite mild and the impedances always seem to reinforce each other (rather than destroying each other, as always happens with reactive air-wound chokes).

The three chokes described and shown in the photograph deliver a high resistive impedance over at least a 2:1 frequency range using only two or three of the oval Fair-Rite cores. Their performance is a major advance over most other balun and EMC chokes that are being used. Once again, in order to achieve this performance you are reminded that you *must* use the Fair-Rite 2643167851 / Farnell 1463420 ferrite cores!

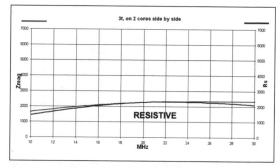

Fig 8.22: Performance of the high-bands choke.

4:1 CURRENT BALUNS

The balun is often combined with a transmission line *impedance transformer*, as explained by Ward Silver, N0AX, in the January 2007 *QST*. Although they are often called 'baluns', they actually combine the functions of a choke balun and an impedance transformer. Impedance transformers don't change the impedances of whatever is connected to them, but they do convert electrical energy from one ratio of voltage to current (impedance) to another. Impedance ratios of 4:1 and 9:1 are common. For example, a 4:1 impedance transformer has half the current and twice the voltage at the load as it does at the input.

By using a single bifilar winding, the primary and secondary of the transformer become a transmission line. If the transmission line is then wound on a toroidal core as shown in **Fig 8.23**, it becomes a 1:1 choke balun. The high impedance presented to common-mode currents allows us to treat the end labeled A'B' as if it were a separate signal source. **Fig 8.24** shows how to change the 1:1 to a 4:1 balun by connecting the load between the input and output, instead of across the output. (This design is known as a *Ruthroff balun*.) Here is how it works: First, the current *i* at B is equal to and out of phase with the current flowing into A. The current *i* flowing into B' must be equal to the current at

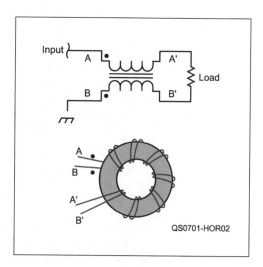

Fig 8.23: By making the transformer windings bifilar, a transmission line is created. Winding the transmission line on the toroid core creates the same choking effect as winding a coaxial cable on the core (reprinted with permission of the American Radio Relay League).

What are those strange dots often seen on transformer symbols, such as those in Fig 8.23? They are known as phasing dots. An increasing voltage at one dot produces an increasing voltage at the other. Current entering one dot causes current to leave the other dot. If two windings are shown with a dot at the same end of the winding symbol, it means that both windings should be wound on the core in the same direction.

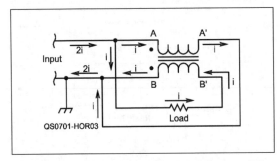

QS0701-HOR03

Fig 8.24: The common-mode impedance of the transmission line allows ends A-B and A'-B' to be treated independently at RF, while the magnitude and directions of the currents in the two windings must be equal and opposite. The effect is to cause the input source to see a quarter of the load impedance (reprinted with permission of the American Radio Relay League).

B, so it is equal to the current i at A. (Similarly at A' and B.) The sum of currents from the input signal source is $2i$, twice what flows in the load. Since no power is created or lost, the product of voltage and current must be the same in the source and load, meaning the source voltage must be one-half that across the load at twice the current. Thus, the source is presented with a quarter of the impedance of the load.

Having the bifilar winding act as a transmission line is a good thing, but the electrical length of the line (and the various connections) adds a small delay. That delay means that the signal at A'B' is out of phase a little bit with that at AB. The phase difference also means currents don't sum exactly and so the impedance the input source sees is not exactly one quarter of the load impedance. The higher the frequency, the longer the line becomes electrically, and the greater the delay and error.

At low frequencies, the common-mode impedance drops to the point where the ends of the line are no longer isolated. These two errors put a definite upper and lower frequency limit on the use of any transmission line transformer.

Building a 4:1 current balun

This balun can be configured for 1:1 or 4:1 impedance ratios and will handle 1kW of power from 160 to 10m. You will need an SWR analyser, such as an MFJ-259, to test the balun or you can experiment with it on the air. (Use low power during tests!)

An FT-240-61 core is selected because type 61 material is designed for use in the HF range, the permeability ($\mu = 125$) creates enough reactance, and the 240 size core is large enough to handle the necessary power.

Carefully straighten a pair of 7ft enamelled wires so that there are no kinks or sharp bends. Use small strips of electrical tape to hold the wire together every 2 - 3in. Use paper labels to show which wire is A, B, A' and B'. Wind the balun as shown in Fig 8.23, spreading the windings evenly around the core and secure the ends of the winding with electrical tape.

Create the 4:1 configuration by connecting an SO-239 connector centre conductor to wire A and the shell to B. Connect wire A' to the shell and leave wire B' unconnected.

Connect the analyser to the SO-239. Solder a 220Ω resistor load between wire B' and wire A. Set the analyser to 10MHz and confirm that the SWR is about 1:1. If the analyser has a resistance meter, it should show slightly more than 50Ω. Replace the 220Ω resistor with a 390Ω resistor. The SWR should now be about 2:1 and the resistance value slightly less than 100Ω. Experiment with different resistor values to confirm the 4:1 impedance transformation.

Change to a 1:1 configuration by disconnecting A' from the shell and removing the resistor load. Attach a 100Ω resistor between A' and B'. Confirm with the analyser that the SWR is about 2:1. Experiment with other resistor values to confirm the 1:1 impedance ratio.

Reconfigure the balun for 4:1 using the 220Ω resistor load. Find the frequencies above and below 10MHz at which the SWR becomes 1.5:1 (resistance value of 75Ω). These are the frequencies at which the assumptions of negligible line length and sufficient choking reactance break down. Anywhere in the middle, you can use your balun on the air!

9 Antenna Masts and Rigging

THE PRACTICAL ASPECTS of installing antennas are just as important in many respects as the electrical ones. There are safety issues to consider. Falling antennas or masts can cause damage and injury, and although injury or damage is less likely in the case of wire antennas, it is still a possibility that needs to be taken seriously. Installing an antenna in the correct fashion can extend its life as well as ensuring that it operates correctly. In summary, the installation can often add as much to the antenna as the design and location.

SAFETY

One of the first things to emphasise when installing an antenna is that of safety. Although amateur radio is generally a very safe hobby, accidents can and do happen. To prevent accidents from occurring it is always necessary to think of the safety aspects of antennas and their installation. Do not take risks, especially as they may involve other people. Not only consider the actual installation, but also the long term life of the antenna itself. If it falls, will it fall in a dangerous fashion, and is it likely to cause injury?

The following safety rules may seem obvious, but plan before you begin. Start by asking yourself, when designing your system:

♦ What risks would the antenna present while it is up?
♦ Could anyone touch a 'hot' part of it and get and RF bum?
♦ Could visiting or trespassing children climb a tower and get hurt?
♦ Could pranksters or vandals easily undo or cut a guy wire?
♦ Have you thought of lightning?
♦ What would be the consequences if any part of the installation fails in foul weather or due to corrosion?
♦ Are there any other safety considerations that may be applicable to the particular installation?

Consider this technique: make that part of the installation capable of doing most damage because of its weight or location as solid as you can. Most often this will be the mast or tower, or at least its lower part. All other parts of your installation such as mast tops, antennas proper etc, are then constructed much lighter. If something is going to give, one of them will, without wreaking too much havoc on the way down.

More accidents happen during antenna erection or removal than at any other time. Be particularly wary of power lines. Do you have liability insurance, just in case? If you must climb to get your antenna up, observe these rules:

Do:
♦ Wear suitable clothing: long-sleeved pull-over shirt, long trousers, shoes with non-slip soles and well-defined heels, gloves.
♦ Always use a safety belt.
♦ Check your safety belt, ropes and pulleys before each use.

♦ Tie your tools and gloves with string so they will not fall far if you drop them.
♦ Wear a hard hat when ground-crewing for a climber.
♦ Consider other points that will assist in improving safety.

Don't:

♦ Climb a wet tower, roof or ladder.
♦ Remain aloft when tired or cold.
♦ Climb an extended crank-up tower.
♦ Leave a tilt-over tower unlocked when upright.
♦ Do anything else that might compromise safety.

If safety is kept in mind at all times, it will make sure that accidents do not happen and ensure that amateur radio remains the very enjoyable hobby that it is.

ROPES

One major element of the installation is the use of guys, ropes and rigging. Rope comes in a wide variety of sizes, materials and forms of construction. In Britain, rope was traditionally measured by its circumference in inches. Very roughly, the diameter of rope is about one third of its circumference, so a ¾-inch rope is about ¼-inch in diameter. With metrication, however, this has changed and rope is now measured by its diameter in millimetres: what was a ¾-inch rope is now a 6mm rope.

Natural ropes such as hemp, manila, cotton and sisal all absorb water and will eventually rot. Until recently antenna mast guys were therefore usually made of galvanised wire, although this, too, eventually corrodes. Galvanised wire guys also have to be split up into short lengths by insulators to reduce the absorption of RF.

Modern ropes made from synthetic fibres do not rot and are generally much stronger than natural fibre ropes so are ideally suited for use as guys. Synthetic ropes melt, but this feature can be turned to advantage as it obviates the necessity of whipping the ends to prevent fraying - instead the end is fused in a clean flame. This is best done before cutting; rotate a 1in section of rope in a clean flame until fused all round, then cut through with a sharp knife when cool. The two jobs can be done in one by using a hot soldering iron.

Types of synthetic rope

Nylon was one of the first synthetic rope fibres and is still the strongest. It can stretch up to 20% before breaking - which makes nylon quite unsuitable for supporting a mast. It is useful as an antenna halyard, but is expensive.

Polyester rope (known as Terylene in the UK, Dacron in USA and Trevira in Germany) is very similar in appearance to nylon but not quite as strong. It stretches very little and the small amount of stretch can be reduced by a pre-stretching process during manufacture, making Terylene a virtual non-corrosive substitute for wire with the added advantage of also being non-conductive. Pre-stretched Terylene is, therefore, the ideal rope to use for mast guys and halyards, but it is also, unfortunately, the most expensive.

Polythene was the first cheap general purpose synthetic rope fibre and is often referred to as 'Courlene'. The rope is hard, wiry and very smooth; the surface always feels 'greasy', so this rope is easily recognised. It is about 50% stronger than natural fibre ropes but not as strong as nylon or polyester. It stretches a little less than nylon but more than polyester. It is very light and about half the cost of polyester.

Polypropylene is the most popular general purpose rope due to its excellent compromise with regard to performance and price. It has 90% of the strength of polyester yet is only half the price. It stretches slightly more than polyester but much less than nylon or polythene.

For amateur radio use, pre-stretched polyester makes ideal guys and halyards, but is expensive. As this material suffers less from ultra-violet degradation than most other fibres, its use is especially recommended in those parts of the world with high levels of UV. In the UK and other places which would welcome more sunshine, monofilament polypropylene is an excellent general-purpose rope equally suitable for use as guys or halyards which will give years of reliable service at little cost.

GUYING THE MAST

Apart from the conventional 'flagpole' type mast, a wide variety of ideas has been successfully tried by ingenious amateurs. In view of the difficulties of transportation, a lot will depend on what can be obtained locally. Different techniques will be required depending on whether the mast is to support a wire antenna or a large beam.

Excellent masts have been made from builder's scaffold poles, especially the dural variety, or lengths of galvanised gas or water pipe screwed together. (Plastic fall-pipes can also be stacked to make good mast radiators - wire verticals - by taping one or more lengths of wire to the outside.)

For most applications 6mm diameter polyester or polypropylene rope will be ample for wire antenna halyards. Wire antennas should be kept under constant tension to prevent fractures due to movement in the wind. This is especially the case if a tree is to be used as a support for a wire antenna. One method of achieving this is to hang a weight on the lower end of the halyard, as shown in **Fig 9.1**. A small spring of the type used to tension small boat steering wires could also be incorporated, close to the insulator at the far end of the wire.

Polyester or polypropylene also make excellent guys for radio masts. For light masts such as a 10m (32ft) by 1in ex-army mast, 6mm diameter rope with a breaking

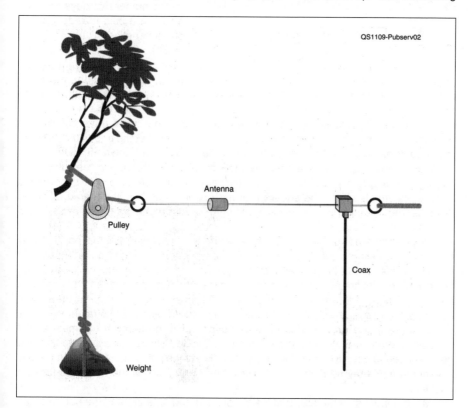

Fig 9.1: Using a weight to keep a tree-supported wire antenna under tension (reprinted with permission of the American Radio Relay League).

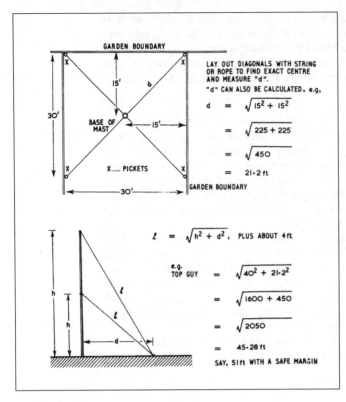

Within the figure:

GARDEN BOUNDARY

LAY OUT DIAGONALS WITH STRING OR ROPE TO FIND EXACT CENTRE AND MEASURE "d".

"d" CAN ALSO BE CALCULATED, e.g,

$$d = \sqrt{15^2 + 15^2}$$
$$= \sqrt{225 + 225}$$
$$= \sqrt{450}$$
$$= 21 \cdot 2 \text{ ft}$$

15'

30'

BASE OF MAST

15'

X ..... PICKETS

30'

GARDEN BOUNDARY

$$\ell = \sqrt{h^2 + d^2}, \text{ PLUS ABOUT 4 ft}$$

e.g.
$$\text{TOP GUY} = \sqrt{40^2 + 21 \cdot 2^2}$$
$$= \sqrt{1600 + 450}$$
$$= \sqrt{2050}$$
$$= 45 \cdot 28 \text{ ft}$$

SAY, 51 ft WITH A SAFE MARGIN

h

d

Fig 9.2: Guying a mast.

load of 1200lb will probably suffice, but for anything heavier, or in case of doubt, the 8mm diameter size is preferred. This offers an 80% increase in strength for only a 50% increase in cost and is well worth the extra to sleep peacefully through the winter storms. Bear in mind that it is normally accepted that the maximum *working load* of a fibre rope should not exceed one sixth of its ultimate strength. All ropes (natural and synthetic) suffer varying degrees of degradation from prolonged exposure to excessive ultra-violet radiation so it pays to err on the generous side regarding size and accept the increased strength as a bonus.

It is impossible to lay down any hard and fast rules regarding the number of sets of guys or the number of guys to a set as so much depends on the characteristics of the particular mast and the ground area available. As a rough guide, three guys to a set on a pitch circle diameter at least equal to the height of the mast is a good basis on which to start. A thin, flexible mast, such as the 10m (30ft) ex-army mast mentioned will require guying every 5m (15ft) or so, whereas a sturdy flagpole may manage with one set at the top only. In theory only three guys per set are necessary but it may be more convenient to use four; a mast at the end of the average rectangular garden can then be anchored to the corners and down the sides.

Guy lengths can be measured by drawing a scale diagram or calculated by Pythagoras' theorem (**Fig 9.2**). As the guy forms the hypotenuse of a right-angled triangle, its length will be the square root of the sum of its height squared, plus the distance from the base squared. Then add three or four feet extra for splices, hitches etc.

Guys should *not* be set too tight; once the mast is being held in position any further tension simply puts the mast under compression, which tends to buckle it in the middle if it cannot be pushed into the ground and this is why high-stretch ropes like nylon and polythene are unsuitable. As a general rule the guys should *look* tight but not *feel* tight. If the mast is to support a wire antenna it should be given a slight rake away from the direction of pull so that the antenna will tend to straighten it. This will obviously put a greater strain on the guys behind the mast. If the mast is stiff enough to support itself without an antenna it should only be necessary to use two guys, spaced about 100° apart, at the top, to balance the pull of the antenna. If the pull is very strong it may be necessary to provide a second set at the middle to prevent buckling.

Much depends on the size and weight of mast and antenna and the nature of the ground but, as a general guide, a length of 50mm (2in) outside diameter galvanised pipe driven into the ground at an angle for 2 - 3ft will make a good anchorage. The guy may then be tied directly to the stake. Surplus rope should be bound to the guy to prevent any possibility of slip and to tidy the loose end. In soft ground it may be necessary to back up the stake with a similar one a foot or so behind, taking a stout lashing from the top of the first one to the bottom of the second.

Lengths of 50 x 50mm (2 x 2in) angle iron also make excellent stakes. Unlike tube or rod, however, the guy cannot be tied directly to the angle iron; in this case a hole must be drilled near the top and a shackle fitted.

PULLEYS

For reliable service in any weather conditions, only genuine marine fittings should be used. They cost somewhat more than cheap washing-line pulleys but are a much better investment as they do not corrode, jam or seize, and require no lubrication or maintenance. Modern marine pulley blocks may be made with synthetic resin bonded fibre cheeks and sheaves and chromium-plated manganese bronze bearding and straps, or with stainless steel cheeks and nylon sheaves. The stainless type costs fractionally more than the other type but there is little to choose between the two in terms of strength and reliability. There is a minimum diameter of sheave for every size of rope and there may be up to three sheaves in one block.

For a simple halyard pulley, a straightforward single sheaved block will suffice but to make up a tackle for raising a mast one of the pair of blocks must be provided with a *becket*. This is simply a point of attachment below the block for securing the fixed end of the rope.

The apparent power gain varies directly as the number of ropes at the moving block. Thus, two single-sheaved blocks, one with becket, will give a 2:1 advantage in one direction and 3:1 in the other. A single and double gives 3:1 or 4:1, and a pair of doubles gives a 4:1 or 5:1 advantage according to the direction of pull. The various arrangements are shown in **Fig 9.3**.

The term 'apparent power gain' is used because power is a function of time and although a lifting tackle may be rigged to give a 4:1 advantage, it will take four times as long (and five times as much rope) to do the job. In fact about 25% of the advantage will be lost through friction in the sheaves.

RAISING THE MAST

Raising the mast itself is potentially the most dangerous activity contemplated when setting up an amateur radio station, so do ensure you have sufficient help. Plan carefully exactly what you are going to do and make sure everyone who is helping understands what is expected of them. Those who are *not* helping should be kept well away from the site. If you have not erected a mast before, or if you have a limited amount of help, do not be too ambitious.

Here, we look at the practical aspects of raising a mast made of scaffold poles,

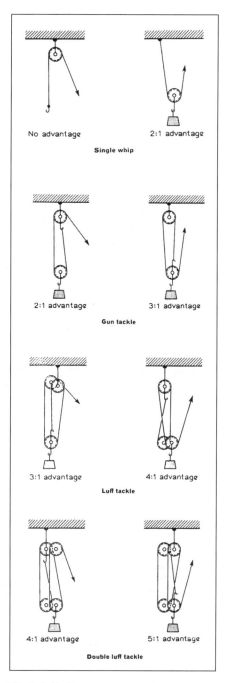

Fig 9.3: Pulley arrangements.

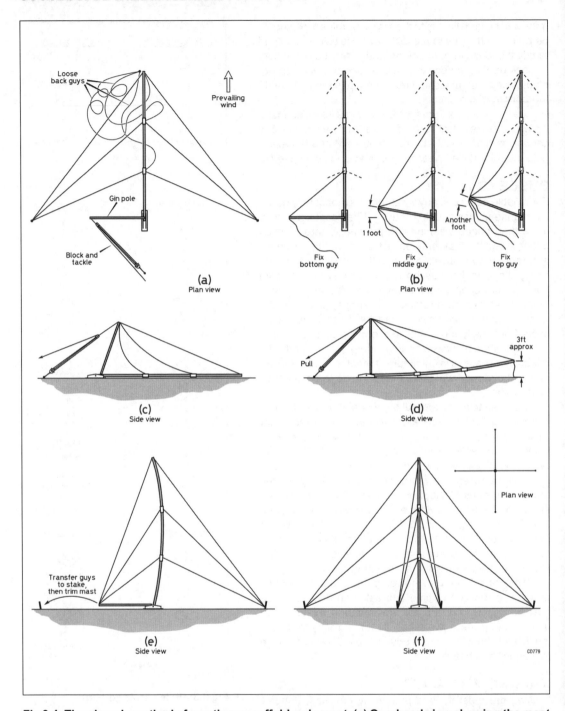

Fig 9.4: The gin pole method of erecting a scaffold-pole mast. (a) Overhead view showing the mast and gin pole laid out on the ground prior to erection. (b) Setting the pre-bend; the amount varies depending on the top load. (c) Side view showing the gin pole being raised using the block and tackle. (d) As the guys take the strain, the mast should be slightly bent as shown. (e) With the mast in position, the gin pole's guys are transferred to stakes and adjusted to remove the bend (the other two sets of guys are not shown for clarity). (f) The mast in its final position. Note the procedure should be reversed to lower the mast, ideally lowering into the wind.

such as is often used at Field Day sites, with the aid of a *gin pole*. Thick-wall scaffold poles should always be used, not the thin-wall TV antenna masts which tend to buckle very easily.

The sections of scaffold pole should be joined with external sleeve clamps, not the interior expanding type of connector. When using a sleeve with a bolted flange, arrange the flanges to *oppose* the bending during lifting, or better still weld two more ribs at 90° to the bolt flange to provide additional rigidity.

The person in charge of the group erecting the antennas should check personally that all of the bolts have been tightened. It is worthwhile using shake-proof washers.

Using a gin-pole to raise a 40ft scaffold mast.

A gin pole is practically essential, and if properly constructed will simultaneously ease erection of the mast and increase the overall safety of the operation. See **Fig 9.4**.

As a rule of thumb, the gin pole should be a third of the length of the mast. If a base plate is being used it should be securely fixed to prevent slipping when lifting the mast. There should be a ring of four guys for each section of the mast. Calculate the length of guys beforehand and have them already prepared and clearly marked – allow a reasonable amount of spare for handling and tying off. The guy stakes should be placed on a circle with a radius not less than half the height of the mast. Use substantial lengths of angle iron driven into the ground at an angle away from the mast. The depth required will depend on the soil composition but usually if they are driven in about 60 to 90cm they should be adequate for most installations. Strips of reflective material to mark the low end of guys and stakes may help to prevent people from walking into them in the dark.

If there is a wind blowing always raise (and, if possible, also lower) the antenna into the wind. The force that can be applied by a strong gust may take the guys right out of everyone's hands. Be prepared to accept reduced height rather than risk the loss of the entire installation to a powerful gust of wind.

Use gloves to handle rope, and everyone working close to the mast should wear some form of protective head gear. The side guys should be securely tied to the stakes, as shown in the plan view in Fig 9.4, though they will probably need adjustment once the mast is up. The back guys should be tied to the back stakes rather than risk the mast going 'over the top'. The gin pole must always have side guys and these should be tied to the side guy stakes. It is best to allow some slack when side-guying the gin pole.

If the mast does get out of control and starts to fall, call to everyone on site to stand clear and if possible, let it fall gradually. Heroics could mean a trip to the hospital – antennas are easier to mend than bones!

Generally, with a knowledgeable and experienced team, it is realistic to think in terms of heights of up to 60ft for a gin pole erected mast which will support only wire antennas (or up to 40ft for a mast supporting some sort of beam).

Finally, *never* erect any masts near overhead power lines.

Advice given in this chapter is believed to be good general practice. However, each installation is different and must be assessed accordingly. No responsibility can be accepted for any consequences arising from the use of information contained within this book.

Appendix

WIRE SIZE REFERENCE AND CONVERSION TABLE

Wire gauge number	SWG inches	mm	AWG inches	mm	Nearest metric reference to SWG
6	0.192	4.88	0.162	4.11	
7	0.176	4.47	0.144	3.66	
8	0.160	4.06	0.128	3.26	
9	0.144	3.66	0.114	2.90	
10	0.128	3.25	0.102	2.59	
11	0.116	2.95	0.091	2.30	
12	0.104	2.64	0.081	2.05	
13	0.092	2.34	0.072	1.83	
14	0.081	2.03	0.064	1.63	
15	0.072	1.83	0.057	1.45	
16	0.064	1.63	0.051	1.29	
17	0.056	1.42	0.045	1.15	1.5
18	0.048	1.22	0.040	1.02	1.25
19	0.040	1.02	0.036	0.91	1.00
20	0.036	0.92	0.032	0.81	
21	0.032	0.81	0.028	0.72	0.8
22	0.028	0.71	0.025	0.64	0.71
23	0.024	0.61	0.023	0.57	
24	0.023	0.56	0.020	0.51	0.56
25	0.020	0.51	0.018	0.45	0.5
26	0.018	0.46	0.016	0.40	
27	0.016	0.41	0.014	0.36	0.4
28	0.014	0.38	0.013	0.32	
29	0.013	0.35	0.011	0.29	
30	0.012	0.305	0.010	0.25	0.315

SWG = Standard Wire Gauge
AWG = American Wire Gauge
Diameters in millimetres have been derived from the original measurements in inches

CHARACTERISTICS OF RADIO FREQUENCY CABLES

(a) Coaxial RF Cables - British UniRadio Series

UR No.	Nominal Impedance Z_0 (ohms)	Overall diameter (inches)	Inner Conductor (inches)	Capacitance (pF / ft)	Maximum operating RMS voltage	Typical Attenuation dB / 100ft 10MHz	100MHz	Approx RG Equiv-alent
43	52	0.195	0.032	29	2750	1.3	4.3	58/U
57	75	0.405	0.044	20.6	5000	0.6	1.9	11A/U
67	50	0.405	7/0.029	30	4800	0.6	2.0	213U
70	75	0.228	7/0.0075	20.5	6270	1.5	4.9	
76	51	0.195	19/0.0066	29	1800	1.6	5.3	58C/U
90	75	0.242	0.022	20	2500	1.1	3.5	59B/U
95	50	0.09	0.0018	30	900	2.6	8.2	174A/U

Above cables have solid dielectric and a velocity factor of 0.66

UR No.	Nominal Impedance Z_0 (ohms)	Overall diameter (inches)	Inner Conductor (inches)	Capacitance (pF / ft)	Maximum operating RMS voltage	Typical Attenuation dB / 100ft 10MHz	100MHz	Approx RG Equiv-alent
202	75	0.20	7/0.0098	17		1.2	3.4	TV down lead
203	75	0.285	0.044	17		0.084	2.3	Low loss TV

The two cables above have a cellular polythene dielectric

(b) Coaxial RF Cables - USA RG Series

RG Number	Nominal Impedance Z_0 (ohms)	Cable diameter (inches)	Velocity factor	Typical Attenuation dB / 100 Feet 10MHz	100MHz	Capacitance (pF / ft)	Maximum operating RMS voltage
RG-8A/U	50.5	0.405	0.66	0.55	2.0	30.5	4000
RG-11A/U	75	0.405	0.66	0.7	2.3	20.5	5000
RG-58/U	53.5	0.195	0.66	1.25	4.65	28.5	1900
RG-59A/U	75	0.242	0.66	1.1	3.4	20.5	2300
RG-62A/U	93	0.242	0.84	0.85	2.7	13.5	750
RG-174A/U	50	0.110	0.66	3.4	10.6	30.3	1000
RG-213/U	50	0.405	0.66	0.6	1.9	29.5	5000

(C) Ribbon / flat RF cables

Type of cable	Nominal impedance Z_0 (ohms)	Dimensions (inches) Each conductor	Overall	Capacitance (pF / ft)	Approx velocity factor	Typical attenuation dB / 100ft 50MHz	100MHz
Flat twin (Permanoid 302)	80	0.036	0.16 x 0.10	20	0.7	2.9	5.1
Flat twin (Permanoid 306B)	300	14/0.0076	0.4 x 0.08	4.5	0.85	1.0	1.9
Slotted twin (Bofa GMP6)	300	7/0.012	0.4 x 0.11	3.36	0.9	0.64	1.4

COIL INDUCTANCE TABLE

Coil inductance calculations can be diffuclt to undertake and as there are many variables, they may not be particularly accurate. As a guide to the approximate levels of inductance, the table below provides values that might be expected for air-cored coils that might be used in antenna applications.

Winding details for four values of inductance

Inductance (μH)	Wire (SWG)	Diameter (inches)	(cm)	Length (inches)	(cm)	Number of turns
40	18	2.5	6.35	2.00	5.08	28
40	14	2.5	6.35	4.25	10.80	34
20	18	2.5	6.35	1.25	3.18	17
20	14	2.5	6.35	2.75	6.99	22
8.6	16	2.0	5.08	2.00	5.08	16
8.6	14	2.5	6.35	3.00	7.62	15
4.5	16	2.0	5.08	1.25	3.18	10
4.5	14	2.5	6.35	4.00	10.16	12

Index